The Be
Acoustic Guitar Chord Songbook

This publication is not authorised for sale in the United States of America and/or Canada.

Wise Publications
part of The Music Sales Group
London/New York/Paris/Sydney/Copenhagen/Berlin/Madrid/Tokyo

Published by
Wise Publications,
8/9 Frith Street, London W1D 3JB, England.

Exclusive Distributors:
Music Sales Limited,
Distribution Centre, Newmarket Road, Bury St Edmunds,
Suffolk, IP33 3YB, England.
Music Sales Pty Limited,
120 Rothschild Avenue, Rosebery, NSW 2018, Australia.

Order No. AM91231
ISBN 0-7119-3479-7

Compiled by Lucy Holliday.
Printed in the United Kingdom.

Adia

Words & Music by
Sarah McLachlan & Pierre Marchand

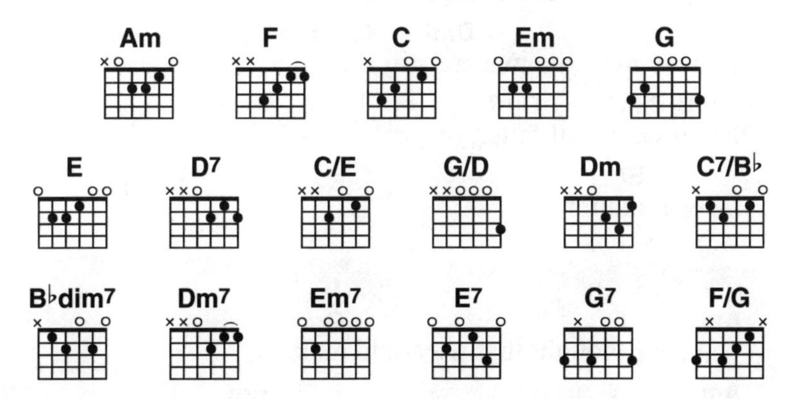

Capo third fret

Verse 1

Am F C
Adia I do believe I failed you
Am F Em G
Adia I know I've let you down.
C F
Don't you know I tried so hard
C E Am
To love you in my way
D7 C G
It's easy, let it go...

Verse 2

Am F C
Adia I'm empty since you left me,
Am F Em G
Trying to find a way to carry on
C F
I search myself and everyone
C/E G/D
To see where we went wrong

Pre-chorus 1

Dm G
There's no-one left to finger,
C F
There's no-one here to blame
Dm G
There's no-one left to talk to honey,
C C7/B♭ F
And there ain't no-one to buy our innocence.

Chorus 1

G C B♭dim7
'Cause we are born innocent,

F Dm7 G Em7
Believe me Adia, we are still innocent.

B♭dim7 Dm7
It's easy, we all falter,

E7
Does it matter?

Verse 3

Am F C
Adia I thought that we could make it

Am F Em G
I know I can't change the way you feel.

C F
I leave you with your misery

C/E G/D
A friend who won't betray.

Pre-chorus 2

Dm G
I pull you from your tower

C F
I take away your pain,

Dm G C
And show you all the beauty you possess

C7/B♭ F
If you'd only let yourself believe that,

Chorus 2

G C B♭dim7
We are born innocent,

F Dm7 G Em7
Believe me Adia, we are still innocent,

B♭dim7 Dm7
It's easy, we all falter

E7
Does it matter?

Instrumental | D7 | C | G | Am D7 | G | G7 |

```
                              C              B♭dim7
Chorus 3          'Cause we are born innocent,

                           F              Dm7      G    Em7
                  Believe me Adia, we are still innocent.

                      B♭dim7        Dm7
                  It's easy, we all falter . . .

                                             F/G    G
                  But does it matter?


                           C             Em                 F
Outro             Believe me Adia, we are still innocent.
                  Dm7       G        C              B♭dim7
                     'Cause we are born innocent,

                           F              Dm7      G    Em7
                  Believe me Adia, we are still innocent.

                      B♭dim7        Dm7
                  It's easy, we all falter . . .

                                             G      E7
                  But does it matter?
```

All My Loving

Words & Music by
John Lennon & Paul McCartney

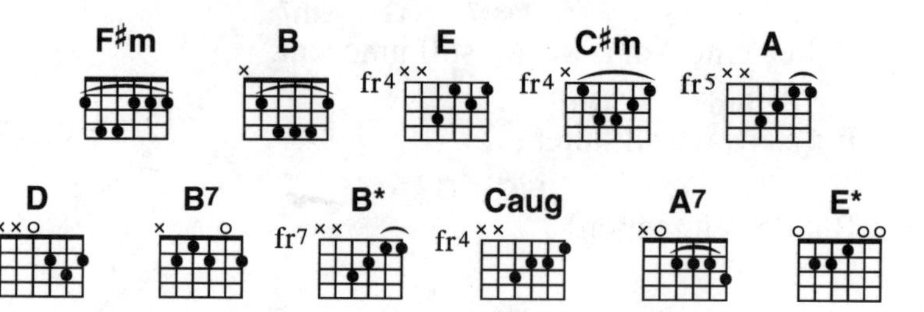

Verse 1

N.C. F♯m B
Close your eyes and I'll kiss you,
E C♯m
Tomorrow I'll miss you,
A F♯m D B7
Remember, I'll always be true.
F♯m B
And then while I'm away
E C♯m
I'll write home every day,
A B* E
And I'll send all my loving to you.

Verse 2

N.C. F♯m B
I'll pretend that I'm kissing
E C♯m
The lips I am missing
A F♯m D B7
And hope that my dreams will come true.
F♯m B
And then while I'm away
E C♯m
I'll write home every day,
A B E
And I'll send all my loving to you.

Chorus 1

C♯m Caug E
All my loving I will send to you,
C♯m Caug E
All my loving, darling I'll be true.

Solo

| A7 | A7 | E* | E* |

| B7 | B7 | E* | E* ||

Verse 3

N.C. F♯m B
Close your eyes and I'll kiss you,
E C♯m
Tomorrow I'll miss you,
A F♯m D B7
Remember, I'll always be true.
F♯m B
And then while I'm away
E C♯m
I'll write home every day,
A B E
And I'll send all my loving to you.

Chorus 2

C♯m Caug E
All my loving I will send to you,
C♯m Caug E
All my loving, darling I'll be true.
C♯m
All my loving,
E
All my loving oo-ooh,
C♯m
All my loving
E*
I will send to you.

Always On My Mind

Words & Music by
Mark James, Wayne Thompson & Johnny Christopher

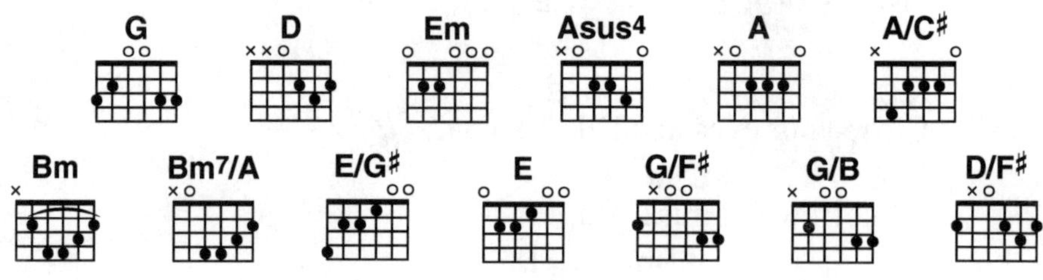

Intro | G | D | Em | Asus4 A ||

Verse 1

D A/C#
Maybe I didn't love you,
Bm Bm7/A G A
Quite often as I could have.
D A/C#
And maybe I didn't treat you,
Bm Bm7/A E/G# E
Quite as good as I should have.
G D
If I made you feel second best,
G G/F# Em G/B
Girl I'm sorry I was blind.
A Bm A/C# D Em D/F#
You were always on my mind,
G A D G A
You were always on my mind.

Verse 2

D A/C#
And maybe I didn't hold you,
Bm Bm7/A G A
All those lonely, lonely times.
D A/C#
I guess I never told you,
Bm Bm7/A E/G# E
I'm so happy that you're mine.

cont.

```
G                                           D
    Little things I should have said and done,
G           G/F#                Em      G/B
    I just never took the time.
A                   Bm      A/C#    D       Em      D/F#
    You were always on   my mind,
G                   A                   D       G   A
    You were always on my mind.
```

Middle

```
D     A/C#  Bm    Bm7/A
Tell____  me,
G                       G/F#                    Em      A
Tell me that your sweet love hasn't died.
       D     A/C#  Bm    Bm7/A
And give            me,
          G                             G/F#                Em
Give me one more chance to keep you satis - fied,
A                             (D)
    I'll keep you satis - fied.
```

Guitar solo

```
| D        | A/C#  A | Bm  Bm7/A | G     A |
| D        | A/C#    | Bm  Bm7/A | E/G#  E ||
```

Verse 3

```
G                                           D
    Little things I should have said and done.
G           G/F#                Em      G/B
    I just never took the time.
A                   Bm      A/C#    D       Em      D/F#
    You were always on my mind,
G                   A                   D
    You were always on my mind.
```

Outro

```
A                   Bm      A/C#    D       Em      D/F#
    You were always on   my mind,
G                   A                   D
    You were always on my mind.
```

America

Words & Music by
Paul Simon

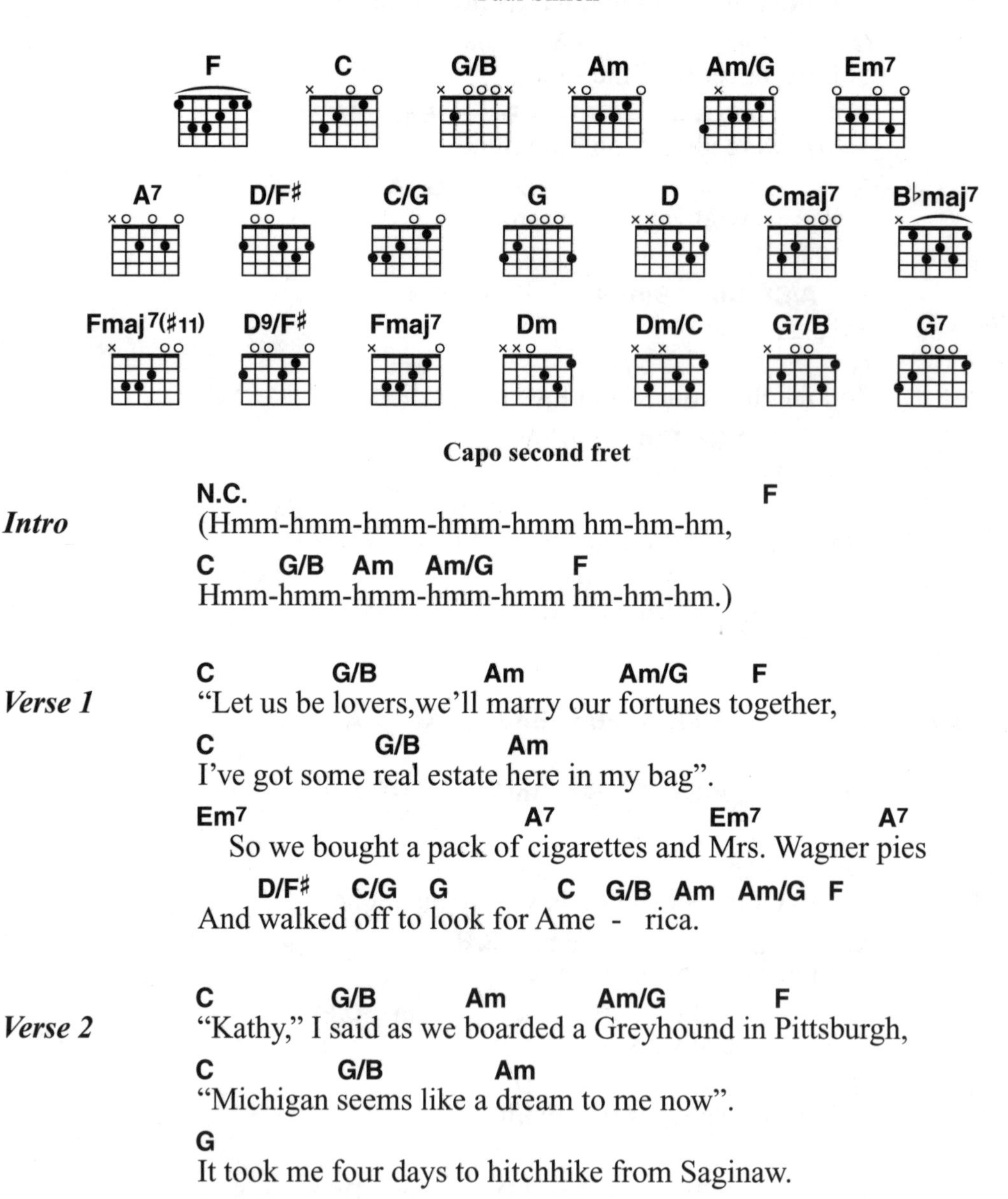

Capo second fret

Intro

N.C. F
(Hmm-hmm-hmm-hmm-hmm hm-hm-hm,

C G/B Am Am/G F
Hmm-hmm-hmm-hmm-hmm hm-hm-hm.)

Verse 1

C G/B Am Am/G F
"Let us be lovers,we'll marry our fortunes together,

C G/B Am
I've got some real estate here in my bag".

Em7 A7 Em7 A7
So we bought a pack of cigarettes and Mrs. Wagner pies

D/F♯ C/G G C G/B Am Am/G F
And walked off to look for Ame - rica.

Verse 2

C G/B Am Am/G F
"Kathy," I said as we boarded a Greyhound in Pittsburgh,

C G/B Am
"Michigan seems like a dream to me now".

G
It took me four days to hitchhike from Saginaw.

D G D Cmaj7
I've gone to look for America.

```
            B♭maj7
*Middle*       Laughing on the bus,
                    Cmaj7
            Playing games with the faces:
            B♭maj7                                   Cmaj7
            She said the man in the gabardine suit was a spy.
            F                    Fmaj7(♯11)        C      G/B  Am  Am/G
            I said, "Be careful his bowtie is really a camera".


Link        | D9/F♯      | Fmaj7      ||


            C          G/B        Am           Am/G      F
Verse 3     "Toss me a cigarette, I think there's one in my raincoat".
            C               G/B        Am
            "We smoked the last one an hour ago".
            Em7                 A7        Em7              A7
              So I looked at the scenery,   she read her magazine
                   D/F♯  C/G  G      C  G/B   Am   Am/G  F
            And the moon rose   over an o  -  pen field.


            C           G/B   Am            Am/G         F
Verse 4     "Kathy, I'm lost," I said, though I knew she was sleeping,
               C         Em         Am
            I'm empty and aching and I don't know why.
            G
            Counting the cars on the New Jersey Turnpike,
                   D  G      D          Cmaj7
            They've all  gone to look for America,
            D  G      D          Cmaj7
            All gone to look for America,
            D  G      D          Cmaj7
            All gone to look for America.


Coda        ||: C   G/B | Am  Am/G | Dm  Dm/C | G7/B  G7 :||   Repeat to fade
```

Always The Last To Know

Words & Music by
Justin Currie

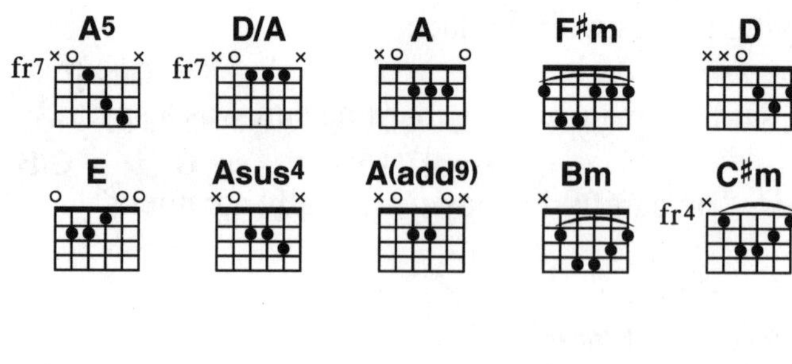

Intro ‖: A5 D/A | A5 D/A :‖ *Play 2 times*

‖: A | A | F♯m | D :‖

| E | E ‖

Verse 1

A
So in you're in love with someone else,
F♯m
Someone who burns within your soul
D E A
And it looks like I am the last to know.
A
I hear you've never felt so alive,
F♯m
So much desire beyond control,
D E Asus4 A
And as usual I am the last to know.

Chorus 1

Aadd9 A F♯m D
The last to know how you're feeling,
A F♯m
The last to know where you are,
D Bm
The last to know if you're happy now,
C♯m
Or if he's treating you like I treated you,
D E A
Or if he's cruel I'll be the last to know.

Verse 2

```
                A
We spent summers out beyond the bay,
                    F#m
And you said these are such perfect days
            D                       E                       Asus4 A Aadd9 A
But if the bomb drops baby I wanna be the last to know.
                    A
But now you're living up behind the hill
                    F#m
And though we share the same city, and feel the same sun
            D               E               Asus4  A
When your winter comes I'll be the last to know.
```

Chorus 2

```
Aadd9           A       F#m             D
   Always the last to know how you're feeling,
            A               F#m
The last to know where you are,
            D           Bm
The last to know if you're happy now,
        C#m
Or if he's pleaded with you like I pleaded with you
    D       E               D
If you go, don't let me be the last to know,
    E                           A5  D/A  A5  D/A
Don't_ let me be the last to know.
```

Bridge

```
Bm              C#m
   Creation's gone crazy,
D               A
   The TV's gone mad,
    Bm          D               E
Now you're the only sane thing that I've had.
```

Guitar solo

‖: A | A | F♯m | D :‖

| E | E | E ‖

Chorus 3

E F♯m D
Always the last to know how you're feeling
A F♯m
The last to know where you are,
D Bm
The last to know if you're happy now,
C♯m
Or if he's cheated on you like I cheated on you,
D E D
Oh,__ and you were the last to know,
E D
You__ were the last to know,
E E A5 D/A A5 D/A
Don't let me be the last___ to know.

Outro

‖: A | A :‖ *Play 3 times*

| A | A | A ‖
Oh, oh, oh,

A
Don't let me be the last to know.

No, no, no, no, no, no...

To fade

Baby, Now That I've Found You

Words & Music by
Tony Macauley & John MacLeod

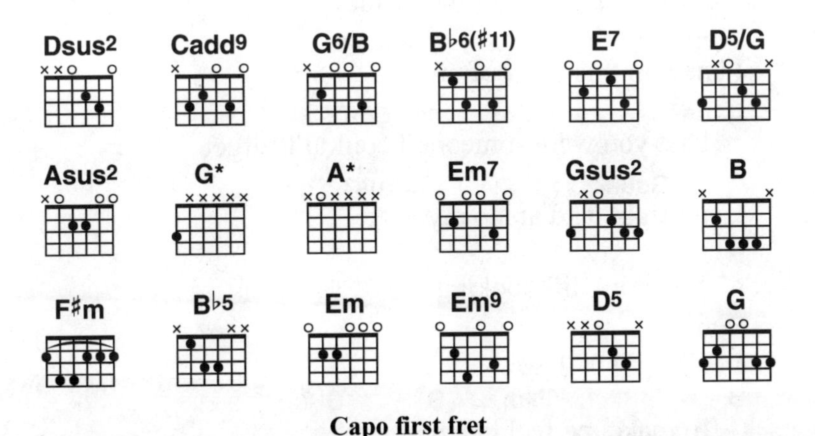

Capo first fret

Intro | Dsus2 | Cadd9 | G6/B | B♭6(♯11) | Dsus2 | E7 | D5/G | Asus2 |

Verse 1

Dsus2 Cadd9
Baby, now that I've found you
G6/B
I won't let you go
B♭6(♯11)
I built my world around you
Dsus2
I need you so,
E7
Baby even though
D5/G Asus2
You don't need me now.
Dsus2 Cadd9
Baby, now that I've found you
G6/B
I won't let you go
B♭6(♯11)
I built my world around you
Dsus2
I need you so,
E7
Baby even though
D5/G
You don't need me,

```
                    Asus2      | Dsus2   |
cont.     You don't need me, no, no.

          | Cadd9   G*   A* | Dsus2    | Cadd9   G*   A* |

          Dsus2                Em7
Verse 2     Baby, baby, when first we met
            Gsus2                   Asus2
          I knew in this heart of mine,
          Dsus2                         Em7
            That you were someone I couldn't forget
                 Gsus2               Asus2
          I said right, and abide my time.
          B
             Spent my life looking
          F#m
          For that somebody
          B                F#m     B        Bb5
            To make me feel like new
          Asus2                         Em
            Now you tell me that you wanna leave me
          G                      Asus2         Dsus2 Cadd9  G6/B  Bb6(#11)
            But darling, I just can't let you,                ooh.

                                                                              x2
Instrumental ||: Dsus2 | Cadd9 | G6/B | Bb6(#11) | Dsus2 | E7 | D5/G | Asus2 :||

          Dsus2                Em7
Verse 3     Baby, baby, when first we met
            Gsus2                   Asus2
          I knew in this heart of mine
          Dsus2                         Em7
            That you were someone I couldn't forget
                 Gsus2               Asus2
          I said right, and abide my time.
          B
             Spent my life looking
          F#m
          For that somebody
          B                F#m     B        Bb5
            To make me feel like new
          Asus2                         Em9
            Now you tell me that you wanna leave me
          G                      Asus2         Dsus2 Cadd9  G6/B  Bb6(#11)
            But darling, I just can't let you. __________
```

Verse 4

```
Dsus2  Cadd9
       Now that I found you
G6/B           B♭6(♯11)
  I built my world around you
 Dsus2                 E7                          D5/G          Asus2
I need you so, baby even though you don't need me now.
Dsus2  Cadd9
Baby, now that I've found you
       G6/B
I won't let you go
          B♭6(♯11)
I built my world around you
Dsus2
I need you so,
  E7
Baby even though,
          D5/G
You don't need me
          Asus2        | Dsus2  | Cadd9   G*  A* |
You don't need me, no, no.
```

Outro

```
||: Dsus2  | Cadd9   G*  A* :|| D5 |
```

Beautiful Ones

Words & Music by
Brett Anderson & Richard Oakes

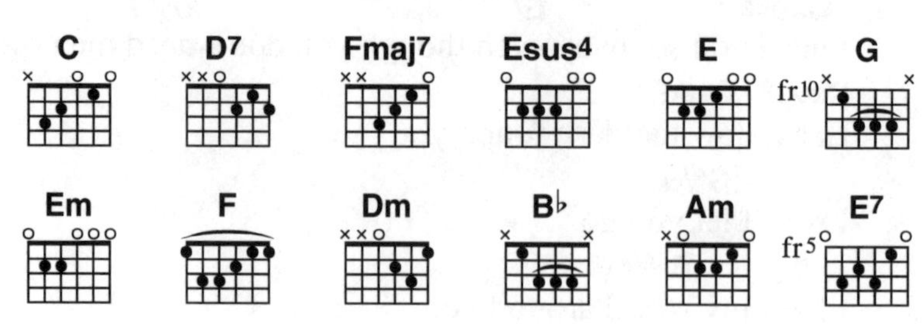

Tune guitar down one semitone

Intro ||: C | D7 | Fmaj7 | Esus4 E :||

Verse 1

C D7
Ooh, high on diesel and gasoline,
Fmaj7
Psycho for drum machine,
Esus4 E
Shaking their bits to the hits, oh.
C D7
Drag acts, drug acts, suicides,
Fmaj7
In your dad's suit you hide,
Esus4 E
Staining his name again, oh.

Verse 2

C D7
Cracked up, stacked up, twenty-two,
Fmaj7
Psycho for sex and glue,
Esus4 E
Lost it in Bostik, yeah.
C D7
Oh, shaved heads, rave heads, on the pill,
Fmaj7
Got too much time to kill,
E G
Get into the bands and gangs, oh.

```
               C
*Chorus 1*     Here they come,
                    Em
               The beautiful ones,
                    F
               The beautiful ones,
               Dm   B♭
               La la la la.
               C
               Here they come,
                    Em
               The beautiful ones,
                    F
               The beautiful ones,
               Dm   B♭   Am  E7
               La la la la la,  la la.

               C                   D7
*Verse 3*      Loved up, doved up, hung around,
                         Fmaj7
               Stoned in a lonely town,
                              Esus4      E
               Shaking their meat to the beat, oh.
               C                  D7
               High on diesel and gasoline,
                         Fmaj7
               Psycho for drum machine,
                              Esus4      E   G
               Shaking their bits to the hits,  oh.

               C
*Chorus 2*     Here they come,
                    Em
               The beautiful ones,
                    F
               The beautiful ones,
               Dm   B♭
               La la la la.
               C
               Here they come,
                    Em
               The beautiful ones,
                    F                Dm
               The beautiful ones, oh oh.
```

Bridge

```
B♭                    C
  You don't think about it,
                      Em
You don't do without it,
                    F          Dm
Because you're beautiful, yeah, yeah.
B♭             C             Em
  And if your baby's going crazy,
                    F          Dm
That's how you made me, la la.
B♭             C             Em
  And if your baby's going crazy,
                    F          Dm
That's how you made me, woah woah,
B♭             C             Em
  And if your baby's going crazy,
                    F
That's how you made me,
Dm    B♭    Am   E7
La la, la la, la.  La, la.
```

Outro

```
    C            D7
|: La la la la, la,
                 Fmaj7
La la la la la, la.
                   Esus4
La la la la la la,
       E
La la la, oh.  :|   Repeat to fade
```

Behind Blue Eyes

Words & Music by
Pete Townshend

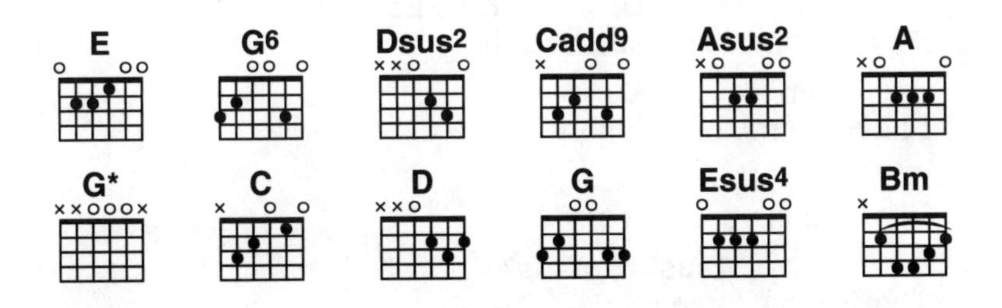

Intro | E | G6 | Dsus2 | Dsus2 |
| Cadd9 | Cadd9 | Asus2 | Asus2 ||

Verse 1

```
E                        G6
No one knows what it's like
           Dsus2
To be the bad man,
           Cadd9
To be the sad man,
    A    G*    A
Be - hind blue eyes.
E                              G6
And no one knows what it's like
     Dsus2
To be hated,
     Cadd9
To be fated,
           A    G* A
To telling on - ly lies.
```

Chorus 1

```
          C    D                G
But my dreams, they aren't as empty
         C           D         E     Esus4 E
As my conscience seems to be
        Bm          C
I have hours, only lonely
              D
My love is vengeance
                  Asus2 | Asus2 |
That's never free.
```

Verse 2

```
E                         G6
No one knows what it's like
                 Dsus2
To feel these feelings
         Cadd9
Like I do,
                 Asus2
And I blame you!
E                     G6
No one bites back as hard
            Dsus2
On their anger,
                Cadd9
None of my pain and woe
             Asus2
Can show through.
```

Chorus 2 As Chorus 1

Bridge

```
             E       G6     Dsus2
Discover    L - I - M - P,      say it,
             Cadd9             Asus2
Discover         L - I - M - P,      say it,
             E       G6     Dsus2
Discover    L - I - M - P,      say it,
             Cadd9             Asus2
Discover         L - I - M - P,      say it,
```

Verse 3

E G6
No one knows what it's like
Dsus2
To be mis - treated,
Cadd9
To be de - feated,
Asus2
Be - hind blue eyes.
E G6
And no one knows how to say
Dsus2
That they're sorry,
Cadd9
And don't worry,
Asus2
I'm not telling lies.

Chorus 3

As Chorus 1

Outro

E G6
No one knows what it's like
Dsus2
To be the bad man,
Cadd9
To be the sad man,
A G* A
Be - hind blue eyes.

Bird On A Wire

Words & Music by
Leonard Cohen

A E D Asus4 Bm Esus4

Verse 1

```
           A          E
Like a bird on the wire,
           A                 D
Like a drunk in a midnight choir
         A          E          A     Asus4
I have tried in my way to be free.
           A           E
Like a worm on a hook,
           A                           D
Like a knight from some old fashioned book,
         A            E          A
I have saved all my  ribbons for thee.
```

Bridge 1

```
D                           A
   If I, if I have been unkind,
Bm                                A
   I hope that you can just let it go by.
D                           A
   If I, if I have been untrue
Bm                                 E     Esus4  E
   I hope you know it was never to you.
```

Verse 2

```
                A         E
Oh, like a baby, stillborn,
           A          D
Like a beast with his horn,
         A       E                       A      Asus4
I have torn everyone who reached out for me.
```

```
              A            E
cont.      But I swear by this song
                 A                    D
           And by all that I have done wrong
           A            E       A     Asus4 A
              I will make it all up to thee.

           D                                   A
Bridge 2      I saw a beggar leaning on his wooden crutch,
           Bm                                A
              He said to me, "You must not ask for so much."
           D                                       A
              And a pretty woman leaning in her darkened door,
           Bm                             E           Esus4 E
              She cried to me, "Hey, why not ask for more?" ______

                    A          E
Verse 3    Oh like a bird on the wire,
               A                 D
           Like a drunk in a midnight choir
               A         E      D      A
           I have tried in my way to be free. ____
```

Blackbird

Words & Music by
John Lennon & Paul McCartney

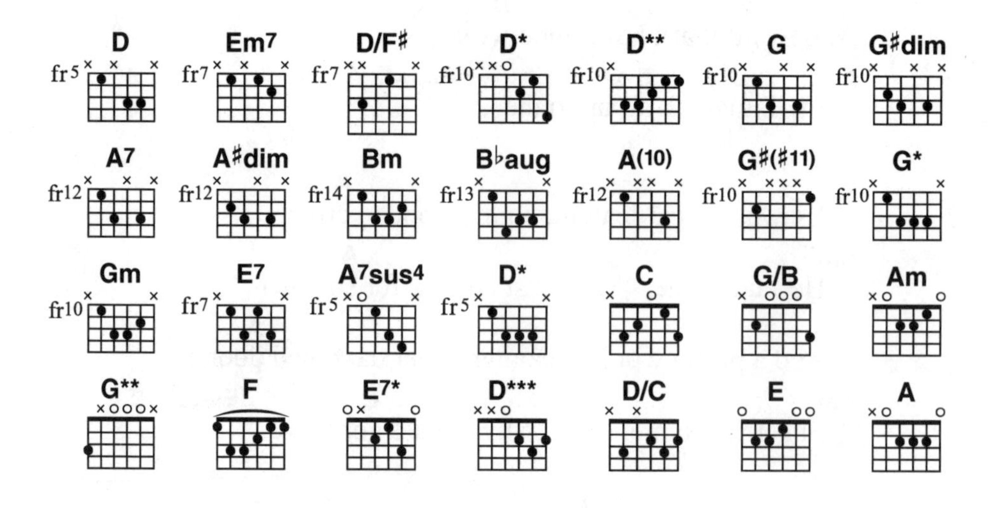

Intro | D Em7 D/F♯ D* | D** ‖

Verse 1

D Em7 D/F♯ D* D**
Blackbird singing in the dead of night
G G♯dim A7 A♯dim Bm
Take these broken wings and learn to fly
B♭aug A10 G♯(♯11) G* Gm
All your life,
D/F♯ E7 A7sus4 D
You were only waiting for this moment to arise.

| G D/F♯ E7 | A7sus4 ‖

Verse 2

D Em7 D/F♯ D* D**
Blackbird singing in the dead of night
G G♯dim A7 A♯dim Bm
Take these sunken eyes and learn to see
B♭aug A10 G♯(♯11) G* Gm
All your life
D/F♯ E7 A7sus4 D
You were only waiting for this moment to be free.

Chorus 1

C G/B Am G** F G**
Black - bird fly,
C G/B Am G** F E7*
Black - bird fly,
A7sus4 D Em7 D/F♯ D* D**
Into the light of a dark black night.

Bridge 1
(vocal ad lib.)

| G G♯dim A7 A♯dim | 6/4 Bm B♭aug A10 G♯(♯11) |
| 4/4 G* Gm | D/F♯ E7 | A7sus4 D ||

Chorus 2

C G/B Am G** F G**
Black - bird fly,
C G/B Am G** F E7*
Black - bird fly,
A7sus4 D Em7 D/F♯ D* D**
Into the light of a dark black night.

Instr.

Solo string section based on D***

Bridge 2

D*** D/C
Blackbird singing in the dead of night,
E A
Blackbird singing in the dead of night.

Verse 3

D Em7 D/F♯ D* D**
Blackbird singing in the dead of night
G G♯dim A7 A♯dim Bm
Take these broken wings and learn to fly
B♭aug A10 G♯(♯11) G* Gm
All your life,
D/F♯ E7 A7sus4 D
You were only waiting for this moment to arise,

Outro

G D/F♯ E7 A7sus4 D
You were only waiting for this moment to arise,
G D/F♯ E7 A7sus4 D**
You were only waiting for this moment to arise.

A Boy Named Sue

Words & Music by
Shel Silverstein

Capo first fret

Intro | A | A | A | A ||

Verse 1

```
Well my daddy left home when I was three
                 D7
And he didn't leave much to ma and me,
     E7                                    A
Just this old guitar and an empty bottle of booze.

Now, I don't blame him 'cause he run and hid
          D7
But the meanest thing that he ever did
         E7                                A     | A     |
Was be - fore he left, he went and named me "Sue."
```

Verse 2

```
Well, he must o' thought that it was quite a joke
          D7
And it got a lot of laughs from a' lots of folk,
  E7                             A
It seems I had to fight my whole life through.

Some gal would giggle and I'd get red
     D7
And some guy'd laugh and I'd bust his head,
 E7                                      A     | A     |
I tell ya, life ain't easy for a boy named "Sue."
```

Verse 3

Well, I grew up quick, and I grew up mean,
D7
My fist got hard and my wits got keen,
E7 A
I'd roam from town to town to hide my shame.

But I made me a vow to the moon and stars
D7
That I'd search the honky-tonks and bars
E7 A
And kill that man that gave me that awful name.

Verse 4

Well, it was Gatlinburg in mid-July
D7
And I just hit town and my throat was dry,
E7 A
I thought I'd stop and have myself a brew.

At an old saloon on a street of mud,
D7
There at a table, dealing stud,
E7 A
Sat the dirty, mangy dog that named me "Sue."

Verse 5

Well, I knew that snake was my own sweet dad
D7
From a worn-out picture that my mother'd had,
E7 A
And I knew that scar on his cheek and his evil eye.

He was big and bent and grey and old,
D7
And I looked at him and my blood ran cold
E7 A
And I said: "My name is "Sue!" How do you do!

Now you gonna die!"

Yeah, that's what I told him!

Verse 6

```
Well, I hit him hard right between the eyes
     D7
And   he went down, but to my surprise,
    E7                                             A
He come up with a knife and cut off a piece of my ear.

But I busted a chair right across his teeth
          D7
And we crashed through the wall and into the street
E7                                                        A
Kicking and a' gouging in the mud and the blood and the beer.
```

Verse 7

```
I tell ya, I've fought tougher men
       D7
But I really can't remember when,
    E7                                        A
He kicked like a mule and he bit like a croco - dile.

I heard him laugh and then I heard him cuss,
D7
  He went for his gun and I pulled mine first,
    E7                                     A
He stood there lookin' at me and I saw him smile.
```

Verse 8

```
And he said: "Son, this world is rough
          D7
And if a man's gonna make it, he's gotta be tough
      E7                                      A
And I knew I wouldn't be there to help you a - long.

So I give you that name and I said goodbye
 D7
I knew you'd have to get tough or die
     E7                                   A
And it's the name that helped to make you strong." Yeah.
```

Verse 9

He said: "Now you just fought one hell of a fight

D7
And I know you hate me, and you got the right

E7 A
To kill me now, and I wouldn't blame you if you do.

But you ought to thank me, before I die,

D7
For the gravel in ya guts and the spit in ya eye

E7 A
'Cause I'm the son-of-a-bitch that named you "Sue."

Verse 10

Yeah what could I do, what could I do?

D7 E7
I got all choked up and I threw down my gun

D7
And I called him my pa, and he called me his son,

E7 A
And I come away with a different point of view.

And I think about him, now and then,

D7 E7
Every time I try and every time I win,

N.C.
And if I ever have a son, I think I'm gonna name him

A
Bill or George! Anything damn thing but Sue! I still hate that name!

Bohemian Like You

Words & Music by
Courtney Taylor-Taylor

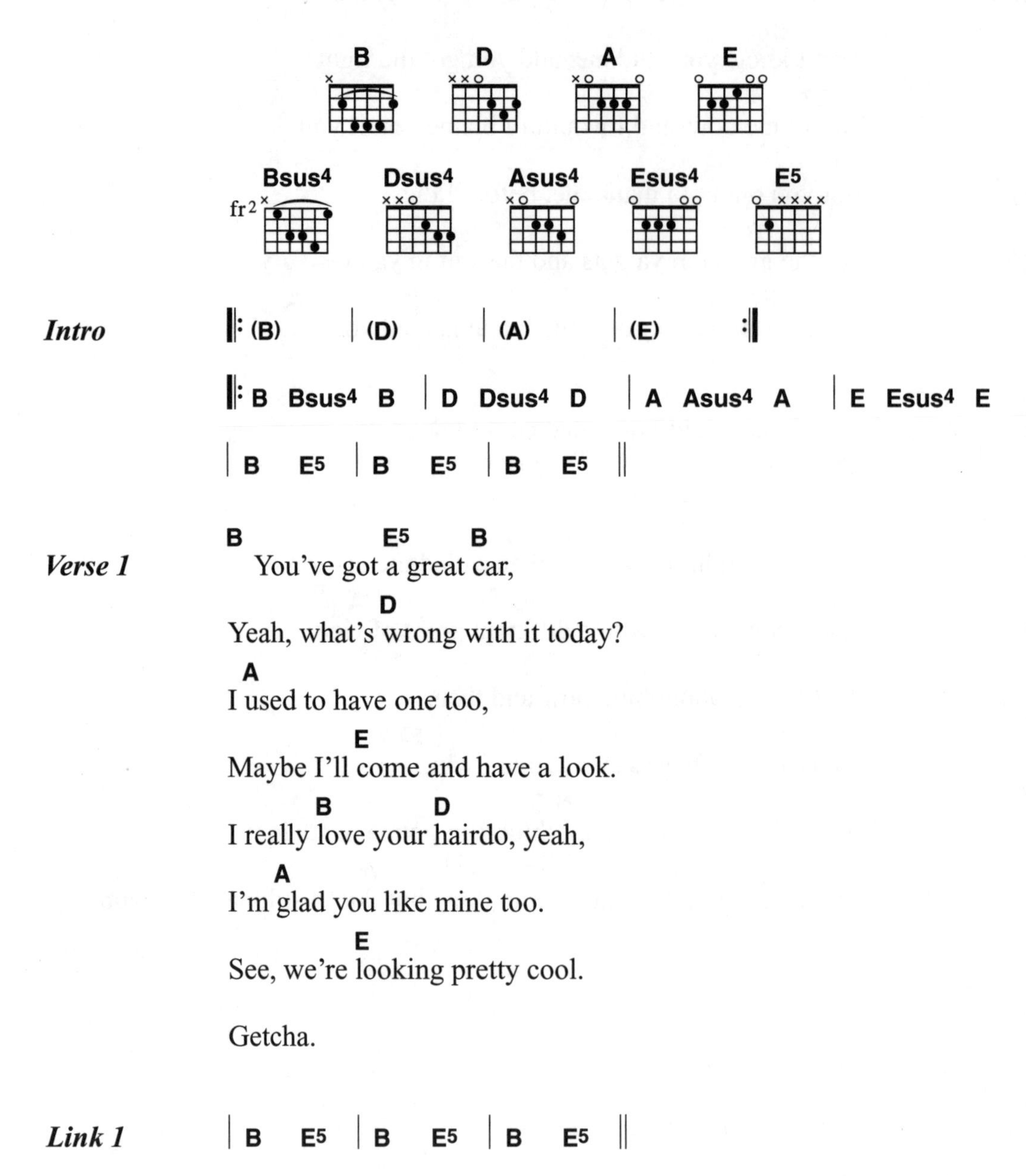

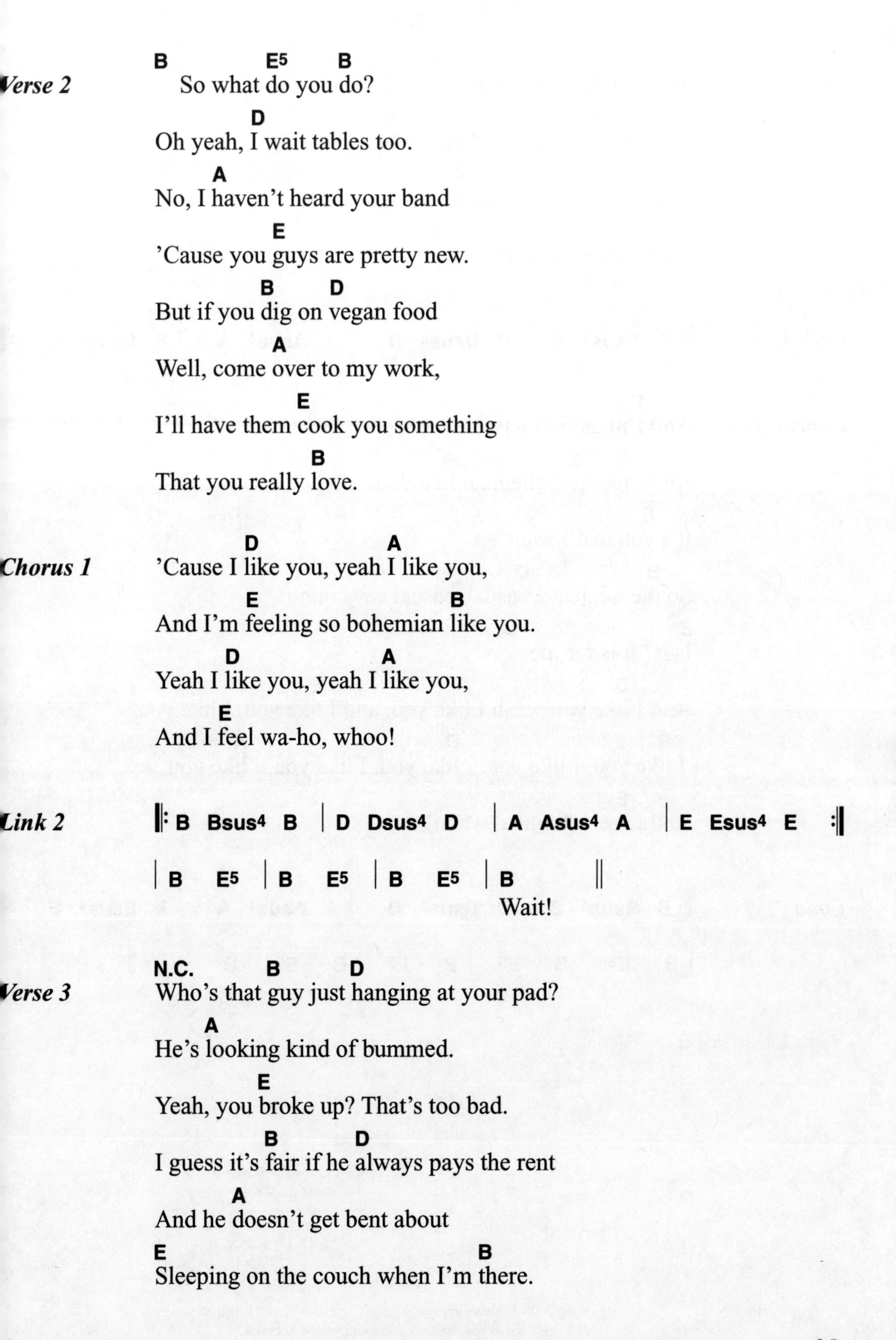

Verse 2

B E5 B
So what do you do?
D
Oh yeah, I wait tables too.
A
No, I haven't heard your band
E
'Cause you guys are pretty new.
B D
But if you dig on vegan food
A
Well, come over to my work,
E
I'll have them cook you something
B
That you really love.

Chorus 1

D A
'Cause I like you, yeah I like you,
E B
And I'm feeling so bohemian like you.
D A
Yeah I like you, yeah I like you,
E
And I feel wa-ho, whoo!

Link 2

𝄆 B Bsus4 B | D Dsus4 D | A Asus4 A | E Esus4 E 𝄇

| B E5 | B E5 | B E5 | B ‖
Wait!

Verse 3

N.C. B D
Who's that guy just hanging at your pad?
A
He's looking kind of bummed.
E
Yeah, you broke up? That's too bad.
B D
I guess it's fair if he always pays the rent
A
And he doesn't get bent about
E B
Sleeping on the couch when I'm there.

Chorus 2

```
               D                   A
'Cause I like you, yeah I like you,
               E                   B
And I'm feeling so bohemian like you.
         D                  A
Yeah I like you, yeah I like you,
        E
And I feel wa-ho, whoo!
```

Link 3

```
|: B  Bsus4  B  | D  Dsus4  D  | A  Asus4  A  | E  Esus4  E  :|
```

Chorus 3

```
      B
And I'm getting wise
        D                A
And I feel so bohemian like you.
     E
It's you that I want
   B              D              A
So please, just a casual, casual easy thing.
E                  B
Is it? It is for me.
        D                 A              E
And I like you, yeah I like you, and I like you, I like you,
  B                    D                   A
 I like you, I like you, I like you, I like you, I like you
        E
And I feel who-hoa, whoo!
```

Coda

```
|: B  Bsus4  B  | D  Dsus4  D  | A  Asus4  A  | E  Esus4  E  :|

| B   E5  | B   E5  | B   E5  | B   E5  | B        ||
```

Brown Eyed Girl

Words & Music by
Van Morrison

G C D D7 Em

Intro | G | C | G | D |
| G | C | G | D ‖

```
           G                    C
Verse 1      Hey, where did we go
           G                  D
             Days when the rains came?
           G              C
             Down in the hollow,
           G          D
             Playing a new game.
           G                      C
             Laughing and a runnin', hey hey,
           G                        D
             Skipping and a - jumpin'
           G                   C
             In the misty morning fog with
           G                D
             Our, our hearts a - thumpin' and

           C      D7                 G     Em
Chorus 1   You,    my brown eyed girl.
           C                 D7          G   D
             And you, my     brown eyed girl.
```

Verse 2

G   C
  And what ever happened
G   D
  To Tuesday and so slow?
G   C
  Going down to the old mine
          G   D
With a transistor radio.
G   C
  Standing in the sunlight laughing,
G   D
  Hiding behind a rainbow's wall.
G   C
  Slipping and a - sliding
G   D
  All along the waterfall with

Chorus 2

C   D7   G   Em
You,   my brown eyed girl.
C   D7   G   D7
  You, my   brown eyed girl.

Do you remember when
                  G
We used to sing
               C
Sha la la la la la la,
G   D7
La la la la de da.

Just like that
G   C
  Sha la la la la la la,
G   D7
La la la la de da,
          (G)
La de da.

Link | G | G | G | G | G | C | G | D ‖

Verse 3

G C
So hard to find my way
G D
Now that I'm all on my own
G C
I saw you just the other day
G D
My how you have grown
G C
Cast my memory back there, Lord
G D
Sometimes I'm overcome thinkin' about it
G C
Makin' love in the green grass
G D
Behind the stadium with

Chorus 3

C D7 G Em
You, my brown eyed girl
C D7 G D7
And you, my brown eyed girl.

Do you remember when
G
We used to sing
G C
||: Sha la la la la la la,
G D7
La la la la de da.
(Lying in the green grass)
G C
Sha la la la la la la,
G D7
La la la la de da, :|| *Repeat ad lib. to fade*

A Case Of You

Words & Music by
Joni Mitchell

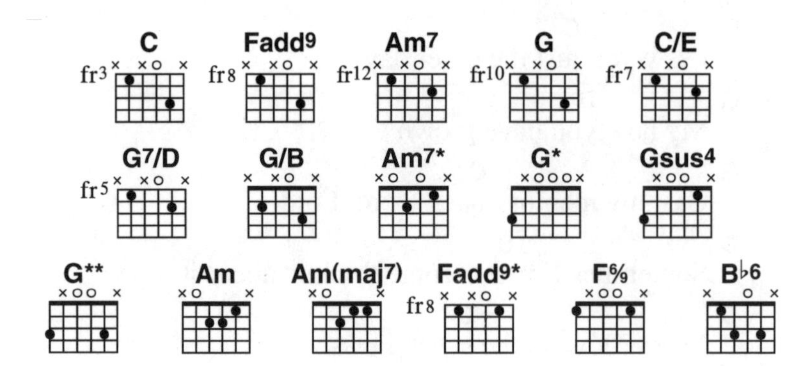

Capo first fret

Intro | C Fadd9 | Am7 G Am7 | Fadd9 C/E G7/D | C/E |
| G7/D C | G/B C Am7* | Gsus4 G* Gsus4 | G** ||

Verse 1

C G/B Am7*
Just before our love got lost you said,

"I am as constant as a northern star."

G7/D C
And I said, "Constantly in the darkness

G/B
Where's that at?

Am7 Gsus4 G* Gsus4 G**
If you want me I'll be in the bar."

C G/B
On the back of a cartoon coaster

Am7
In the blue TV screen light

G7/D C
I drew a map of Canada

C G/B Am Am(maj7) Am7*
Oh Ca - na - da_______________

G7/D C G/B
With your face sketched on it twice.

```
                Fadd9*                          C/E
Chorus 1        Oh,      you're in my blood like holy wine
                Fadd9                 C/E
                  You taste so bitter   and so sweet
                  C                   G**  Am
                Oh I could drink a case of  you, darling
                             Fadd9     C/E          G7/D
                And I would        still   be on my feet

                Oh I would still be on my (feet.)

Intro reprise 1 | C    Fadd9    | Am7  G  Am7  | Fadd9  C/E G7/D | C/E     |
                  feet.
                | G7/D    C     | G/B  C  Am7* | Gsus4 G* Gsus4 | G**     ||

                  C        G/B      Am7*
Verse 2         Oh I am a lonely  painter

                I live in a box of paints
                G7/D                C
                  I'm frightened by   the devil
                          G/B       Am7*               Gsus4  G* Gsus4  G**
                And I'm drawn to those ones that ain't a - fraid
                    C                                   G/B
                I re - member that time you told me,   you said,
                                  Am7         Am(maj7)
                "Love is touching    souls"
                Am7*
                Surely you touched mine
                      G7/D                C
                'Cause    part of you pours   out of me
                G/B        Am7*              G*   Gsus4  G**
                  In these lines from time to time.

                  Fadd9*                         C/E
Chorus 2        Oh,        you're in my blood like    holy wine
                   Fadd9                 C/E
                You taste so bitter and,    so sweet
                  C                   G**    Am  Am(maj7)  Am7*
                Oh I could drink a case of you,_______________ darling,
                G7/D    C            G/B
                  Still, I'd be on my feet

                I would still be on (my feet.)
```

Intro reprise 2

```
| C     Fadd9    | Am7  G  Am7  | Fadd9 C/E G7/D | C/E   |
  my________       feet.
| G7/D    C      | G/B  C  Am7* | Gsus4 G* Gsus4 | G**   ||
```

Verse 3

```
            C
I met a woman
            G/B
She had     a mouth like yours
                     Am
She knew your life
                     Am(maj7)      Am7*
She knew your devils and your deeds

And she said,
G7/D                C
   "Go to him,      stay with him if you can
G/B
   But be prepared to bleed."
```

Chorus 3

```
           Fadd9*                          C/E
Oh but you are in my blood, you're my      holy wine
           Fadd9        C/E
You're so       bitter,     bitter and so sweet
    C                        G      Am  Am(maj7)  Am7*
Oh, I could drink a case of you,________________ darling
G7/D   C        G/B
Still I'd be on my feet

I would still be (on my feet.)
```

Outro

```
| C     Fadd9    | Am7  G  Am7  | Fadd9 C/E G7/D | C/E   |
  on    my         feet._____________
| G7/D    C      | G/B  C  Am7* | Gsus4 G* Gsus4 | G**   ||

| G**     F%     | B♭6          ||
```

Champagne Supernova

Words & Music by
Noel Gallagher

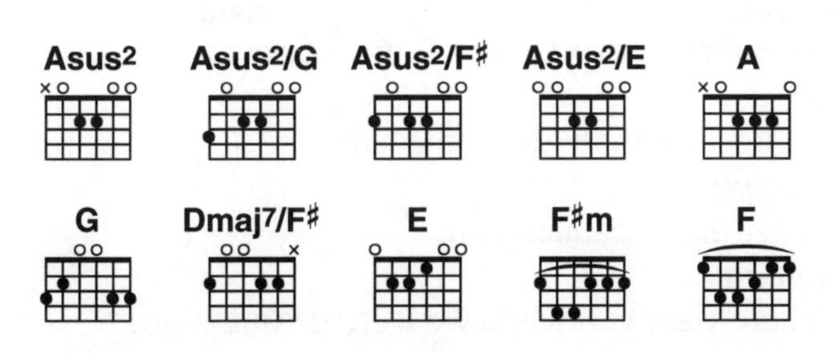

Intro ‖: Asus2 | Asus2/G | Asus2/F♯ | Asus2/E :‖

Verse 1

Asus2
How many special people change?
Asus2/G
How many lives are living strange?
Asus2/F♯   Asus2/E
Where were you while we were getting high?
Asus2
   Slowly walkin' down the hall
Asus2/G
Faster than a cannon ball.
Asus2/F♯   Asus2/E
Where were you while we were getting high?

Chorus 1

                    Asus2   Asus2/G
Some day you will find me caught beneath the landslide
     Asus2/F♯   Asus2/E
In a champagne supernova in the sky.
                    Asus2   Asus2/G
Some day you will find me caught beneath the landslide
     Asus2/F♯
In a champagne supernova,
   Asus2/E
A champagne supernova in the (sky.)

| Asus2 | Asus2/G | Asus2/F♯ | Asus2/E ‖
   sky.

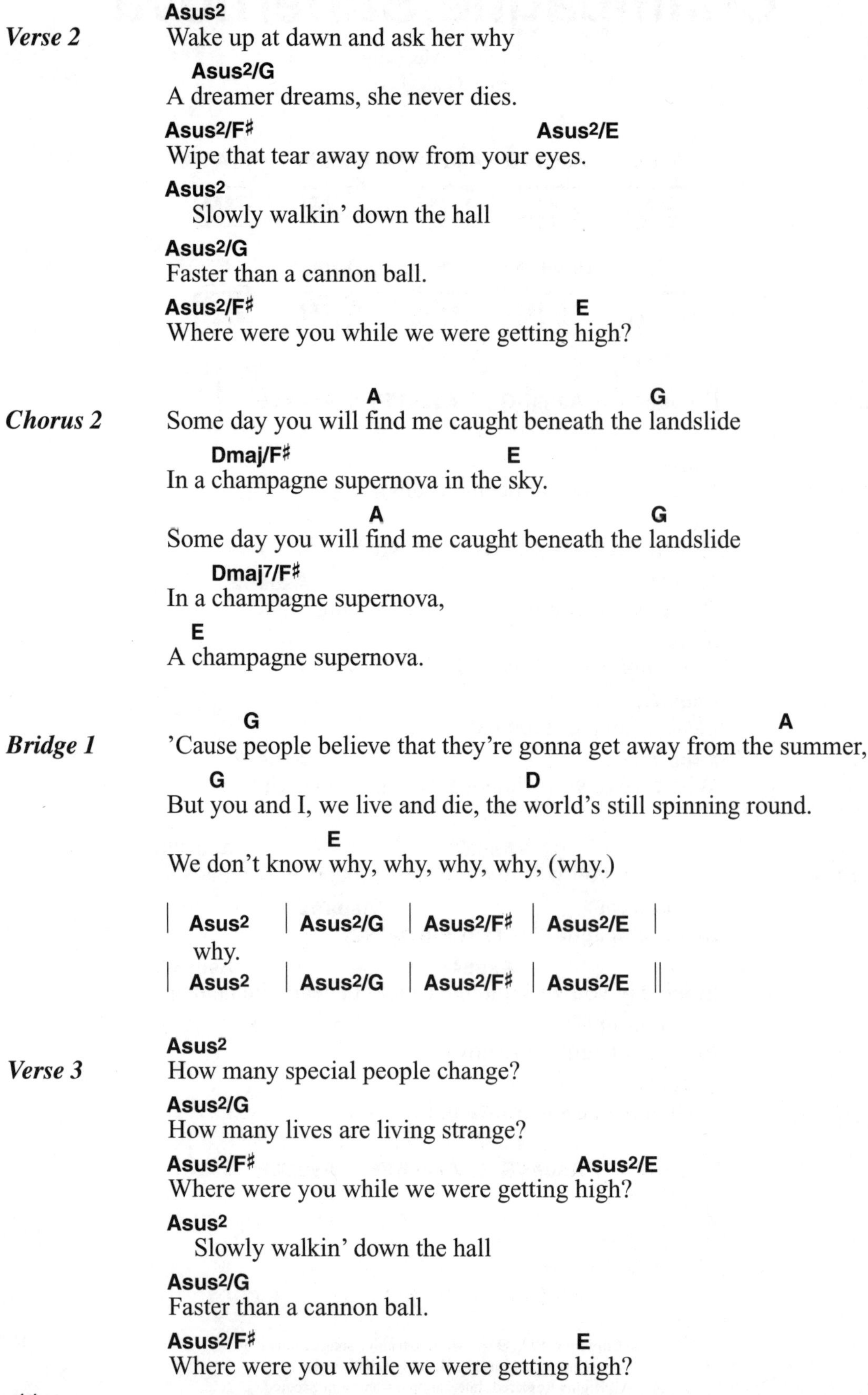

Verse 2

Asus2
Wake up at dawn and ask her why
Asus2/G
A dreamer dreams, she never dies.
Asus2/F♯ Asus2/E
Wipe that tear away now from your eyes.
Asus2
Slowly walkin' down the hall
Asus2/G
Faster than a cannon ball.
Asus2/F♯ E
Where were you while we were getting high?

Chorus 2

A G
Some day you will find me caught beneath the landslide
Dmaj/F♯ E
In a champagne supernova in the sky.
A G
Some day you will find me caught beneath the landslide
Dmaj7/F♯
In a champagne supernova,
E
A champagne supernova.

Bridge 1

G A
'Cause people believe that they're gonna get away from the summer,
G D
But you and I, we live and die, the world's still spinning round.
E
We don't know why, why, why, why, (why.)

| Asus2 | Asus2/G | Asus2/F♯ | Asus2/E |
why.
| Asus2 | Asus2/G | Asus2/F♯ | Asus2/E ||

Verse 3

Asus2
How many special people change?
Asus2/G
How many lives are living strange?
Asus2/F♯ Asus2/E
Where were you while we were getting high?
Asus2
Slowly walkin' down the hall
Asus2/G
Faster than a cannon ball.
Asus2/F♯ E
Where were you while we were getting high?

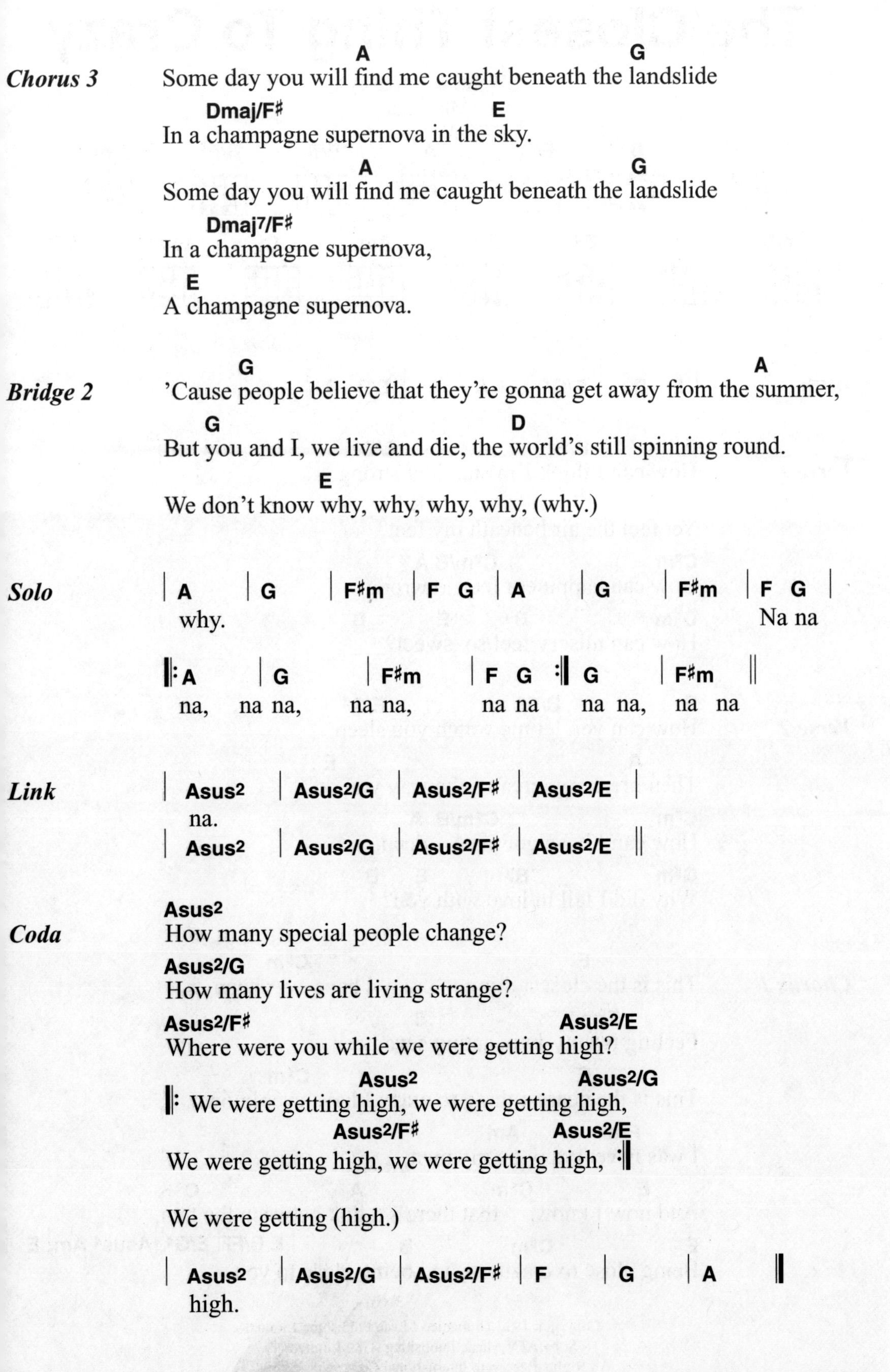

Chorus 3

A G
Some day you will find me caught beneath the landslide
Dmaj/F♯ E
In a champagne supernova in the sky.
A G
Some day you will find me caught beneath the landslide
Dmaj7/F♯
In a champagne supernova,
E
A champagne supernova.

Bridge 2

G A
'Cause people believe that they're gonna get away from the summer,
G D
But you and I, we live and die, the world's still spinning round.
E
We don't know why, why, why, why, (why.)

Solo

| A | G | F♯m | F G | A | G | F♯m | F G |
why. Na na

‖: A | G | F♯m | F G :‖ G | F♯m ‖
na, na na, na na, na na na na, na na

Link

| Asus2 | Asus2/G | Asus2/F♯ | Asus2/E |
na.
| Asus2 | Asus2/G | Asus2/F♯ | Asus2/E ‖

Coda

Asus2
How many special people change?
Asus2/G
How many lives are living strange?
Asus2/F♯ Asus2/E
Where were you while we were getting high?
Asus2 Asus2/G
‖: We were getting high, we were getting high,
Asus2/F♯ Asus2/E
We were getting high, we were getting high, :‖

We were getting (high.)

| Asus2 | Asus2/G | Asus2/F♯ | F | G | A ‖
high.

The Closest Thing To Crazy

Words & Music by
Mike Batt

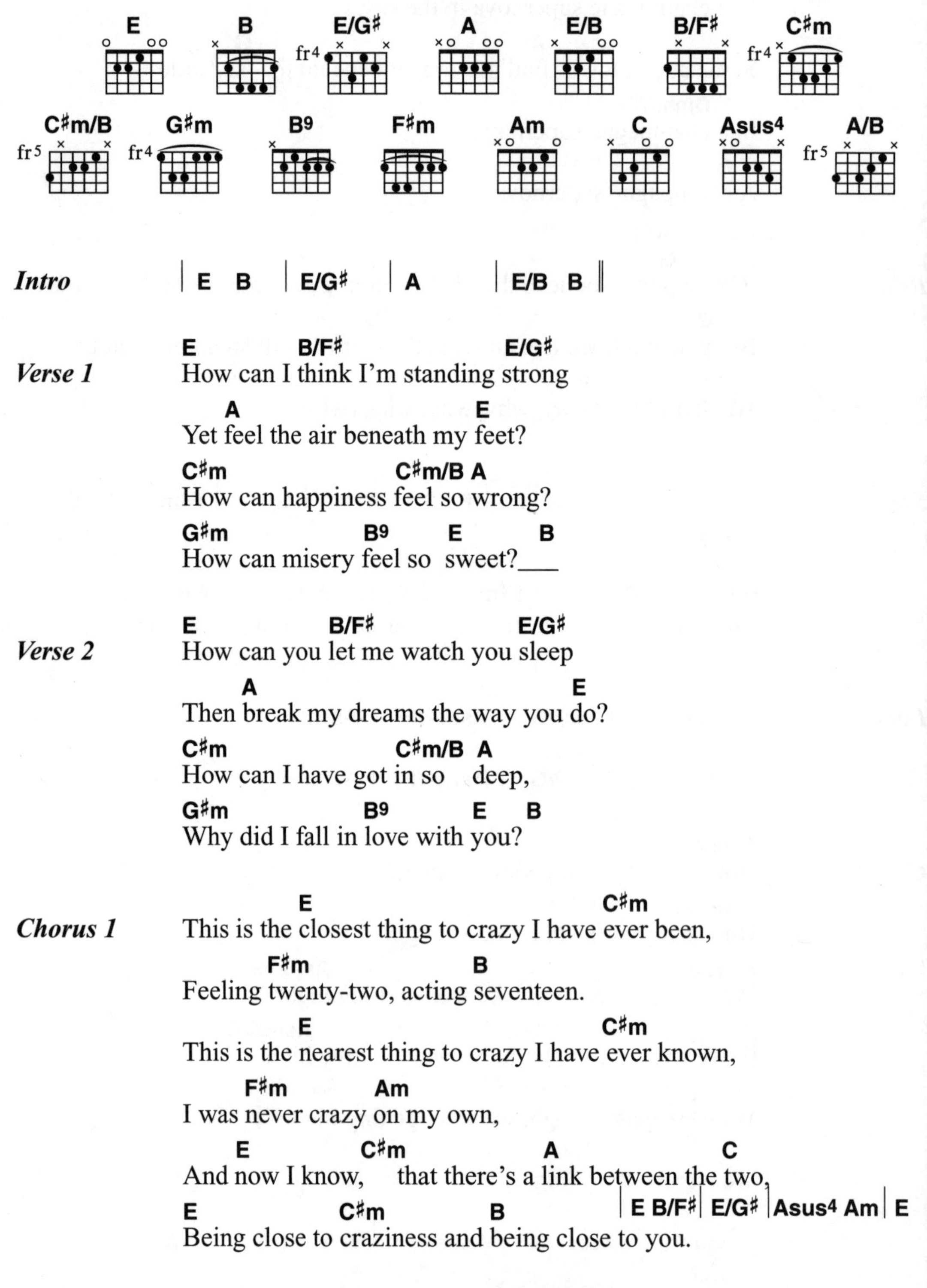

Intro | E B | E/G♯ | A | E/B B ||

Verse 1

E B/F♯ E/G♯
How can I think I'm standing strong
A E
Yet feel the air beneath my feet?
C♯m C♯m/B A
How can happiness feel so wrong?
G♯m B9 E B
How can misery feel so sweet?___

Verse 2

E B/F♯ E/G♯
How can you let me watch you sleep
A E
Then break my dreams the way you do?
C♯m C♯m/B A
How can I have got in so deep,
G♯m B9 E B
Why did I fall in love with you?

Chorus 1

E C♯m
This is the closest thing to crazy I have ever been,
F♯m B
Feeling twenty-two, acting seventeen.
E C♯m
This is the nearest thing to crazy I have ever known,
F♯m Am
I was never crazy on my own,
E C♯m A C
And now I know, that there's a link between the two,
E C♯m B | E B/F♯ | E/G♯ | Asus4 Am | E
Being close to craziness and being close to you.

Verse 3

E B/F♯ E/G♯
How can you make me fall a - part

A E
Then break my fall with loving lies?

C♯m C♯m/B A
It's so easy to break a heart,

G♯m B9 E B
It's so easy to close your eyes.

Verse 4

E B/F♯ E/G♯
How can you treat me like a child?

A E
Yet like a child I yearn for you.

C♯m C♯m/B A
How can anyone feel so wild?

G♯m B9 E B
How can anyone feel so blue?

Chorus 2

E C♯m
This is the closest thing to crazy I have ever been,

F♯m B
Feeling twenty-two, acting seventeen.

E C♯m
This is the nearest thing to crazy I have ever known,

F♯m Am
I was never crazy on my own,

E C♯m A C
And now I know, that there's a link between the two,

E C♯m B | E C♯m |
Being close to craziness and being close to you,

Outro

A B E C♯m
And being close to you,

A A/B E
And being close to you.

A Day In The Life

Words & Music by
John Lennon & Paul McCartney

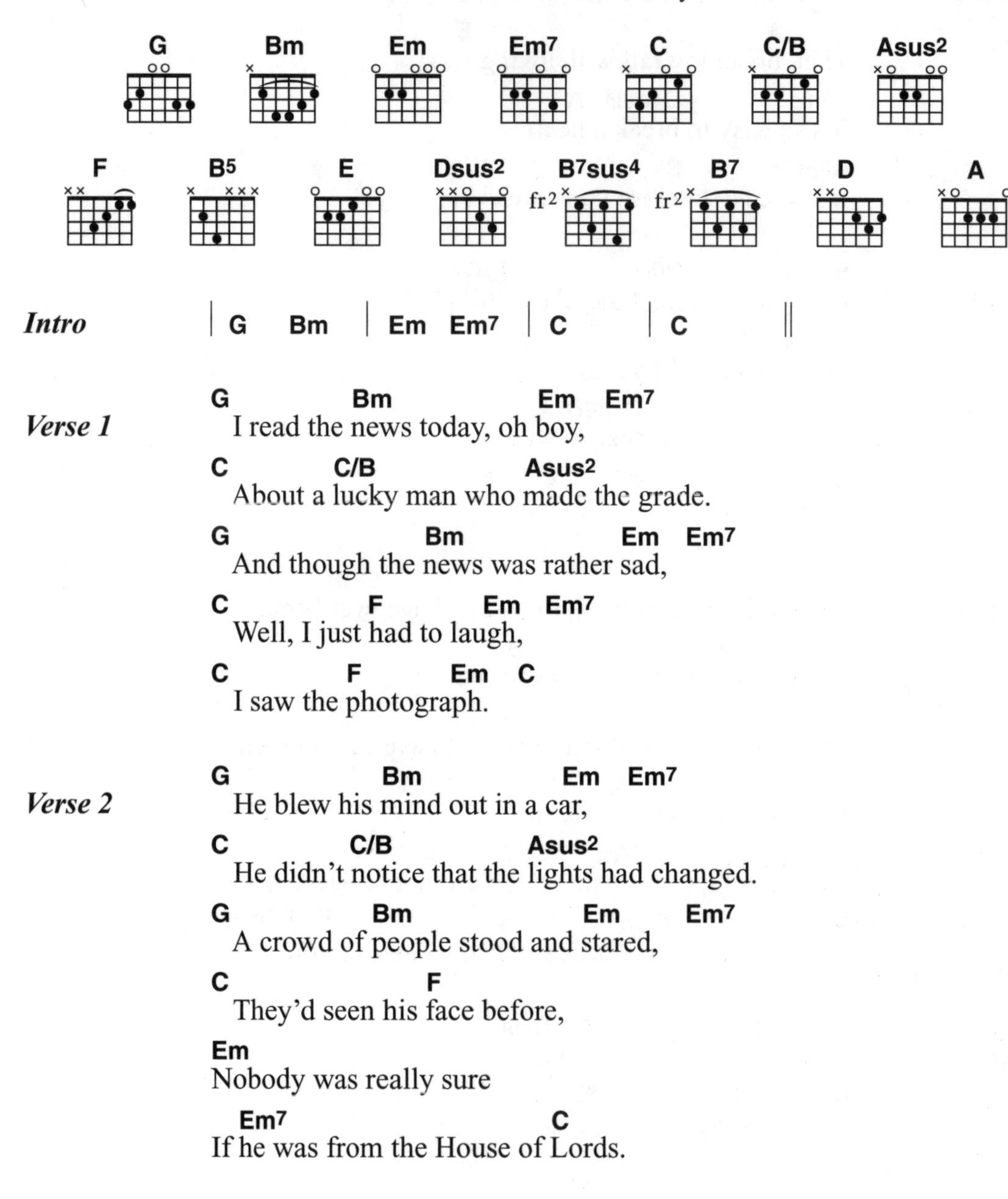

Intro | G Bm | Em Em7 | C | C ||

```
            G              Bm                  Em   Em7
Verse 1       I read the news today, oh boy,
            C          C/B                 Asus2
              About a lucky man who made the grade.
            G                       Bm                 Em    Em7
              And though the news was rather sad,
            C              F           Em   Em7
              Well, I just had to laugh,
            C            F          Em   C
              I saw the photograph.

            G              Bm                  Em   Em7
Verse 2       He blew his mind out in a car,
            C          C/B                 Asus2
              He didn't notice that the lights had changed.
            G              Bm                  Em         Em7
              A crowd of people stood and stared,
            C                    F
              They'd seen his face before,
            Em
            Nobody was really sure
               Em7                      C
            If he was from the House of Lords.
```

Verse 3

G Bm Em Em7
I saw a film today, oh boy,

C C/B Asus2
The English army had just won the war.

G Bm Em Em7
A crowd of people turned away,

C F Em
But I just had to look,

Em7 C
Having read the book,

N.C.(B5)
I'd love to turn you on.

Instrumental ‖: N.C. | N.C. | N.C. | N.C. | N.C. :‖ E | E ‖

Middle

(E) Dsus2
Woke up, got out of bed, dragged a comb across my head,

E B7sus4
Found my way downstairs and drank a cup

E B7sus4 B7
And looking up I noticed I was late. Ha, ha, ha.

E
Found my coat and grabbed my hat,

Dsus2
Made the bus in seconds flat,

E B7sus4
Found my way upstairs and had a smoke

E B7sus4
And somebody spoke and I went into a dream.

Interlude

C G D A E C G D A | E D C D ‖
Ah,__ ah,__ ah,__ ah,__ ah.__

Verse 4

G Bm Em Em7
I read the news today, oh boy,

C C/B Asus2
Four thousand holes in Blackburn, Lancashire.

G Bm Em Em7
And though the holes were rather small,

C F
They had to count them all;

Em Em7 C
Now they know how many holes it takes to fill the Albert Hall.

N.C.(B5)
I'd love to turn you on.

Instrumental ‖: N.C. | N.C. | N.C. | N.C. | N.C. :‖ E ‖

Days

Words & Music by
Ray Davies

A E D F C G Am

Intro | A | A |

Verse 1

```
A                          E
   Thank you for the days _____
      D      A          D          A         E      A
Those endless days, those sacred days   you gave   me.
                           E
I'm thinking of the days ______
 D      A     D     A        E       A
I won't forget a single day believe me.
 D       A
I bless the light,
 D       A         D        A     E        A
I bless the light that lights on you believe me.
    D          A
And though you're gone
         D       A     D      A     E          A
You're with me every single day believe me.
```

Chorus 1

```
F            C              G
Days I'll remember all my life,
F                C                  G
Days when you can't see wrong from   right,
   F       C
You took my   life
    F     C          F    C          G    C
But then I knew that very soon you'd leave me.
    F     C
But it's alright,
     F        C          F      C        G     C
Now I'm not frightened of this world believe me.
```

```
                 E                   Am
Bridge      I wish today, could be tomorrow,
                     E
            The night is long
                      Am     G    F
            It just brings sorrow let it wait,
                E
            Ah. ___

                                A        E
Verse 2     Thank you for the days _____
                 D        A          D         A          E       A
            Those endless days, those sacred days   you gave   me.
                                         E
            I'm thinking of the days ______
             D        A     D      A       E        A
            I won't forget a single day believe me.

Chorus 2    As Chorus 1

            E
Link        Days._______

Verse 3     As Verse 2

             D       A
Outro       I bless the light
             D       A          D        A      E        A
            I bless the light that shines on you believe me
                D           A
            And though you're gone
                   D          A      D      A      E        A
            You're with me every single day believe me.
            A
            Days._______
```

Dolphins

Words & Music by
Fred Neil

A A7 Bm E B♭7

Capo first fret

Intro |: A | A | A7 | A7 :|

Verse 1
```
A                 A7
  Sometimes I think about
Bm      E
  Saturday's child
A           A7
  And all about the times
Bm                          E
  When we were running wild.
```

Chorus 1
```
     Bm                      E                A    A7
I've been a-searchin' for the dolphins in the sea. __
Bm                          E               A      A7
  Ah, but sometimes I wonder, do you ever think of me?
```

Verse 2
```
A                    A7
  This old world will never change
Bm            E
  The way it's been
A               A7
  And all our ways of war
Bm                        E
  Can't change it back again.
```

Chorus 2
```
              Bm                   E            A    A7
I've been a - searchin' for the dolphins in the sea. __
Bm                          E               A      A7
  Ah, but sometimes I wonder, do you ever think of me?
```

Verse 3

A A7
Lord, I'm not the one to tell
Bm E
This old world how to get along
A A7
I only know that peace will come
Bm E
When all our hate is gone.

Chorus 3

Bm E A A7
I've been a-searchin' for the dolphins in the sea. ___
Bm E A A7
Ah, but sometimes I wonder, do you ever think of me?

Outro

A A7
This old world will never change,
A A7
This old world will never change,
A
This old world
A7 B♭7 A
Will never change. ___

Ebony And Ivory

Words & Music by
Paul McCartney

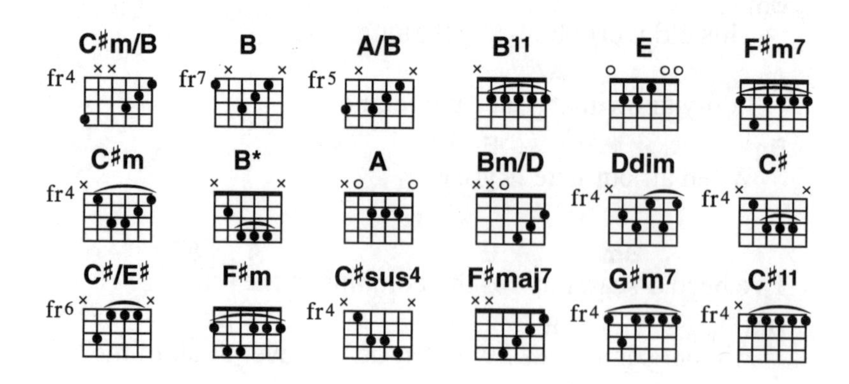

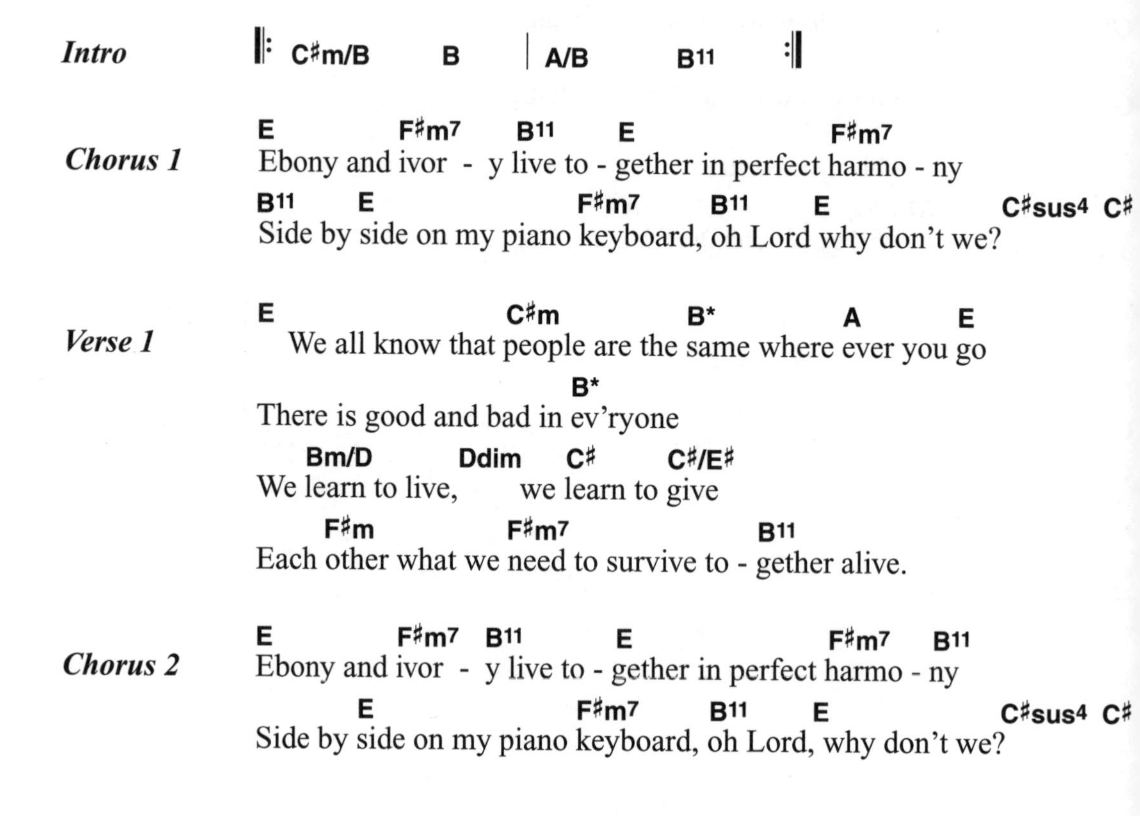

Intro ‖: C♯m/B B | A/B B11 :‖

Chorus 1

E F♯m7 B11 E F♯m7
Ebony and ivor - y live to - gether in perfect harmo - ny
B11 E F♯m7 B11 E C♯sus4 C♯
Side by side on my piano keyboard, oh Lord why don't we?

Verse 1

E C♯m B* A E
We all know that people are the same where ever you go
B*
There is good and bad in ev'ryone
Bm/D Ddim C♯ C♯/E♯
We learn to live, we learn to give
F♯m F♯m7 B11
Each other what we need to survive to - gether alive.

Chorus 2

E F♯m7 B11 E F♯m7 B11
Ebony and ivor - y live to - gether in perfect harmo - ny
E F♯m7 B11 E C♯sus4 C♯
Side by side on my piano keyboard, oh Lord, why don't we?

Bridge

| F#maj7 | G#m7 C#11 | F#maj7 | G#m7 C#11 ||

F#maj7 G#m7 C#11
Ebony, ivory living in perfect harmony

F#maj7 B11
Ebony, ivory, ooh.

Verse 2

E C#m B* A E
We all know that people are the same where ever you go

B*
There is good and bad in ev'ryone

Bm/D Ddim C# C#/E#
We learn to live, we learn to give

F#m F#m7 B11
Each other what we need to survive to - gether alive.

Chorus 3

E F#m7 B11 E F#m7 B11
Ebony and ivor - y live to - gether in perfect harmo - ny

E F#m7 B11 E C#sus4 C#
Side by side on my piano keyboard, oh Lord why don't we?

F#m7 B11
Side by side on my piano keyboard, oh Lord

E F#m7 B11 | E | F#m7 B11 |
Why don't we?——

Outro

| E | F#m7 B11 | E | F#m7 B11 |

E F#m7 B11
||: Ebony, ivory living in perfect harmony. :|| *Repeat to fade*

Every Breath You Take

Words & Music by
Sting

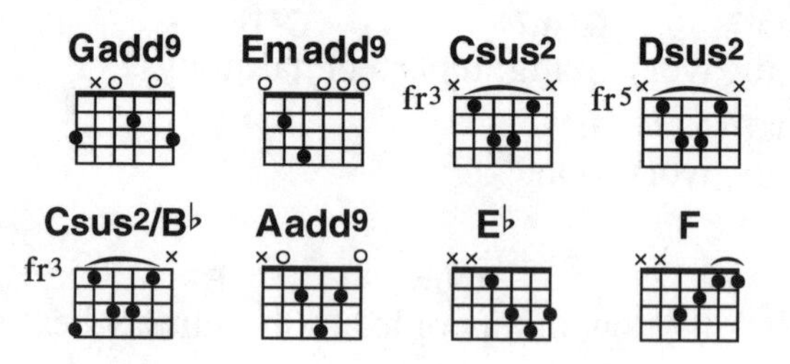

Intro | Gadd9 | Gadd9 | Emadd9 | Emadd9 |

| Csus2 | Dsus2 | Gadd9 |

Verse 1

Gadd9
Ev'ry breath you take,
Emadd9
Ev'ry move you make,
Csus2
Ev'ry bone you break,
Dsus2
Ev'ry step you take,
Emadd9
I'll be watching you.

Gadd9
Ev'ry single day,
Emadd9
Ev'ry word you say,
Csus2
Ev'ry game you play,
Dsus2
Ev'ry night you stay,
Gadd9
I'll be watching you.

horus 1

Csus2
Oh, can't you see
Csus2/B♭ Gadd9
You belong to me,
Aadd9
How my poor heart aches
Dsus2
With ev'ry step you take.
Gadd9
Ev'ry move you make,
Emadd9
Ev'ry vow you break,
Csus2
Ev'ry smile you fake,
Dsus2
Ev'ry claim you stake
Emadd9
I'll be watching you.

iddle

E♭
Since you've gone, I've been lost without a trace,
F
I dream at night I can only see your face,
E♭
I look around but it's you I can't replace,
F
I feel so cold and I long for your embrace,
E♭
I keep crying baby, baby please.

nstrumental

‖: Gadd9 | Gadd9 | Emadd9 | Emadd9 |
| Csus2 | Dsus2 | Gadd9 | Gadd9 :‖

horus 2

As Chorus 1

utro

Emadd9 Csus2
Ev'ry move you make,
Dsus2
Ev'ry step you take
Emadd9
I'll be watching you.
Emadd9
I'll be watching

‖: Gadd9 | Gadd9 | Emadd9 | Csus2 :‖
you. | | | I'll be watching *Repeat to fade*

Everything I Own

Words & Music by
David Gates

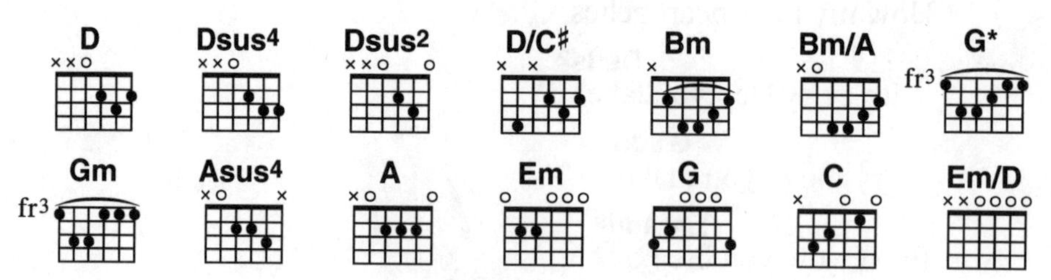

Capo seventh fret
Tune guitar slightly sharp

Intro | D Dsus4 D Dsus2 D | D Dsus4 D Dsus2 D ||

Verse 1

```
D        D/C#              Bm    Bm/A
   You sheltered me from harm,
            G*    Gm           D    Asus4 A
Kept me warm,    kept me wa - rm.
D        D/C#           Bm   Bm/A
   You gave my life to me,
          G*  Gm          D   Asus4 A
Set me free,    set me free.________
```

Link 1

```
Em             G               A Asus4 A
   The finest years I ever knew,
Em               G                 A
   Were all the years I had with you.
```

Chorus 1

```
      G              D     Em      A
And I would give any - thing I own,
G               D      Em         A
Give up my life, my heart, my home.
G              D      Em     A
I would give every - thing I own
        G                 D      Dsus4 D Dsus2 D
Just to have you back a - gain.
```

Verse 2

```
D        D/C#                  Bm    Bm/A
  You taught me how to laugh
          G*   Gm          D      Asus4  A
What a time,     what a time.
D                D/C#
  You never said too much
   Bm
But still you showed the way
      C      G                      D  Dsus4  D  Dsus2  D
And I knew     from watching you.
```

Link 2

```
Em          G                       A  Asus4  A
  Nobody else could never know
Em             G                A
  The part of me that can't let go.
```

Chorus 2

```
G                      D      Em      A
And I would give any - thing I own,
G             D          Em        A
Give up my life, my heart, my home.
G                D         Em      A
I would give every - thing I own
          G                     D
Just to have you back a - gain.
```

Bridge

```
           Bm
Is there someone you know
          Bm/A
You're loving them so,
      G
But taking them all for granted?
             Em
You may lose them one day,
             Em/D
Someone takes them away,
             C                                    A
And they don't hear the words you long to say...
```

Chorus 3

As Chorus 2

Outro

```
          G                   D
Just to touch you once again.
```

Feel

Words & Music by
Robbie Williams & Guy Chambers

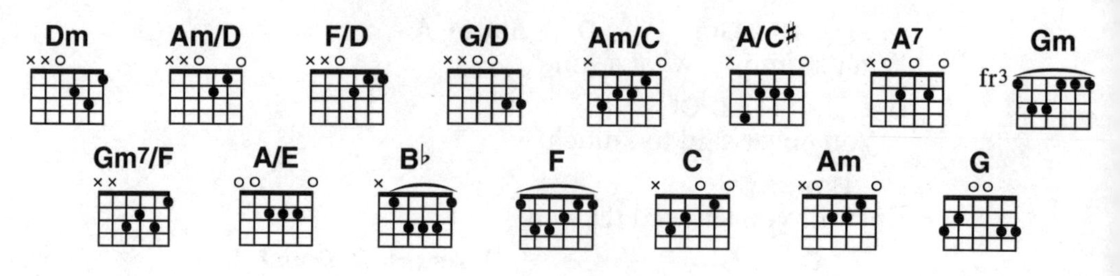

Intro ‖: Dm Am/D | F/D G/D :‖

Verse 1

```
                Dm
Come and hold my hand,
Am/C                     A/C♯
   I wanna contact the living.
A7                  Gm
   Not sure I under - stand,
Dm/F                    A/E
   This role I've been given.
A7                Dm
   I sit and talk to God,
Am/C                          A/C♯
   And he just laughs at my plans.
A7                  Gm
   My head speaks a language,
Dm/F            A/E
   I don't under - stand.
```

Chorus 1

```
A7                 B♭        F
   I just wanna feel real love,
                         C      | C      |
Feel the home that I live in.
                         B♭
'Cause I got too much life,
                         F
Running through my veins,
              C
Going to waste.
```

Verse 2

```
                    Dm
I don't wanna die,
Am/C                          A/C#
   But I ain't keen on living either.
A7                  Gm
   Before I fall in love,
Dm/F                         A/E
   I'm preparing to leave   her.
A7                   Dm
   I scare myself to death,
Am/C                        A/C#
   That's why I keep on running.
A7                  Gm
   Before I've arrived,
Dm/F                      A/E
   I can see myself coming.
```

Chorus 2

```
A7                   B♭        F
   I just wanna feel real love,
                             C  | C  |
Feel the home that I live in.
                              B♭
'Cause I got too much life,
                              F
Running through my veins,
              C    | C    |
Going to waste.
                    B♭      F
And I need to feel real love,
                         C  | C  |
And a life ever after,
                  (Dm)
I cannot give it up.
```

Instrumental ||: Dm Am/D | F/D G/D | Dm Am/D | F/D G/D :|| *Play 4 times*

Chorus 3

```
                    B♭        F
I just wanna feel real love,
                         C   | C    |
Feel the home that I live in.
                     B♭
I got too much love,
                             F
Running through my veins,
              C  | C    |
To go to waste.
```

Chorus 4

```
                    B♭       F
I just wanna feel real love,
                    C   | C    |
In a life ever after.
                              B♭
There's a hole in my soul,
                             F
You can see it in my face,
                     C  | C    |
It's a real big place.
```

Interlude

```
||: Dm   Am/D | F/D   G/D :||
```

Outro

```
                           Dm    Am
Come and hold my hand.
F                   G     Dm    Am
  I wanna contact   the living,
F            G        Dm    Am
  Not sure I under - stand,
F                G     Dm     Am
  This role I've been given.
F            G        Dm    Am
  Not sure I under - stand,
F            G        Dm    Am
  Not sure I under - stand,
F            G        Dm    Am
  Not sure I under - stand,
F            G        Dm  Am/E | F    G | Dm (fermata)  ||
  Not sure I under - stand.
```

Fernando

Words & Music by
Benny Andersson, Bjorn Ulvaeus & Stig Anderson

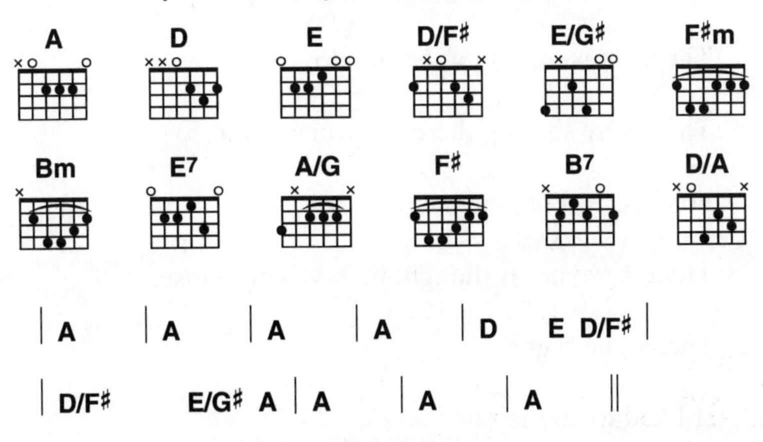

Intro | A | A | A | A | D E D/F♯ |
| D/F♯ E/G♯ A | A | A | A ||

Verse 1
A
Can you hear the drums Fernando?
F♯m
I remember long ago another starry night like this.
Bm
In the firelight Fernando,
E
You were humming to yourself and softly strumming your guitar.
I could hear the distant drums
A
And sounds of bugle calls were coming from afar.

Verse 2
A
They were closer now Fernando.
F♯m
Ev'ry hour, ev'ry minute seemed to last eternally.
Bm
I was so afraid Fernando,
E
We were young and full of life and none of us prepared to die.
And I'm not ashamed to say
A
The roar of guns and cannons almost made me cry.

```
            A                              E7
Chorus 1    There was something in the air that night,
                                           A
            The stars were bright, Fernando.
                                           E7
            They were shining there for you and me,
                                A
            For liberty, Fernando.
                      A/G                             F#
            Though we never thought that we could lose,
                       B7
            There's no regret.
                                 E7
            If I had to do the same again,
                                       A
            I would my friend, Fernando.
                                 E7
            If I had to do the same again,
                                       D     E  D/F# | D/F#     E/G#  A |
            I would my friend, Fernando.

            | A        | A  D/A  A | E        | E        | A        ||

            A
Verse 3       Now we're old and grey Fernando,
                                                                  F#m
            And since many years I haven't seen a rifle in your hand.
                                           Bm
            Can you hear the drums Fernando?
                                                                        E
            Do you still recall the fateful night we crossed the Rio Grande?

            I can see it in your eyes,
                                                                A
            How proud you were to fight for freedom in this land.

            A                              E7
Chorus 2    There was something in the air that night,
                                           A
            The stars were bright, Fernando.
                                           E7
            They were shining there for you and me,
                                A
            For liberty, Fernando.
```

cont.

A/G F♯
Though we never thought that we could lose,
B7
There's no regret.
E7
If I had to do the same again,
A
I would my friend, Fernando.

Chorus 3

A E7
There was something in the air that night,
A
The stars were bright, Fernando.
E7
They were shining there for you and me,
A
For liberty, Fernando.
A/G F♯
Though we never thought that we could lose,
B7
There's no regret.
E7
If I had to do the same again,
A
I would my friend, Fernando.
E7
𝄆 If I had to do the same again,
A
I would my friend, Fernando. 𝄇 *Repeat to fade*

The First Cut Is The Deepest

Words & Music by
Cat Stevens

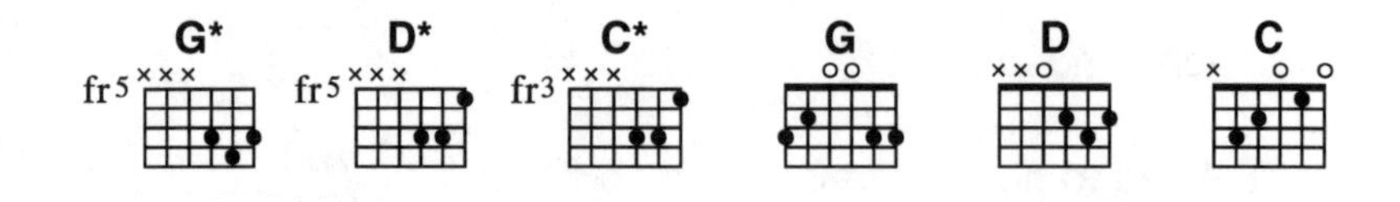

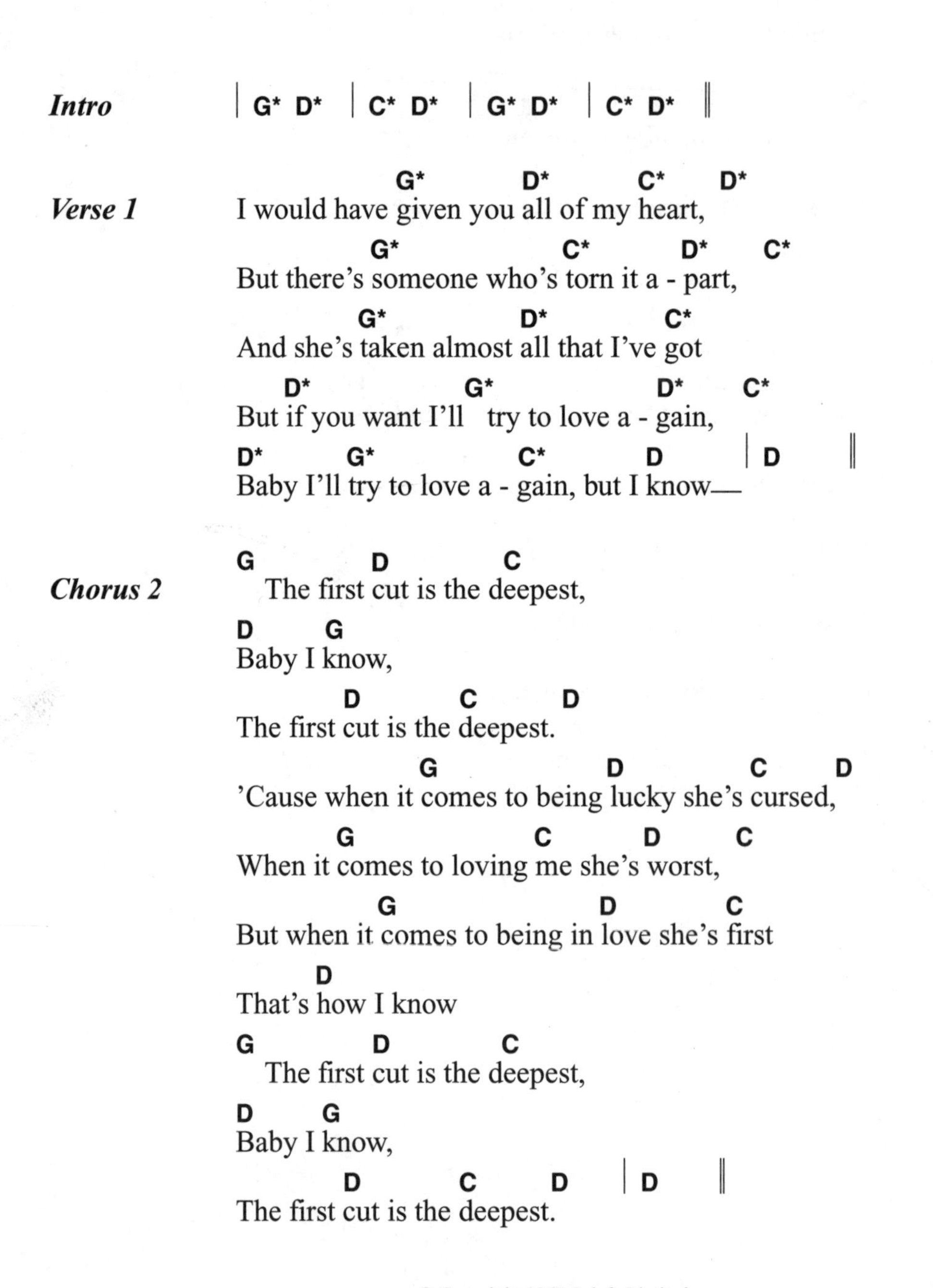

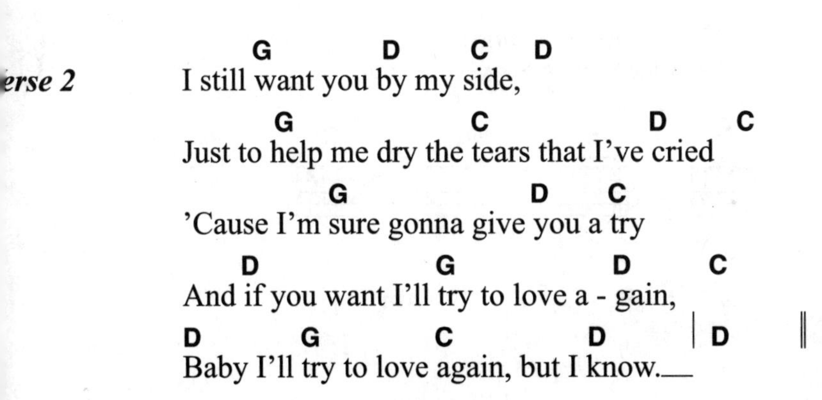

'horus 2 As Chorus 1

ink | G* D* | C* D* ‖
Ba - by I know

'horus 3 As Chorus 1

Fade out during chorus

Fisherman's Blues

Words & Music by
Mike Scott & Steve Wickham

G F Am C

```
Intro      |: G   | G   | F   | F   | Am  | Am  | C   | C   :|

              G                   F
Verse 1    I wish I was a fisherman tumbling on the seas
           Am                           C
              Far away from dry land and its bitter memories,
           G                              F
              Casting out my sweet life with abandonment and love,
           Am                                      C
              No ceiling bearing down on me save the starry sky above.
                             G
           With light in my head,
                             F   G  Am  | Am  ||
           And you in my arms.   Whoo!

Link 1     | G   | G   | F   | F   | Am  | Am  | C   | C   ||

              G                         F
Verse 2    I wish I was the brakeman on a hurtling fevered train
                      Am                                C
           Crashing a-headlong into the heartland like a cannon in the rain
                   G                               F
           With the beating of the sleepers and the burning of the coal,
           Am                                 C
           Counting the towns flashing by and the night that's full of soul.
                             G
           With light in my head,
                             F   G  Am  | Am  ||
           And you in my arms.   Whoo!

Link 2     |: G   | G   | F   | F   | Am  | Am  | C   | C   :|
```

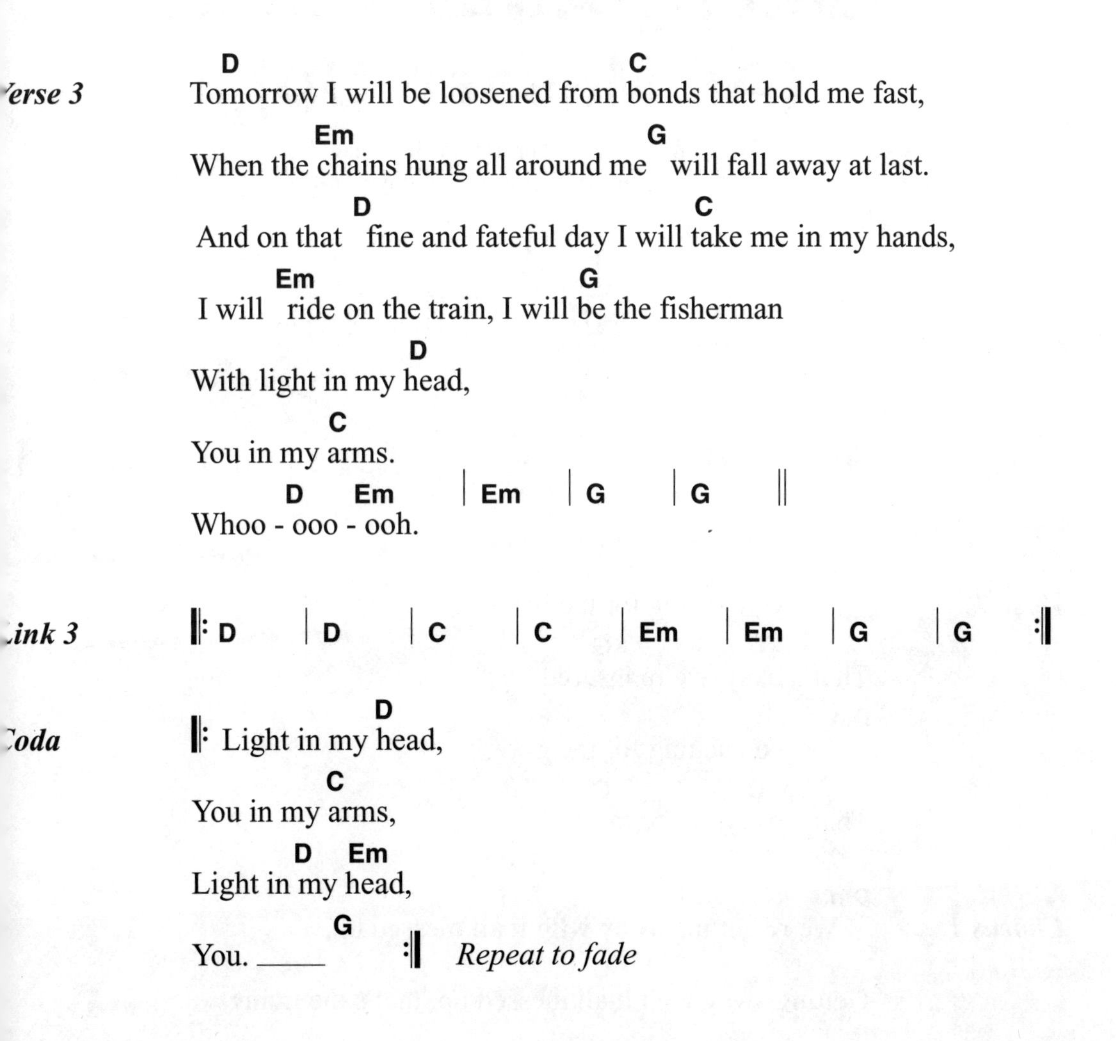

```
            D                                   C
*erse 3     Tomorrow I will be loosened from bonds that hold me fast,
                   Em                            G
            When the chains hung all around me   will fall away at last.
                      D                              C
            And on that   fine and fateful day I will take me in my hands,
                  Em                         G
            I will   ride on the train, I will be the fisherman
                                 D
            With light in my head,
                         C
            You in my arms.
                  D    Em      | Em    | G     | G     ||
            Whoo - ooo - ooh.

ink 3       |: D    | D    | C    | C    | Em    | Em    | G    | G    :|

                               D
oda         |: Light in my head,
                         C
            You in my arms,
                   D   Em
            Light in my head,
                         G
            You. ____          :|   Repeat to fade
```

Getting Away With It (All Messed Up)

Words & Music by Tim Booth, Jim Glennie,
Saul Davies, Mark Hunter & David Baynton-Power

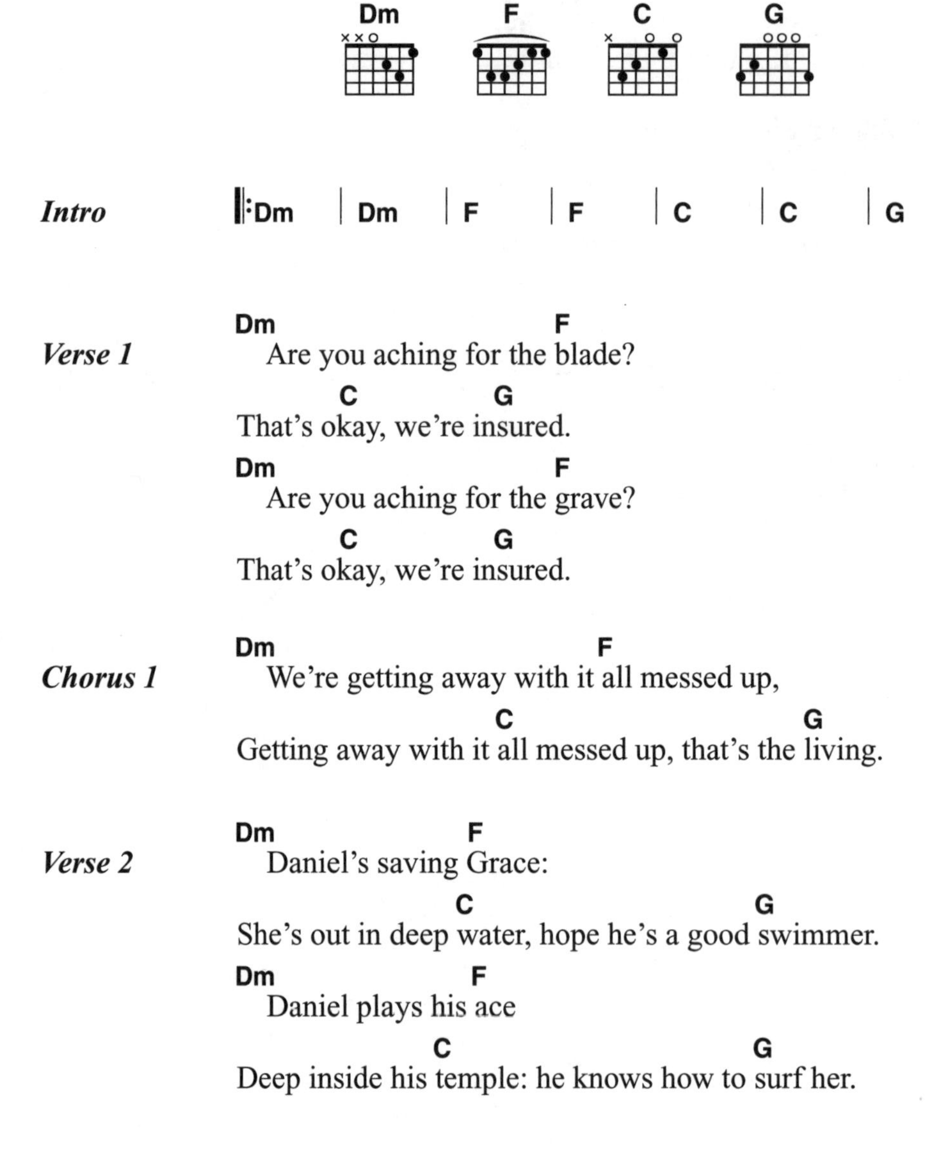

Intro | ‖: Dm | Dm | F | F | C | C | G | G :‖

Verse 1

Dm F
Are you aching for the blade?
C G
That's okay, we're insured.
Dm F
Are you aching for the grave?
C G
That's okay, we're insured.

Chorus 1

Dm F
We're getting away with it all messed up,
C G
Getting away with it all messed up, that's the living.

Verse 2

Dm F
Daniel's saving Grace:
C G
She's out in deep water, hope he's a good swimmer.
Dm F
Daniel plays his ace
C G
Deep inside his temple: he knows how to surf her.

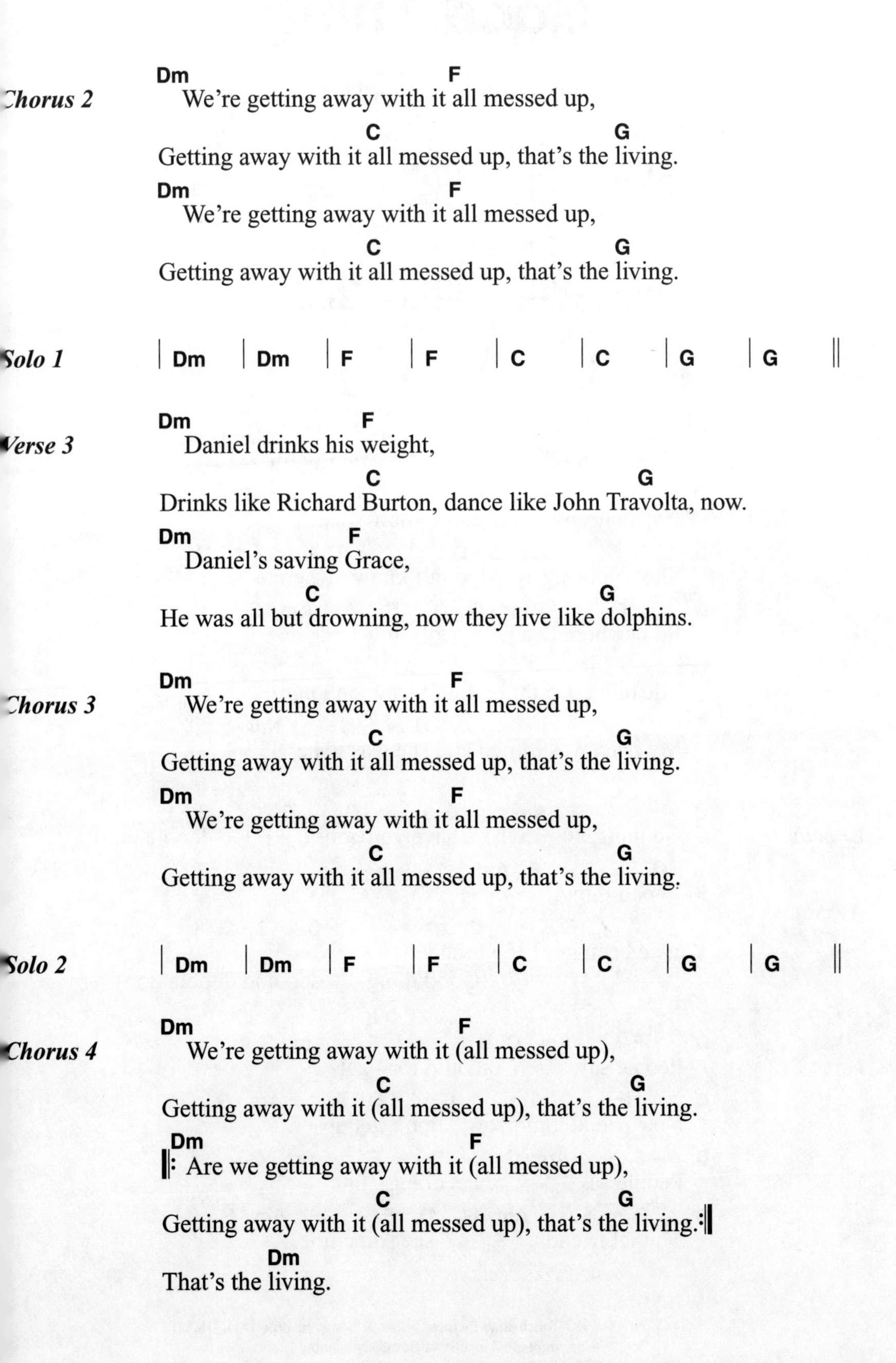

Chorus 2

```
Dm                                  F
   We're getting away with it all messed up,
                          C                           G
Getting away with it all messed up, that's the living.
Dm                                  F
   We're getting away with it all messed up,
                          C                           G
Getting away with it all messed up, that's the living.
```

Solo 1

| Dm | Dm | F | F | C | C | G | G ||

Verse 3

```
Dm                    F
   Daniel drinks his weight,
                          C                           G
Drinks like Richard Burton, dance like John Travolta, now.
Dm                 F
   Daniel's saving Grace,
                  C                          G
He was all but drowning, now they live like dolphins.
```

Chorus 3

```
Dm                                  F
   We're getting away with it all messed up,
                          C                           G
Getting away with it all messed up, that's the living.
Dm                                  F
   We're getting away with it all messed up,
                          C                           G
Getting away with it all messed up, that's the living.
```

Solo 2

| Dm | Dm | F | F | C | C | G | G ||

Chorus 4

```
Dm                                  F
   We're getting away with it (all messed up),
                          C                            G
Getting away with it (all messed up), that's the living.
  Dm                                 F
‖: Are we getting away with it (all messed up),
                          C                          G
Getting away with it (all messed up), that's the living. :‖
               Dm
That's the living.
```

Good Thing

Words & Music by
Roland Gift & David Steele

A9 D F Am G
C Em A F♯m B

Intro | A9 |: D F | Am G | D F | C G :|

Verse 1
D F Am G D F Am G
The one good thing in my life
D F Am G D F Am G
Has gone away, I don't know why.
D F Am G D F Am G
She's gone away I don't know where,
D F Am G D F Am G
Somewhere I can't fol - low her.
Em A
The one good thing didn't stay too long,
F♯m B N.C.
My back was turned and she was gone.

Chorus 1
D F Am G D F C G
Good thing, where have you gone? (Doo doobie doo)
D F Am
My good thing,
G D F C G
You've been gone too long.
(Good thing, doo doo doobie doo).

Verse 2
D F Am G D F Am G
People say I should for - get.
D F Am G D F Am G
New friend tomorrow, don't get upset.
D F Am G D F Am G
People say she's doing fine.
D F Am G D F Am G
Mutual friends I see sometime.

```
              Em                A
cont.           That's not I what I want to hear.
              F#m               B
                I want to hear she wants me near.


Chorus 2      As Chorus 1


Piano solo    | D          F  | Am   G  | D    F  | C    G  |
              (Good thing.)

              ||: D    F  | Am   G  | D    F  | C    G  :||  Play 3 times


              D      F        Am  G  D      F          Am  G
Verse 3         Then one day            she came back
              D   F      Am    G     D  F      Am  G
                I was so happy that I didn't act.
              Em                A
                Morning came into my room,
              F#m                 B          N.C.
                Caught me dreaming like a fool.


              D             F  Am  G    D         F
Chorus 3      Good thing,              my good thing
              C       G   D            F             Am
             { (Doo doo doobie doo)
             {            My, my, my good thing.
              G                 D         F  C       G
             { Where have you gone?
             {                 (Good thing,    doo doo doobie doo)
                  D            F
              My good thing,
              Am  G       D            F
              Hey-hey my good thing
              C        G              D
                (Doo doobie doo, good thing.)
              F     Am  G          D            F
               Girl,           where have you gone?
              C          G         D                  F    Am   G
             { (Doo doo doobie  doo, good thing)
             {                  It's  been              so long.


                     D     F     C      G
Outro         ||: Good God, girl!  (doo doobie doo).
                    D      F    Am  G
              Good God, girl.          :||  Repeat to fade
```

From A Distance

Words & Music by
Julie Gold

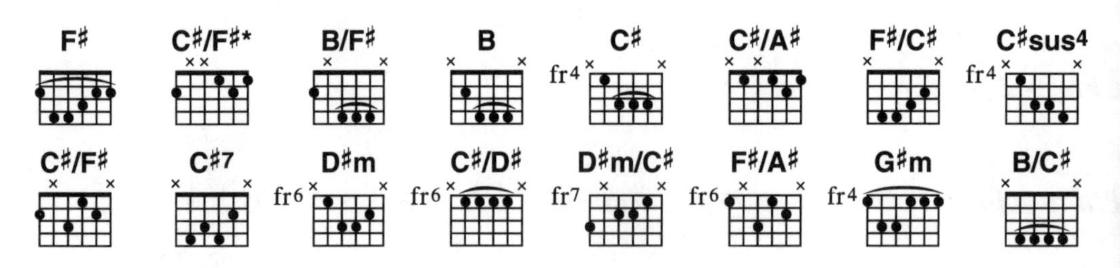

Intro | F♯ C♯/F♯* B/F♯ F♯ | B C♯ |
| F♯ C♯/A♯ B F♯/C♯ | B C♯sus4 ||

Verse 1

F♯ B/F♯ C♯/F♯ F♯
From a distance the world looks blue and green,
B C♯ C♯7 F♯ C♯/F♯ B/F♯ C♯/F♯
And the snow capped moun - tains white.
F♯ B C♯ F♯
From a distance the ocean meets the stream
B C♯ F♯ C♯/F♯ F♯
And the eagle takes to flight.

Chorus 1

B C♯ D♯m C♯/D♯ D♯m
From a distance there is harmony
D♯m/C♯ B F♯/A♯ C♯sus4 C♯
And it echoes through the land.
B F♯
It's the voice of hope,
B F♯
It's the voice of peace,
B C♯ | F♯ C♯/F♯* B/F♯ F♯ | B C♯ |
It's the voice of every man.

```
              F♯            B     C♯        F♯
Verse 2       From a distance we   all have e - nough
                   B          C♯    F♯  C♯/F♯*  B/F♯    F♯
              And no one is in need.
                   F♯             B               C♯      D♯m
              There are no guns, no   bombs, no   di - seases,
                B         C♯          F♯     C♯/F♯  F♯
              No hungry mouths to feed.

              B           C♯   D♯m         C♯/D♯  D♯m
Chorus 2      From a distance we are instruments
                   B        F♯/A♯      C♯sus4  C♯
              Marching in a common band.
                B       F♯
              Playing songs of hope,
                B       F♯
              Playing songs of peace
                      B          C♯  | F♯  C♯/F♯*  B/F♯  F♯ | B  C♯  |
              They're the songs of every man.

              B             C♯
Bridge        God is watching us,
              F♯            D♯m
              God is watching us,
              G♯m           C♯          F♯  C♯/F♯*  B  B/C♯
              God is watching us    from a distance.

Piano solo    ||: F♯   F♯/A♯   | B    C♯   :||

              | F♯  C♯/F♯*  B/F♯  F♯   | B    C♯  |
```

Verse 3

F# B C# F#
From a distance you look like my friend

B C# F# C#/F# B/F#
Even though we are at war.

F# B C# D#m
From a distance I can't comprehend

D#m/C# B C# F# C#/F# F#
What all this war is for.

Chorus 3

B C# D#m C#/D# D#m
From a distance there is harmony

D#m/C# B F#/A# C#sus4 C#
And it echoes through the land.

B F#
It's the hope of hopes,

B F#
It's the love of loves,

B C# D#m C#/D# D#m
It's the heart of every man.

Outro

B F#
It's the hope of hopes,

B F#
It's the love of loves,

B C# F# C#/F# B/F# F# | B C# | F# ‖
It's the song of every man.

Hazey Jane I

Words & Music by
Nick Drake

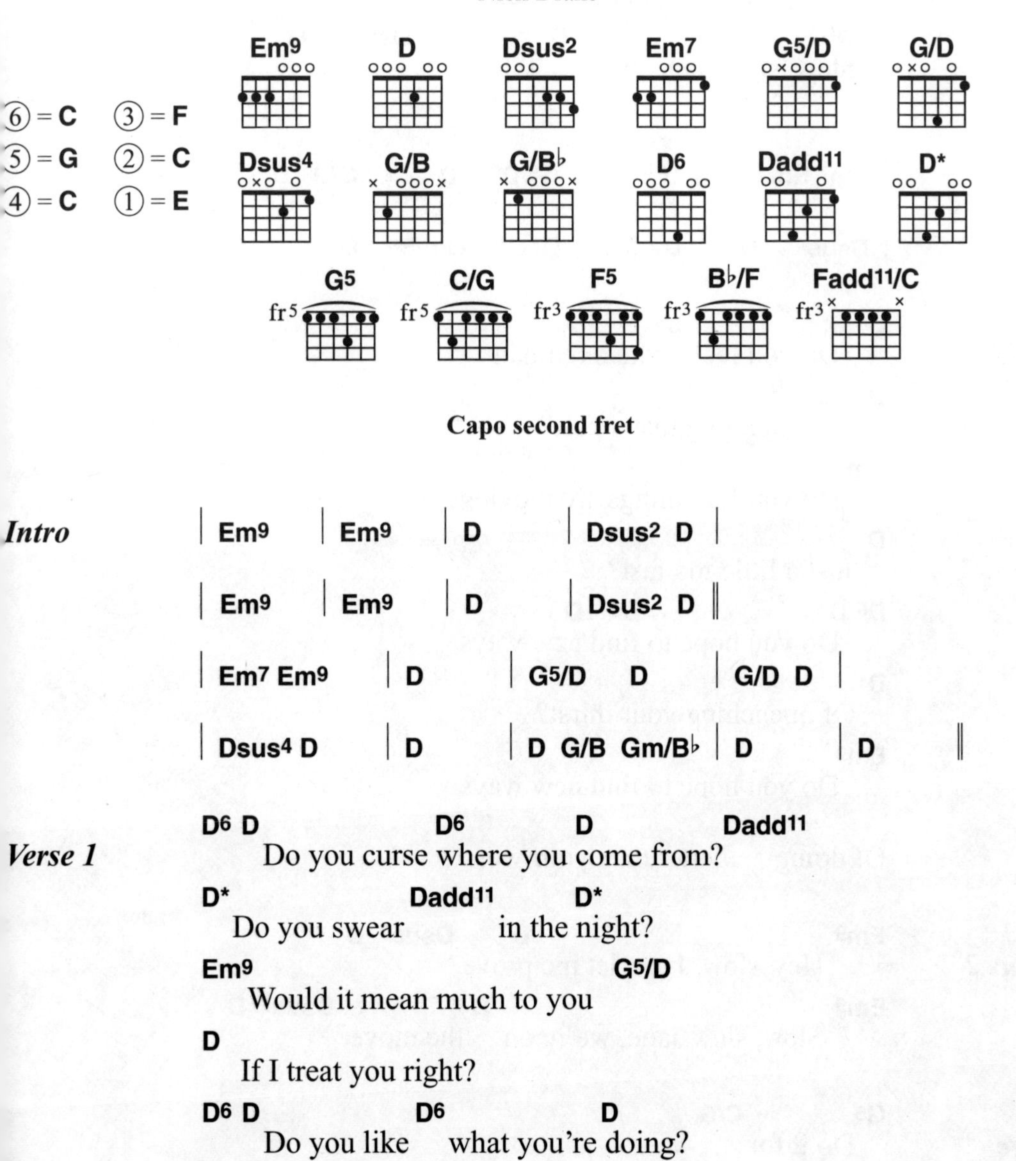

Capo second fret

Intro

Em9	Em9	D	Dsus2 D
Em9	Em9	D	Dsus2 D	
Em7 Em9	D	G5/D D	G/D D
Dsus4 D	D	D G/B Gm/B♭	D	D	

Verse 1

D6 D Do you curse (D6) where you (D) come from? (Dadd11)
D* Do you swear (Dadd11) in the night? (D*)
Em9 Would it mean much to you (G5/D)
D If I treat you right?
D6 D Do you like (D6) what you're (D) doing?
D* Would you do it some more?
Em9 Or will you stop once and wonder
What you're (D) doing it for?

Chorus 1

Em9 D Dsus2 D
Hey, slow, Jane, make sense.
Em9 D Dsus2 D
Slow, slow, Jane, cross the fence.

Link 1

| Em7 Em9 | D | G5/D D | G/D D |

| Dsus4 D | D | D G/B Gm/B♭ | D | D ||

Verse 2

D6 D D6 D
Do you feel like a remnant
D*
Of something that's past?
Em9
Do you find things are moving
D
Just a little too fast?
D6 D D6 D
Do you hope to find new ways
D*
Of quenching your thirst?
Em9
Do you hope to find new ways
D
Of doing better than your worst?

Chorus 2

Em9 D Dsus2 D
Hey, slow, Jane, let me prove,
Em9 D Dsus2 D
Slow, slow Jane, we're on the move.

Bridge

G5 C/G
Do it for you,
G5 F5
I'm sure that you would do the same for me one day.
G5 C/G
So try to be true,
B♭/F Fadd11/C
Even if it's only in your hazey way.

Link 2

| D | D G/B Gm/B♭ D | D | D ||

Verse 3

```
D6 D                D6       D
     Can you tell   if you're moving
D*
  With no mirror to see?
Em9
     If you're just riding a new man,
D
  Looks a little like me.
D6 D          D6      D
     Is it all so con - fusing,
D*
  Is it hard to believe?
Em9
     When the winter is coming
         D
Can you  sign up and leave?
```

Chorus 3

```
Em9                          D   Dsus2 D
     Hey, slow, Jane, clear your eye.
Em9                          D
     Slow, slow Jane, fly on by.
```

Outro

```
| Em9 | Em9 | D | Dsus2 D |
| Em9 | Em9 | D | Dsus2 D | Em9 | Em9 | D ||
```

Hallelujah

Words & Music by
Leonard Cohen

C G Am F E

Intro | C G ||

Verse 1

```
           C                     Am
Now I've heard there was a secret chord
    C                    Am
That David played, and it pleased the Lord
   F              G                C           G
But you don't really care for music, do you?
  C              F          G
It goes like this: the fourth, the fifth,
   Am          F
The minor fall, the major lift,
   G                E           Am
The baffled king composing Hallelujah.
```

Chorus 1

```
     F          Am          F
Hallelujah, Hallelujah, Hallelujah,
     C G C  G
Hallelu  -  jah.
```

Verse 2

```
     C                          Am
Your faith was strong but you needed proof,
    C              Am
You saw her bathing on the roof:
   F              G                 C          G
Her beauty and the moonlight overthrew you.
   C           F      G
She tied you to a kitchen chair,
   Am                       F
She broke your throne, and she cut your hair
    G               E                 Am
And from your lips she drew the Hallelujah.
```

Chorus 2

```
      F              Am            F
Hallelujah, Hallelujah, Hallelujah,
     C  G  C    G
Hallelu  -  jah.
```

Verse 3

```
     C                  Am
You say I took the name in vain,
C               Am
I don't even know the name,
    F                 G                   C          G
But if I did, well really, what's it to you?
           C                     F      G
There's a blaze of light in every word,
  Am                     F
It doesn't matter which you heard:
     G                E                  Am
The holy or the broken Hallelujah.
```

Chorus 3

```
      F              Am            F
Hallelujah, Hallelujah, Hallelujah,
     C  G  C    G
Hallelu  -  jah.
```

Verse 4

```
  C                   Am
I did my best, it wasn't much,
  C                       Am
I couldn't feel, so I tried to touch.
    F                    G                 C          G
I've told the truth, I didn't come to fool you
    C                   F        G
And even though it all went wrong
   Am                   F
I'll stand before the Lord of Song
     G                                E            Am
With nothing on my tongue  but Hallelujah.
```

Chorus 4

```
        F              Am            F
|: Hallelujah, Hallelujah, Hallelujah,
     C  G
Hallelu - jah.   :|   Repeat to fade
```

Happy Xmas (War Is Over)

Words & Music by
John Lennon & Yoko Ono

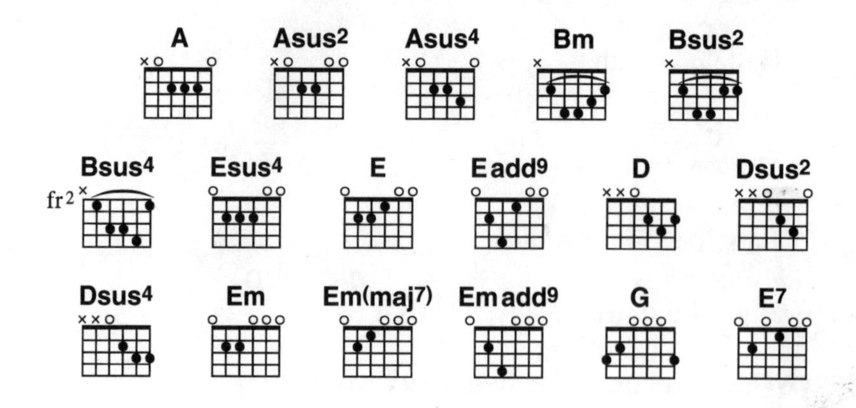

Verse 1

A **Asus2** **Asus4**
So this is Christmas

A **Bm** **Bsus2** **Bsus4**
And what have you done?

Bm **Esus4** **E** **Eadd9**
Another year over,

E **A** **Asus2** **Asus4**
A new one just begun.

A **D** **Dsus2** **Dsus4**
And so this is Christmas,

D **Em** **Em(maj7)** **Eadd9**
I hope you have fun,

Em **Asus4** **A** **Asus2**
The near and the dear ones,

A **D** **Dsus2** **Dsus4**
The old and the young.

Chorus 1

D **G**
A very Merry Christmas

A
And a happy New Year,

Em **G**
Let's hope it's a good one

D **E7**
Without any fear.

Verse 2

A Asus2 Asus4
And so this is Christmas

A Bm Bsus2 Bsus4
For weak and for strong,

Bm Esus4 E Eadd9
The rich and the poor ones,

E A Asus2 Asus4
The road is so long.

E D Dsus2 Dsus4
And so happy Christmas

D Em Em(maj7) Eadd9
For black and for white,

Em Asus4 A Asus2
For the yellow and the red ones,

A D Dsus2 Dsus4
Let's stop all the fights.

Chorus 2

As Chorus 1

Verse 3

A Asus2 Asus4
And so this is Christmas

A Bm Bsus2 Bsus4
And what have we done?

Bm Esus4 E Eadd9
Another year over,

E A Asus2 Asus4
A new one just begun.

A D Dsus2 Dsus4
And so happy Christmas,

D Em Em(maj7) Eadd9
I hope you have fun,

Em Asus4 A Asus2
The near and the dear ones,

A D Dsus2 Dsus4
The old and the young.

Chorus 3

As Chorus 1

Outro

A Asus2 Asus4 A
War is o - ver,

Bm Bsus2 Bsus4 Bm
If you want it,

Esus4 E Eadd9 E A Asus2 Asus4 A
War is o - ver now.

Happy Christmas.

A Hazy Shade Of Winter

Words & Music by
Paul Simon

Am G F E Am7 Cmaj7 C

Capo fifth fret

Intro | (Am) | (G) | (F) | (E) ||

Verse 1

```
Am    Am7  Am   Am7  Am          G
Time, time, time,     see what's become of me:
        F
While I  looked around
                 Cmaj7
For my possibilities
         G
I was so hard to please.
              Am                G
But look around, leaves are brown
          F       E              Am      Am7  Am
And the sky is a hazy shade of winter.
```

Verse 2

```
Am        Am7       G
Hear the Salvation Army band:
F
Down by the riverside, it's bound to be a better ride
       Cmaj7
Than what you've got planned,
              G
Carry your cup in your hand,
              Am                G
And look around, leaves are brown now
          F       E              Am
And the sky is a hazy shade of winter.
```

Verse 3

G
Hang on to your hopes, my friend,
F
That's an easy thing to say, but if your hopes should pass away
Cmaj7
Simply pretend
G
That you can build them again.
Am G
Look around, the grass is high,
F E Am
The fields are ripe, it's the springtime of my life.

Bridge

F C
Ah, seasons change with the scenery
G
Weaving time in a tapestry,
Am
Won't you stop and remember me
G
At any convenient time.
F
Funny how my memory skips while looking over manuscripts
Cmaj7
Of unpublished rhyme,
G
Drinking my vodka and lime.
Am G
I look around, leaves are brown now
F E Am
And the sky is a hazy shade of winter.

Coda

G F
𝄆 Look around, leaves are brown,
E Am
There's a patch of snow on the ground. 𝄇 *Play 3 times*

He Thinks He'll Keep Her

Words & Music by
Mary-Chapin Carpenter & Don Schlitz

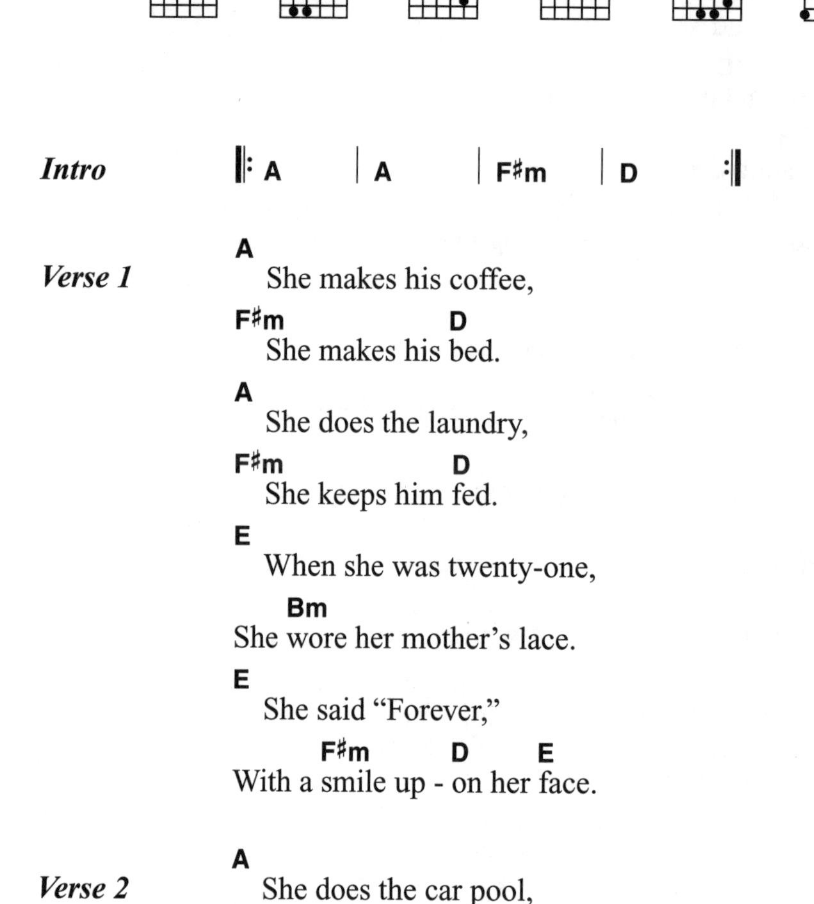

Intro ‖: A | A | F♯m | D :‖

Verse 1

```
A
   She makes his coffee,
F♯m                  D
   She makes his bed.
A
   She does the laundry,
F♯m                  D
   She keeps him fed.
E
   When she was twenty-one,
    Bm
She wore her mother's lace.
E
   She said "Forever,"
          F♯m        D       E
With a smile up - on her face.
```

Verse 2

```
A
   She does the car pool,
F♯m          D
   She P.T.A.'s,
A
   Doctors and dentists,
F♯m                  D
   She drives all day.
```

:ont.

E
When she was twenty-nine,
Bm
She de - livered number three,
E
And every Christmas card,
F♯m D E
Showed a perfect family.

:horus 1

A E D
Every - thing runs right on time,
E A
Years of prac - tise and de - sign,
E D
Spit and polish till it shines.
E
He thinks he'll keep her.
A E D
Every - thing is so be - nign,
E A
Safest place you'll ever find
E D
God for - bid you change your mind,
E
He thinks he'll keep her.

| A | A | F♯m | D ‖

Verse 3

A
She packs his suitcase,
F♯m D
She sits and waits.
A
With no expression,
F♯m D
Upon her face.
E
When she was thirty-six
Bm
She met him at their door,
E
She said "I'm sorry,
F♯m D E
I don't love you any - more."

Chorus 2 As Chorus 1

Link

```
| A      | A      | F#m    | D      ||
```

Verse 4

```
   E
For fifteen years she had a job,
     Bm
And not one raise in pay,
E
   Now she's in the typing pool at,
F#m      D      E
   Min - imum wage.
```

Chorus 3

```
A          E                   D
   Every - thing runs right on time,
          E                  A
Years of practise and de - sign,
          E           D
Spit and polish till it shines.
                    E
He thinks he'll keep her.
A          E              D
   Every - thing is so be - nign,
       E                A
Safest place you'll ever find
                E/G#                 D/F#
At least un - til you change your mind,
                    E
He thinks he'll keep her.
```

Outro

```
|: A     | A      | F#m    | D      :| Play 3 times
| A      | A      | F#m    | D  E   | A      ||
```

A Horse In The Country

Words & Music by
Michael Timmins

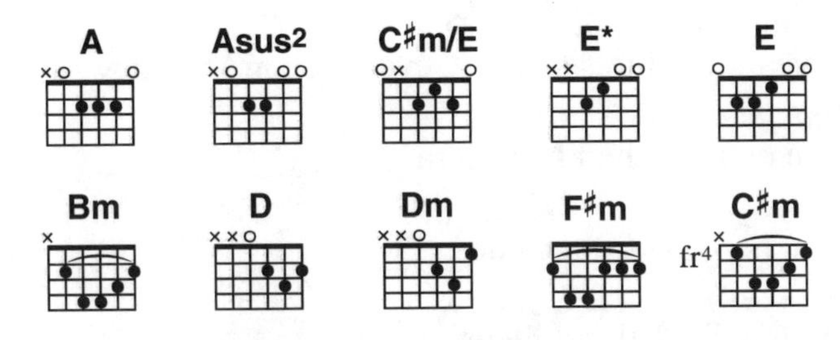

Intro | A | Asus2 A | C♯m/E | E C♯m/E | E | E |

Verse 1

```
A                        Asus2   A
   The money would be pretty good
     E
If a quart of milk, was still a dollar,
Bm                                 A            Asus2  A
   Or even if a quart of milk were still a   quart.
          D
And the hours, well, I don't mind
            A                     (Asus2)    (A)
How they creep on by like an old love of mine
         Bm                        E                       A   Asus2  A
It's the years that simply disappear that are doing me in.
```

Pre-Chorus 1

```
D           E
   Guess I married too young
        A                           D
Yeah, nineteen was just too young,
Bm
   But sometimes you meet someone
             A
And your guts just burn.
D                                  E
   It's not that I don't love him anymore
                 A
It's just that when I hear him
          D
Coming through that front door
     Bm            E                       A        Asus2  A
My heart doesn't race like it did once before.
```

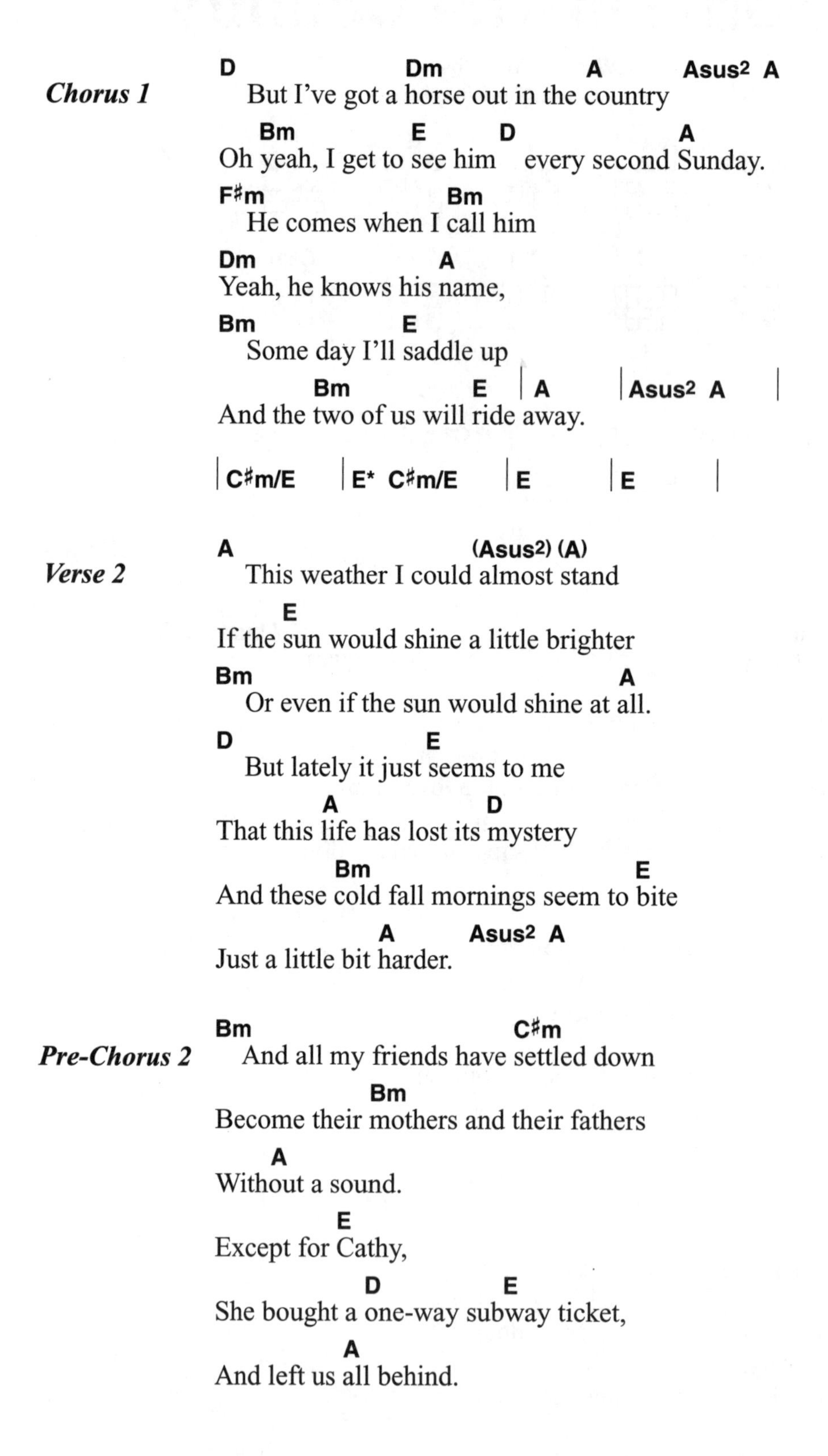

Chorus 1

D Dm A Asus2 A
But I've got a horse out in the country

Bm E D A
Oh yeah, I get to see him every second Sunday.

F♯m Bm
He comes when I call him

Dm A
Yeah, he knows his name,

Bm E
Some day I'll saddle up

Bm E | A | Asus2 A |
And the two of us will ride away.

| C♯m/E | E* C♯m/E | E | E |

Verse 2

A (Asus2) (A)
This weather I could almost stand

E
If the sun would shine a little brighter

Bm A
Or even if the sun would shine at all.

D E
But lately it just seems to me

A D
That this life has lost its mystery

Bm E
And these cold fall mornings seem to bite

A Asus2 A
Just a little bit harder.

Pre-Chorus 2

Bm C♯m
And all my friends have settled down

Bm
Become their mothers and their fathers

A
Without a sound.

E
Except for Cathy,

D E
She bought a one-way subway ticket,

A
And left us all behind.

Chorus 2

```
D                 Dm              A
   But I've got a horse out in the country
    Bm            E        D              A
Oh yeah, I get to see him   every second Sunday.
F#m                Bm
   He comes when I call him
Dm                A
Yeah, he knows his name,
Bm               E
   Some day I'll saddle up
          Bm              E  | A       | Asus2 A     |
And the two of us will ride away.

| C#m/E      | E* C#m/E     | E       | E        |
```

Outro

```
A                        Asus2 A
   This town wouldn't be  so  bad
    E
If a girl could trust her instincts,
Bm              E               A
   Or even if a girl could trust a boy.
```

I Don't Know Where It Comes From

Words & Music by Andy Bell, Mark Gardener,
Laurence Colbert & Stephen Queralt

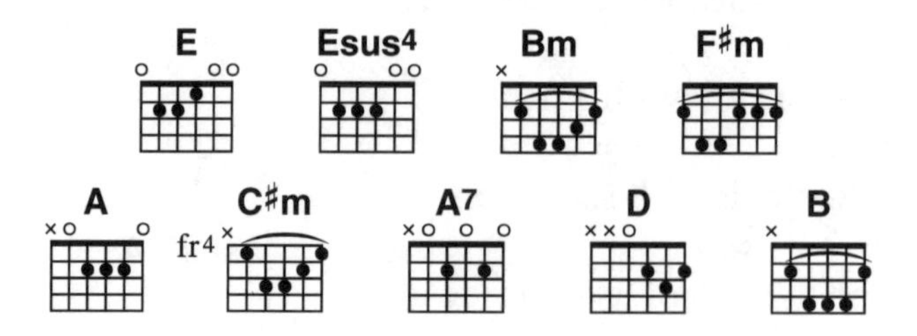

Verse 1

E Esus4 E Bm
There's something moving through the air,

F♯m
Years ago it wasn't there,

F♯m A E Esus4
If people feel it , they don't care.____

Verse 2

E Esus4 E Bm
Seems like every - body's telling lies

F♯m
A piece is missing from their lives

F♯m A E Esus4
They're never going to be surprised.

Chorus 1

E A
I don't know where it comes from,

E C♯m
I don't know where it comes from,

E A
I don't know where it comes from,

A7 E Esus4
Don't ask me where it comes from.

Verse 3

E Esus4 E Bm
Turned on the ra - dio to - night,

F♯m
And I was overwhelmed with shite,

F♯m A E Esus4
I got so low, I couldn't fight.

Verse 4

E Esus4 E Bm
What's going on, I can't de - fine,
F#m
How is it everyone's re - signed,
F#m A E Esus4
We're so uptight, we can't tell why.

Chorus 2

E A
I don't know where it comes from, (don't ask me)
E C#m
I don't know where it comes from, (don't ask me)
E A
I don't know where it comes from, (don't ask me)
A7 E Esus4
Don't ask me where it comes from.

Chorus 3 As Chorus 2

Guitar solo

| A | D | B | E Esus4 | A | D | B | E |
| A | D | B | E Esus4 | A | D | B | B ||

Verse 5 As Verse 1

Verse 6 As Verse 2

Outro

E A
I don't know where it comes from, (don't ask me)
E C#m
I don't know where it comes from, (don't ask me)
E A
I don't know where it comes from, (don't ask me)
A7 E
Don't ask me where it comes from.
E A
I don't know where it comes from, (don't ask me)
E C#m
I don't know where it comes from, (don't ask me)
E A
I don't know where it comes from, (don't ask me)
A7 E
Don't ask me where it comes from.

I Fought In A War

Words & Music by
Belle & Sebastian

Em A C B7 G Am D

Verse 1

```
Em   N.C.
     I fought in a war
        A    N.C.
And I left my friends behind me
        C          N.C.
To go looking for the enemy,
         B7       N.C.
And it wasn't very long
Em   N.C.
     Before I would stand
        A         N.C.
With another boy in front of me,
        C         N.C.
And a corpse that just fell into me
            B7       N.C.
With the bullets flying round.
```

Chorus 1

```
           G                               Am
And I reminded myself of the words you said

When we were getting on.
        C
And I bet you're making shells back home
       B7                            G
For a steady boy to wear, round his neck.
                                  Am
Well it won't hurt to think of you
                                      C
As if you're waiting for this letter to arrive,
                 B7
Because I'll be here quite a while.
```

Verse 2

Em
I fought in a war
A
And I left my friends behind me
C
To go looking for the enemy,
B7
And it wasn't very long
Em
Before I found out
A
That the sickness there ahead of me
C
Went beyond the bedsit infamy
B7 D
Of the decade gone before.

Chorus 2

G Am
I reminded myself of the words you sang
When we were getting on,
C
And I bet you're making shells back home
B7 G
For a steady man to wear, round his neck.
Am
Well it won't hurt to think of you
C
As if you're waiting for this letter to arrive,
B7
Because I'll be here quite a while.

Instrumental

Em	Em	Am	Am
C	C	B7	B7
Em	Em	A	A
C	C	B7	D	

Verse 3

```
Em
   I fought in a war,
 A
I didn't know where it would end.
  C
It stretched before me infinitely,
 B7
I couldn't really think
Em
   Of the day beyond now,
             A
Keep your head down pal, there's trouble plenty.
C
In this hour, this day
           B7
I can see hope, I can see light.
```

Chorus 3

```
    G                              Am
I reminded myself of the looks you gave

When we were getting on.
       C
And I bet you're making shells back home
     B7                              G
For a steady man to wear, round his neck.
                             Am
Well it won't hurt to think of you
                            C
As if you're waiting for this letter to arrive,
              B7            D
Because I'll be here quite a while.
```

Instrumental

```
| Em  | Em  | Am  | Am  |
| C   | C   | B7  | B7  |
| Em  | Em  | A   | A   |
| C   | C   | B7  | D   ||
```

I Say A Little Prayer

Words by Hal David
Music by Burt Bacharach

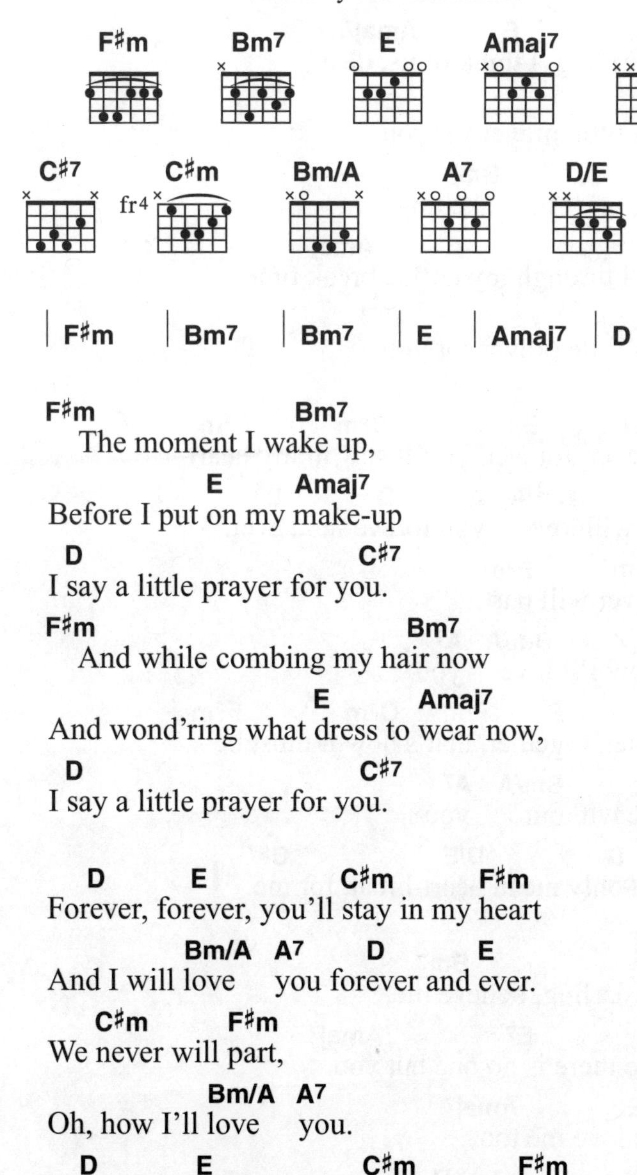

Intro | F♯m | Bm7 | Bm7 | E | Amaj7 | D | C♯7 |

Verse 1

```
F♯m                        Bm7
    The moment I wake up,
                  E        Amaj7
Before I put on my make-up
 D                         C♯7
I say a little prayer for you.
F♯m                                Bm7
    And while combing my hair now
                       E         Amaj7
And wond'ring what dress to wear now,
 D                         C♯7
I say a little prayer for you.
```

Chorus 1

```
    D        E         C♯m       F♯m
Forever, forever, you'll stay in my heart
             Bm/A   A7      D         E
And I will love     you forever and ever.
    C♯m         F♯m
We never will part,
                 Bm/A   A7
Oh, how I'll love       you.
   D         E             C♯m           F♯m
Together, together, that's how it must be.
                  Bm/A      A7
To live without           you
          D            D/E             C♯7
Would only mean heart-break for me.
```

Verse 2

```
F#m                 Bm7
   I run for the bus, dear,
                 E          Amaj7
While riding, I think of us, dear,
  D                          C#7
I say a little prayer for you.
F#m                 Bm7
   At work I just take time
                      E        Amaj7
And all through my coffee break time
  D                          C#7
I say a little prayer for you.
```

Chorus 2

```
      D        E              C#m        F#m
|: Forever, forever, you'll stay in my heart
             Bm/A   A7      D          E
And I will love     you forever and ever.
    C#m        F#m
We never will part,
               Bm/A   A7
Oh, how I'll love     you.
  D        E             C#m         F#m
Together, together, that's how it must be.
             Bm/A   A7
To live without      you
        D          D/E            C#7
Would only mean heart-break for me. :|
```

Middle 1

```
F#m                 Bm7
   My darling, believe me,
                E7         Amaj7
For me there is no one but you.
    D/E          Amaj7
Please love me too,
D/E              Amaj7
I'm in love with you.
D/E            Amaj7
Answer my prayer, baby,
D/E                Amaj7
Say you love me too,
   D/E          Amaj7
Answer my prayer, please.
```

```
                D          E               C#m          F#m
Chorus 3        Forever, forever, you'll stay in my heart
                             Bm/A  A7        D          E
                And I will love    you forever and ever.
                   C#m        F#m
                We never will part,
                               Bm/A  A7
                Oh, how I'll love    you.
                 D          E              C#m           F#m
                Together, together, that's how it must be.
                              Bm/A  A7
                To live without     you
                     D          D/E             C#7
                Would only mean heart-break for me.

                F#m                   Bm7
Outro              My darling, believe me,
                                E7          Amaj7
                For me there is no one but you.
                   D/E          Amaj7
                Please love me too.
                  D/E           Amaj7
                ||: This is my prayer,
                  D/E           Amaj7
                Answer my prayer now, baby. :||   Repeat to fade
                                                  with vocal ad lib.
```

I See A Darkness

Words & Music by
Will Oldham

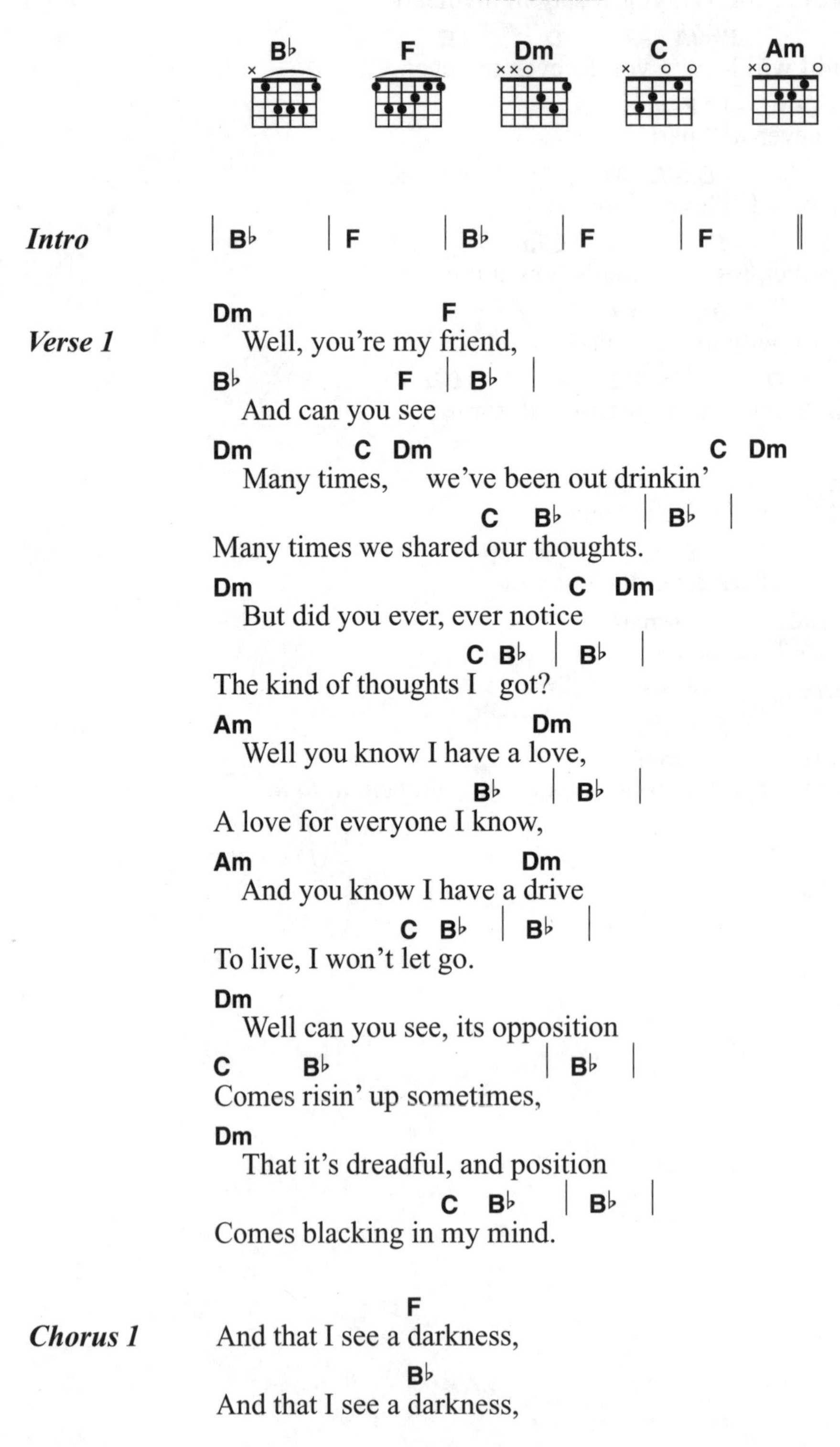

Intro | B♭ | F | B♭ | F | F ||

Verse 1

Dm F
Well, you're my friend,
B♭ F | B♭ |
And can you see
Dm C Dm C Dm
Many times, we've been out drinkin'
C B♭ | B♭ |
Many times we shared our thoughts.
Dm C Dm
But did you ever, ever notice
C B♭ | B♭ |
The kind of thoughts I got?
Am Dm
Well you know I have a love,
B♭ | B♭ |
A love for everyone I know,
Am Dm
And you know I have a drive
C B♭ | B♭ |
To live, I won't let go.
Dm
Well can you see, its opposition
C B♭ | B♭ |
Comes risin' up sometimes,
Dm
That it's dreadful, and position
C B♭ | B♭ |
Comes blacking in my mind.

Chorus 1

F
And that I see a darkness,
B♭
And that I see a darkness,

cont.

```
                  F
And that I see a darkness,
                  B♭
And that I see a darkness.
                            F
Did you know how much I love you?
                             B♭
Is there hope that somehow you
                        F        | F  |
Can save me from this darkness?
```

Verse 2

```
Dm
   Well I hope that someday buddy,
                       F
We have peace in our lives,
                  Dm                        F
Together, or a - part, alone, or with our wives.
                        Dm
And we can stop our whoring,
                         B♭
And pull the smiles in - side,
                     F
And light it up for ever,
                      Am
And never go to sleep,
                       C
My best unbeaten brother,
                 Am  | B♭ |
This isn't all I see.
```

Chorus 2

```
B♭        F
   Or will I see a darkness,
                B♭
Oh no I see a darkness,
                F
Oh no I see a darkness,
                B♭
Oh no I see a darkness.
                            F
Did you know how much I love you?
                             B♭
Is there hope that somehow you
                        F
Can save me from this darkness?
```

I Got You Babe

Words & Music by
Sonny Bono

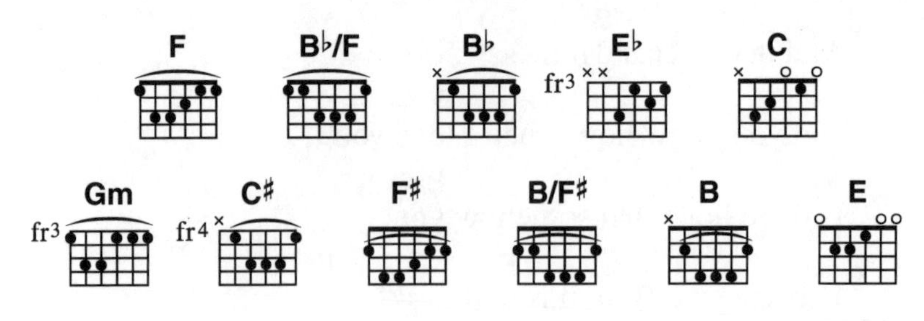

Intro | F B♭/F | F B♭/F ||

Verse 1

F B♭/F
They say we're young and we don't know,
F B♭ E♭ C
We won't find out until ___ we grow.
F B♭/F
Well I don't know if all that's true
F B♭ E♭ C
'Cause you got me and baby I got you.

Chorus 1

F B♭/F F B♭/F
Babe, I got you babe,
F B♭/F
I got you babe.

Verse 2

F B♭/F
They say our love won't pay the rent,
F B♭ E♭ C
Before it's earned, our money's all been spent.
F B♭/F
I guess that's so, we don't have a plot,
F B♭ E♭ C
But at least I'm sure of all the things we got.

Chorus 2

F B♭/F F B♭/F
Babe, I got you babe,
F N.C.
I got you babe.

```
           Gm              C
Bridge     I got flowers in the spring,
             Gm              C
           I got you to wear my ring.
                         F                 B♭/F
           And when I'm sad, you're a clown,
                      B♭                        C         C♯
           And if I get scared you're always around. ____

             F♯                        B/F♯
Verse 3    Don't let them say your hair's too long,
                   F♯                  B     E        C♯
           'Cause I don't care, with you I can't go wrong.
                 F♯               B/F♯
           Then put your little hand in mine,
           F♯                       B          E          C♯
           There ain't no hill or mountain   we can't climb.

           F♯     B/F♯   F♯          B/F♯
Chorus 3   Babe,   I got you babe,
               F♯          B/F♯
           I got you babe.

           | F♯   B/F♯   | F♯    C♯    ||

           F♯                B/F♯             F♯              C♯
Coda          I got you to hold my hand, I got you to understand.
           F♯                B/F♯             F♯              C♯
              I got you to walk with me, I got you to talk with me.
           F♯                B/F♯               F♯            C♯
              I got you to kiss goodnight, I got you to hold me tight.
           F♯              B/F♯             F♯           C♯
              I got you, I won't let go; I got you to love me so.

Outro      | F♯   B/F♯   | F♯    C♯    |

           N.C.    B         F♯        Pause
                 I got you   babe.
           F♯ B/F♯            F♯        C♯
                  I got you   babe.
                  F♯              B/F♯   F♯            C♯
           ||: I got you babe.   I got you babe.       :||   Repeat to fade
```

In The Groove Again

Words & Music by
Simon Eugene

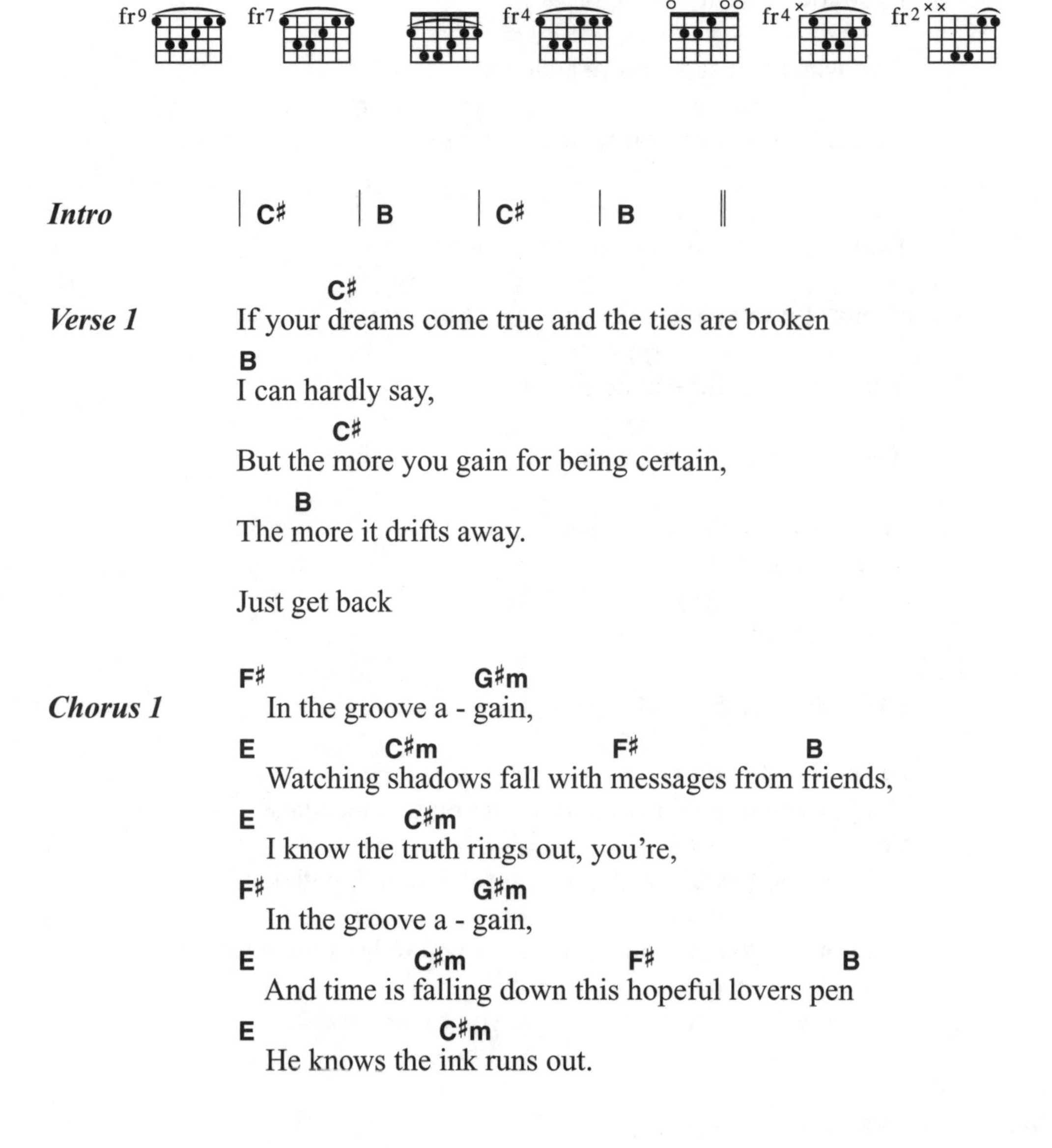

Intro | C♯ | B | C♯ | B ||

Verse 1

C♯
If your dreams come true and the ties are broken
B
I can hardly say,
C♯
But the more you gain for being certain,
B
The more it drifts away.

Just get back

Chorus 1

F♯ G♯m
In the groove a - gain,
E C♯m F♯ B
Watching shadows fall with messages from friends,
E C♯m
I know the truth rings out, you're,
F♯ G♯m
In the groove a - gain,
E C♯m F♯ B
And time is falling down this hopeful lovers pen
E C♯m
He knows the ink runs out.

```
                C#
Verse 2    And the burning light can not be questioned
                  B
           When you really have no say,
                  C#
           'Cause the more you move in the wrong direction,
               B
           The greater is the pain.

           Just get back

           F#                   G#m
Chorus 2     In the groove a - gain,
           E          C#m                 F#            B
             Watching shadows fall with messages from friends,
           E            C#m
             I know the truth rings out, you're,
           F#                   G#m
             In the groove a - gain,
           E             C#m             F#             B
             And time is falling down this hopeful lovers pen
           E               C#m
             He knows the ink runs out.

           G#m        B       C#m         E
Bridge 1     Words that told me,   in arms that hold me
              G#m          B          C#m     F#sus4 F#
           They always help the   wounds to soothe.
                G#m                B
           But the thought of simply hoping
           C#m              E
           Fills me with for - boding,
                        G#m           B          C#    F#sus4 F#
           'Cause there's always things I    fear I'd lose.
```

Verse 3

```
            C#
But if your sun dies down on a ripped up curtain
   B
You really have no say.
   C#                              B
And if by chance you get to hurt it you take away the pain.

If you get back
```

Chorus 3

```
F#                 G#m
  In the groove a - gain,
E          C#m              F#           B
  Watching shadows fall with messages from friends,
E           C#m
  I know the truth rings out, you're,
F#                 G#m
  In the groove a - gain,
E              C#m             F#             B
  And time is falling down this hopeful lovers pen
E               C#m
  He knows the ink runs out.
```

Bridge 2

```
G#m        B      C#m        E
  Heights of chance,    they never stop me
     G#m         B       C#m    F#sus4 F#
From falling down   on my back.
G#m        B     C#m             E
Roots often are faded, memory has in - vaded,
    G#m             B            C#m   F#sus4 F#
And lowers my chin    into my mind.
```

```
                          C#
Verse 4         But if your dreams come true and the ties are broken
                B
                I can hardly say,
                   C#
                But if by chance you get to hurting,
                B
                Take away the pain

                If you get back

                F#                    G#m
Chorus 4          In the groove a - gain,
                E           C#m              F#             B
                  Watching shadows fall with messages from friends,
                E            C#m
                  I know the truth rings out, you're,
                F#                    G#m
                  In the groove a - gain,
                E             C#m              F#            B
                  And time is falling down this hopeful lovers pen
                E               C#m
                  He knows the ink runs out.

                C#
Outro           If you dreams come true and the ties are broken
                B
                I can hardly say,
                     C#
                But the more you gain for being certain,
                   B
                The more it drifts away.
```

In The Summertime

Words & Music by
Ray Dorset

E A6 B6 A B

Intro

| E | E | E | E | A6 | A6 |
| E | E | B6 | A6 | E | E ‖ |

Verse 1

E
In the summertime when the weather is high

You can stretch right up and touch the sky;

A E
When the weather's fine you got women, you got women on your min

B A E
Have a drink, have a drive, go out and see what you can find.

Verse 2

E
If her Daddy's rich take her out for a meal,

If her Daddy's poor just do what you feel,

A E
Scoot along the lane, do a ton or a ton and twenty-five.

B A E
When the sun goes down you can make it make it good in a lay-by.

Verse 3

E
We're no threat, people, we're not dirty, we're not mean.

We love everybody but we do as we please.

A E
When the weather's fine we go fishing or go swimming in the sea.

B A E
We're always happy, life's for living, yeah, that's our philosophy.

Verse 4

```
     E
Sing along with us, di-di-di-di-di,

Da-da-da-da-da, yeah we're hap-happy
A                                    E
Da-da-da, dee-da-da, dee-da-da, da-da-da.
   B                          A           E
Da-da-da-da-da, alright alright, da-da-da-da-da-da.

Alright!
```

Instrumental

```
| E    | E    | E    | E    | A6   | A6   |
| E    | E    | B6   | A6   | E    | E    ||
```

Verse 5

```
                E
When the winter's here, yeah it's party time,

Bring a bottle, wear your wrap, 'cause it'll soon be summer time.
                A                                          E
And we'll sing again, we'll go driving or maybe we'll settle down.
            B
If she's rich, if she's nice,
                 A                      E
Bring your friends and we'll all go into town.
```

Instrumental

```
| E    | E    | E    | E    | A6   | A6   |
| E    | E    | B6   | A6   | E    | E    ||
```

Verse 6 As Verse 1

Verse 7 As Verse 2

Verse 8 As Verse 3

Coda

```
     E
Sing along with us, di-di-di-di-di,

Da-da-da-da-da, yeah we're hap-happy.
A                                    E
Da-da-da, dee-da-da, dee-da-da, da da da.
```

Fade out

If You're Not The One

Words & Music by
Daniel Bedingfield

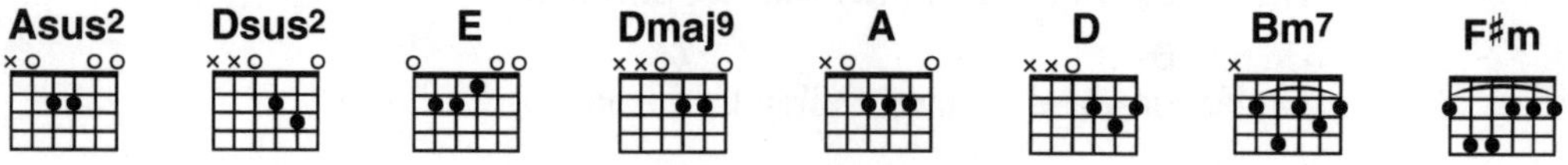

Asus2 Dsus2 E Dmaj9 A D Bm7 F♯m

Capo first fret

Verse 1

Asus2
If you're not the one,
Dsus2
Then why does my soul feel glad today?
Asus2
If you're not the one,
Dsus2
Then why does my hand fit yours this way?
Asus2
If you are not mine,
Dsus2
Then why does your heart return my call?
Asus2
If you are not mine,
Dsus2
Would I have the strength to stand at all?
E Dsus2
I never know what the future brings,
E Dsus2 Dmaj9
But I know you're here with me now.
A
We'll make it through,
D
And I hope you are the one I share my life with.

Chorus 1

A
I don't wanna run away,
Bm7 D A
But I can't take it, I don't understand.
Bm7
If I'm not made for you,
D F♯m
Then why does my heart tell me that I am?
E Bm7 Dsus2
Is there any way that I could stay in your arms?

Verse 2

Asus2
If I don't need you,
Dsus2
Then why am I crying on my bed?
Asus2
If I don't need you,
Dsus2
Then why does your name resound in my head?
Asus2
If you're not for me,
Dsus2
Then why does this distance maim my life?
Asus2
If you're not for me,
Dsus2
Then why do I dream of you as my wife?
E Dsus2
I don't know why you're so far away,
E Dsus2 Dmaj9
But I know that this much is true,
A
We'll make it through,
D
And I hope you are the one I share my life with.
A Dsus2
And I wish that you could be the one I die with.
A Dsus2
And I pray that you're the one I build my home with.
E Dsus2 A
I hope I love you all my life.

Chorus 2

A
I don't wanna run away,
Bm7 D A
But I can't take it, I don't understand.
Bm7
If I'm not made for you,
D F♯m
Then why does my heart tell me that I am?
E Bm7 Dsus2
Is there any way that I could stay in your arms?

```
                 F♯m                                 E
Middle      'Cause I miss you, body and soul so strong,
                                Dsus2
            That it takes my breath away.
                  F♯m
            And I breathe you,
                                 E                    Dsus2
            Into my heart and pray for strength to stand today.
                 F♯m
            'Cause I love you,
                                      E
            Whether it's wrong or right,
                                 A                D
            And though I can't be with you tonight,
                                      E      A
            You know my heart is by your side.

            A
Chorus 3       I don't wanna run away,
                Bm7              D          A
            But I can't take it, I don't understand.
                       Bm7
            If I'm not made for you,
                 D                                    F♯m
            Then why does my heart tell me that I am?
                      E                       Bm7          Dsus2
            Is there any way that I could stay in your arms?

            | Dsus2   | Dsus2 (fermata) ||
```

Kokomo

Words & Music by
Mike Love, Terry Melcher, John Phillips & Scott McKenzie

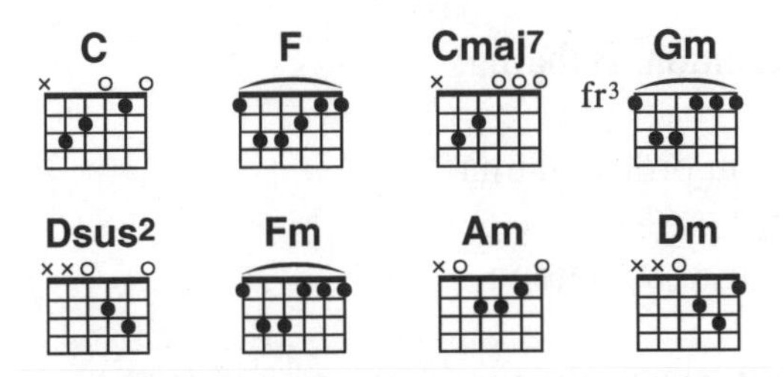

Intro

(C)
Aruba, Jamaica, oooh I wanna take you.
(F)
Bermuda, Bahama,

Come on pretty mama.
(C)
Key Largo, Montego,

Baby why don't we go,
(F)
Jamaica.

Verse 1

C Cmaj7
Off the Florida Keys,
Gm F
There's a place called Kokomo,
Fm C
That's where you wanna go,
Dsus2 G
To get away from it all.
C Cmaj7
Bodies in the sand,
Gm F
Tropical drink melting in your hand.
Fm C
We'll be falling in love,
Dsus2 G
To the rhythm of a steel drum band.

Down in (Kokomo).

Chorus 1

C
Aruba, Jamaica oooh, I wanna take you
F
To Bermuda, Bahama,

Come on pretty mama
C
Key Largo, Montego,
F
Ooo, I wanna take you down to Kokomo,
Fm
We'll get there fast,
C
And then we'll take it slow.
Am Dm G
That's where we wanna go,
C
Way down to Kokomo.

(To Martinique, that Monserrat mystique)

Verse 2

C Cmaj7
We'll put out to sea,
Gm F
And we'll perfect our chemistry,
Fm C Dsus2 G
By and by we'll defy a little bit of gravity.
C Cmaj7
Afternoon delight,
Gm F
Cocktails and moonlit nights.
Fm C
That dreamy look in your eye,
Dsus2 G
Give me a tropical contact high.

Way down in Kokomo,

Chorus 2

As Chorus 1

(Port Au Prince I wanna catch a glimpse).

Instrumental | C | Cmaj7 | Gm | F | Fm | C |
| Dsus2 | G |

```
      C                       Cmaj7
Verse 3   Everybody knows,
      Gm                      F
          A little place like Kokomo.
      Fm          C
          Now if you wanna go,
              Dsus2             G
      And get away from it all

      Go down to (Kokomo).
```

Chorus 3 As Chorus 1 *Repeat to fade*

Jackie's Racing

Words & Music by
Andrew Caldwell, Paul Carroll & Eric Lindsay

A A/E Bm D C#m (fr4) E G

Intro | A A/E | A A/E | A A/E | A A/E |

```
          A                 Bm                A   A/E | A   A/E |
Verse 1   Jackie says that Sunday's are no fun.
             A                        Bm              D  | D  C#m |
          She done no wrong, but she says she's on the run.
          Bm                    E
          Out her head, and she's so proud of it,
          A                     D         C#m
          All the boys tell her she's on air,
          Bm                    E
          Loves tight clothes that don't quite fit.

             D                   A
Chorus 1  It's everything she's re - vealing,
          G                       D
          All the scenes she's been stealing,
               D               A
          She's got no hidden meaning.

Link 1    | Bm  D | A    |

          A                   Bm                     A   A/E | A   A/E |
Verse 2   Jackie says for a good time she's the one,
             A                        Bm              D  | D  C#m |
          She lives for kicks, and she likes her teenage fun.
          Bm            E
          Invitation, her name is on it,
          A                         D          C#m
          She's first there, and she's last to leave.
          Bm                E
          Thursday night till Sunday morning,
```

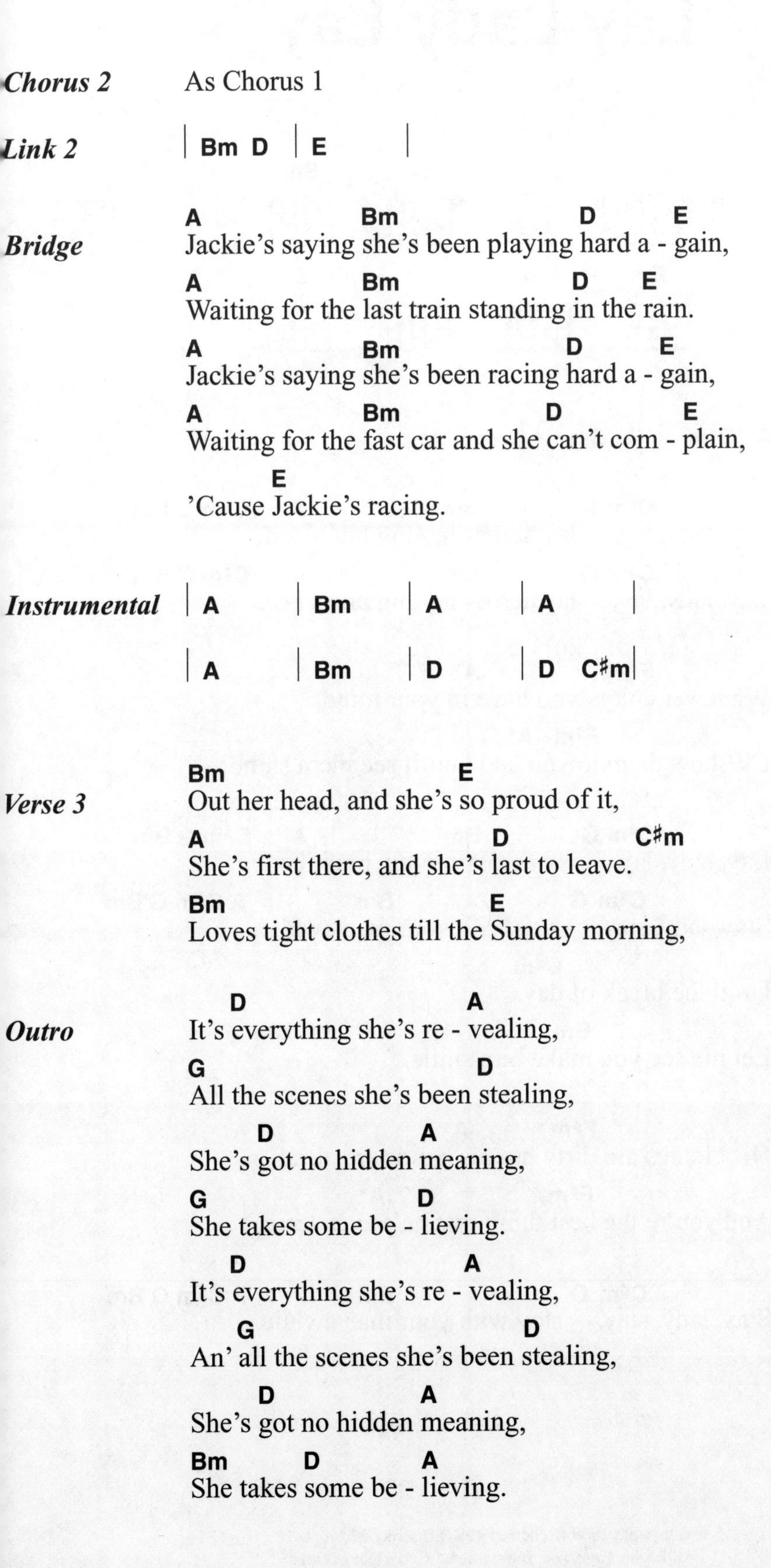

Chorus 2 As Chorus 1

Link 2 | Bm D | E |

Bridge

```
A                  Bm                  D      E
Jackie's saying she's been playing hard a - gain,
A                  Bm                  D     E
Waiting for the last train standing in the rain.
A                  Bm                D      E
Jackie's saying she's been racing hard a - gain,
A                  Bm               D          E
Waiting for the fast car and she can't com - plain,
          E
'Cause Jackie's racing.
```

Instrumental

| A | Bm | A | A |

| A | Bm | D | D C♯m |

Verse 3

```
Bm                          E
Out her head, and she's so proud of it,
A                             D         C♯m
She's first there, and she's last to leave.
Bm                            E
Loves tight clothes till the Sunday morning,
```

Outro

```
    D                       A
It's everything she's re - vealing,
G                           D
All the scenes she's been stealing,
       D                A
She's got no hidden meaning,
G                       D
She takes some be - lieving.
    D                       A
It's everything she's re - vealing,
    G                                 D
An' all the scenes she's been stealing,
       D                A
She's got no hidden meaning,
Bm         D            A
She takes some be - lieving.
```

Lay Lady Lay

Words & Music by
Bob Dylan

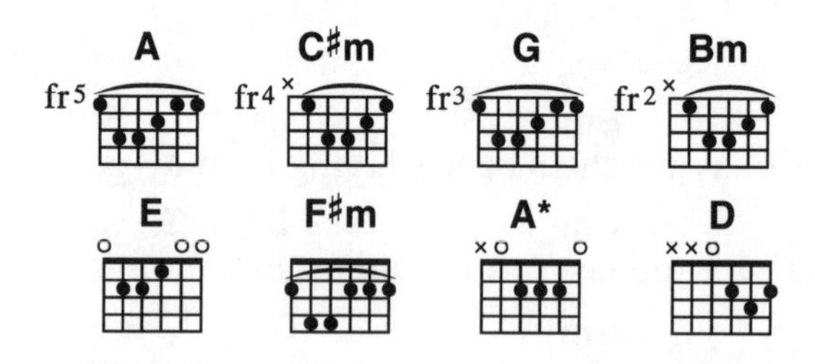

Intro 𝄆 A C♯m | G Bm 𝄇

Chorus 1

A C♯m G Bm A C♯m G Bm
Lay, lady, lay, lay across my big brass bed.

A C♯m G Bm A C♯m G Bm
Lay, lady, lay, lay across my big brass bed.

Verse 1

E F♯m A*
Whatever colors you have in your mind,

E F♯m A*
I'll show them to you and you'll see them shine.

Chorus 2

A C♯m G Bm A C♯m G Bm
Lay, lady, lay, lay across my big brass bed.

A C♯m G Bm A C♯m G Bm
Stay, lady, stay, stay with your man awhile.

A C♯m
Until the break of day,

G Bm A C♯m G Bm
Let me see you make him smile.

Verse 2

E F♯m A*
His clothes are dirty but his hands are clean.

E F♯m A*
And you're the best thing that he's ever seen.

Chorus 3

A C♯m G Bm A C♯m G Bm
Stay, lady, stay, stay with your man awhile.

```
          C#m                              E    D    A*
Bridge 1    Why wait any longer for the world to begin?
          C#m                              Bm      A*
            You can have your cake and eat it too.
          C#m                              E  D  A*
            Why wait any longer for the one you love?
                   C#m                     Bm
          When he's standing in front of you.

          A           C#m G          Bm                 A C#m G Bm
Chorus 4    Lay, lady, lay,    lay across my big brass bed.
          A            C#m G                Bm        A      C#m G Bm
            Stay, lady, stay,    stay while the night is still ahead.

          E           F#m          A*
Verse 3     I long to see you in the morning light.
          E           F#m          A*
            I long to reach for you in the night.

          A            C#m G                Bm        A      C#m G Bm
Chorus 5    Stay, lady, stay,    stay while the night is still ahead.

Coda      | A*  Bm  | C#m  D  | A*         ||
```

Lookin' Up

Words & Music by
Shelby Lynne & Bill Bottrell

A | Em7 | D | Dm | B | F♯m | F | E7

Capo second fret

```
            A
Verse 1     Smokin' and thinkin'
                      Em7
            Of things to do since you're gone
            A
               Sittin' lonely,
                    Em7
            Can't even get stoned.
            D                    Dm
               Takin' a breath of a feeling that
                              A    | Em7    | A     | Em7   |
            Once lived in this house.

            A
Verse 2     Laughin', and dyin'
                    Em7
            At the mirror in the hall
            A
            Talkin' to myself,
                          Em7
            A memory don't remember at all,
            D
               Last thing you told me,
                    Dm                          A     | A
            Was the first thing that brought on these clouds,
                           B
            I'm lookin' up,
                    Dm                    A     | A     |
            For the next thing that brings me down.

            | B      | Dm     | A      | A      |
              Mmm.
```

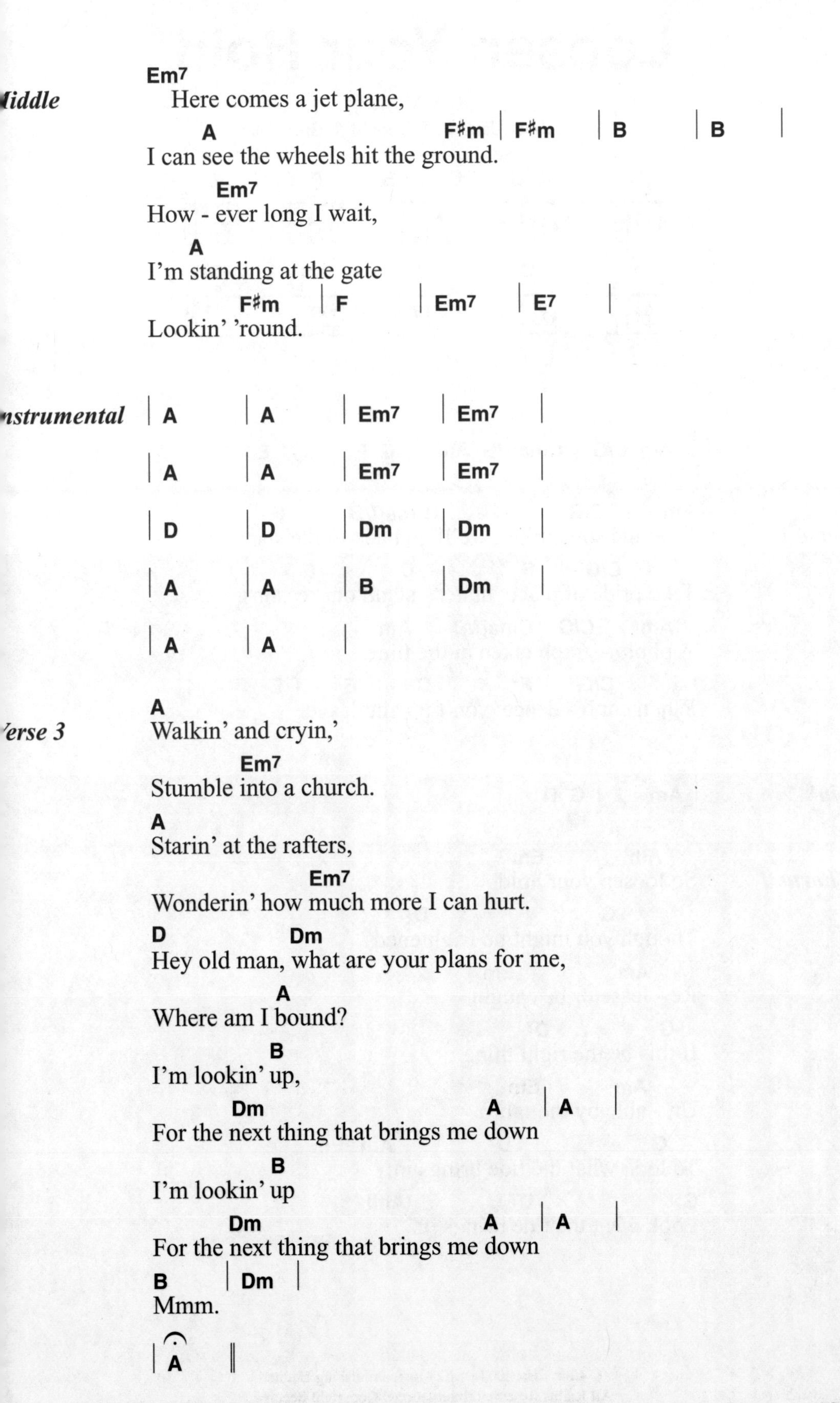

Middle

Em7
Here comes a jet plane,
A | F♯m | F♯m | B | B |
I can see the wheels hit the ground.
Em7
How - ever long I wait,
A
I'm standing at the gate
F♯m | F | Em7 | E7 |
Lookin' 'round.

Instrumental

| A | A | Em7 | Em7 |

| A | A | Em7 | Em7 |

| D | D | Dm | Dm |

| A | A | B | Dm |

| A | A |

Verse 3

A
Walkin' and cryin,'
Em7
Stumble into a church.
A
Starin' at the rafters,
Em7
Wonderin' how much more I can hurt.
D Dm
Hey old man, what are your plans for me,
A
Where am I bound?
B
I'm lookin' up,
Dm A | A |
For the next thing that brings me down
B
I'm lookin' up
Dm A | A |
For the next thing that brings me down
B | Dm |
Mmm.

| A (fermata) ‖

Loosen Your Hold

Words & Music by
Joel Cadbury, James McDonald & Brett Shaw

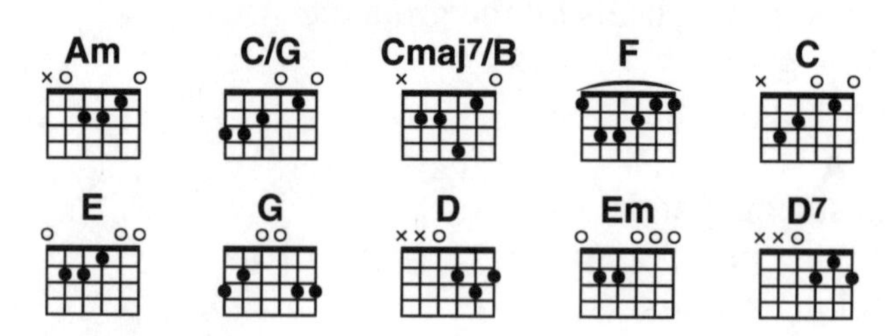

Intro | |: Am C/G | Cmaj7/B Am | C/G F | C E :||

Verse 1

```
Am         C/G                    Cmaj7/B       F
Feed me something, we'll go back to the start
           C/G        F              C            E
Take pride of place, under - stand our reasons.
  Am          C/G    Cmaj7/B      Am
A photo - graph taken at the time
             C/G        F             C         E     | E     |
When confi - dence won't up and leave.
```

Link | Am | G D ||

Chorus 1

```
    Am          Em
So loosen your hold,
           G                    D7
Though you might be frightened
    Am            Em
Re - lease or be caught
  G               D7
If this be the right thing
    Am         Em
Un - able by thought
  G                   D7              Am   Em
To look what the tide brings in,
G                  D7              (Am)
Look what the tide brings in.
```

Link 2 ‖: Am C/G | Cmaj7/B Am | C/G F | C E :‖

Verse 2 As Verse 1

Chorus 2 As Chorus 1

Instrumental ‖: Am Em | G D7 | Am Em | G D7 :‖

```
              Am            Em
Chorus 3      So loosen your hold,
                  G                  D7
              Though you might be frightened
                Am            Em
              Re - lease or be caught
                G              D7
              If this be the right thing
                Am           Em
              Un - able by thought
                G                D7          Am Em | G D7 | Am ‖
              To look what the tide brings in.
```

Love Is All Around

Words & Music by
Reg Presley

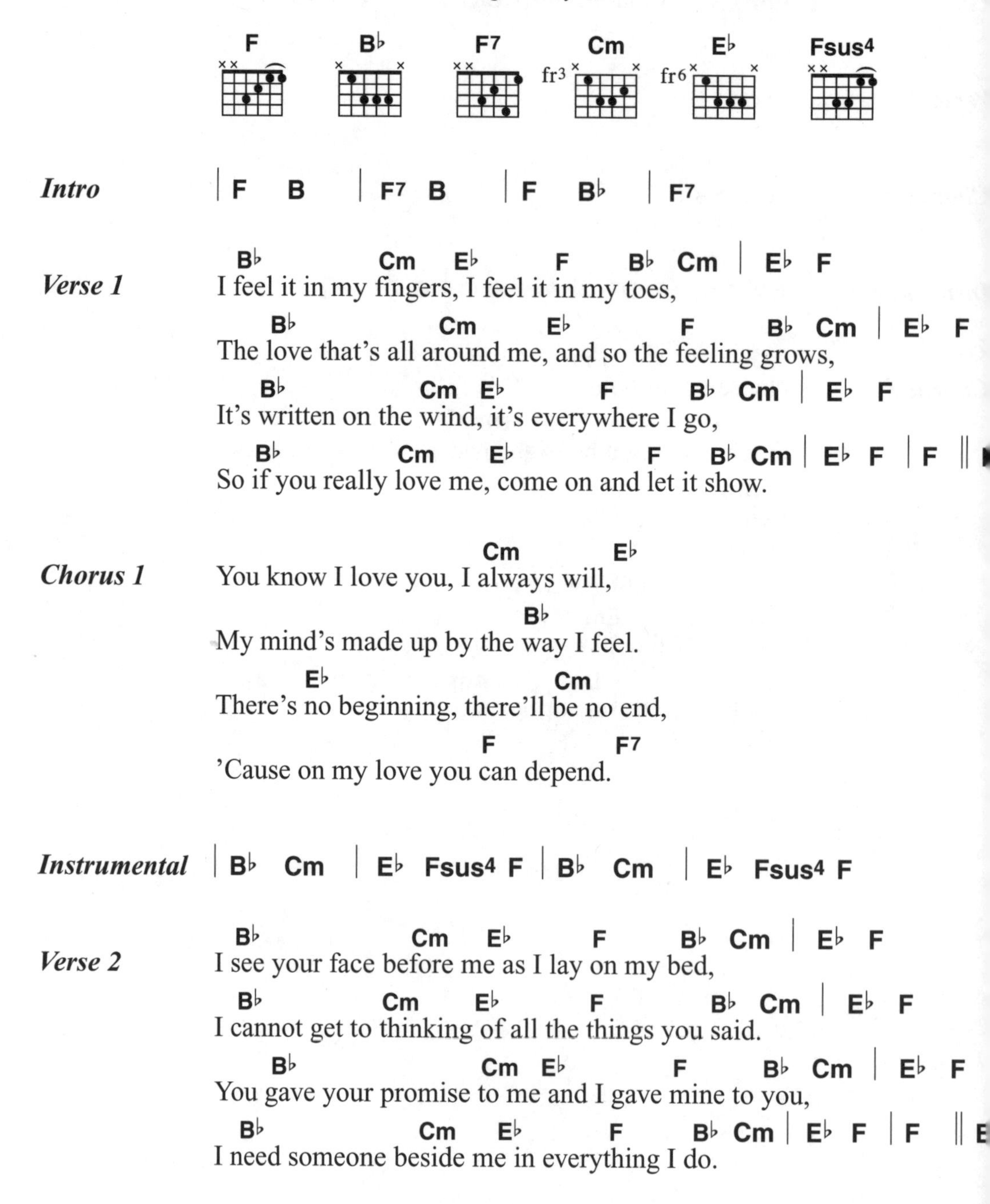

```
             (E♭)                     Cm          E♭
Chorus 2     You know I love you, I always will,
                                           B♭
             My mind's made up by the way I feel.
                      E♭                  Cm
             There's no beginning, there'll be no end,
                                   F              F7   B♭  | F7  B♭  | F
             'Cause on my love you can depend.
                           B♭      F7
             Got to keep it moving.

                  B♭           Cm    E♭        Fsus4  F  B♭  Cm | E♭  F
Verse 3      It's written in the wind, oh, everywhere I   go,
                B♭                  Cm E♭      Fsus4  F   B♭  Cm | E♭
             So if you really love me,  come on and let it show,
                   F
             Come on and let it (show).
                B♭          Cm
             |: Come on and let it,
             E♭           Fsus4  F
             Come on and let       it,
             B♭           Cm   E♭    Fsus4  F
             Come on and let it show.              :|   Repeat to fade
```

Lowdown

Words & Music by
Jim James

D G A F♯m7 Bm

Intro ‖: D | G A | D | G A :‖ x4

Verse 1
D F♯m7
Lowdown, cheatin'
G A
Sure no need for repeatin'
D F♯m7
So love dog, can't you see,
G
That you never gotta fight with me.

Interlude ‖: D | F♯m7 | G | A :‖
| D | Bm A |

D Bm A D Bm
No you never gotta fight with me.
A D Bm A
Oh, oh.

Link 1 ‖: D | G A | D | G A :‖ x4

Verse 2
D F♯m7
Hurtin', beatin',
G A
Ain't no need for repeatin',
D F♯m7
So love dog, can't you see,
G
That you never gotta bleed for me.
D F♯m7
Chancin', glancin',
G A
Sure no mood for romancing.

```
              D                     F#m7
ont.      So love dog, can't you see,
                        G
          That you only gotta dance with me.

          | D          | Bm   A     |

          D            Bm        A         D
            Yeah you only gotta dance with me.
          | Bm   A   | D         | Bm   A   | D         |
                    Oh, oh.
          | Bm   A   | D         | Bm   A   |
                    Oh, oh.
          D            Bm        A         D
            Yeah you only gotta dance with me.
          | Bm   A   | D         | Bm   A
                    Oh, oh.
                       D
                    Oh, oh.
                       Bm        A         D
            Yeah you only gotta dance with me.
          | Bm   A     | D      | Bm   A  | D    | Bm   A   |
                  Woah, oh.
                       | D      | Bm   A  | D    | Bm   A   | D      |
                  Woah, oh.

          | Bm   A     | D (fermata) ||
```

A Little Time

Words & Music by
Paul Heaton & David Rotheray

F   B♭/F   Fsus2   B♭   C   Gm (fr3)   Fmaj7

Intro

| F   B♭/F | F   B♭/F | F   B♭/F ||

Verse 1

```
F   Fsus2      F          B♭/F    F
   I need a little time to think it over,
 B♭/F          F          B♭/F   F
I need a little space just on my own.
 Fsus2         F       B♭/F     F
I need a little time to find my freedom.
 B♭/F
I need a little...
```

Chorus 1

```
F
Funny how quick the milk turns sour,
B♭       C
Isn't it, isn't it?
        F
Your face has been looking like that for hours,
B♭           C
Hasn't it, hasn't it?
B♭                          C
Promises, promises turn to dust,
F                        Gm
Wedding bells just turn to rust,
B♭                C
Trust into mistrust.
```

Verse 2

```
                          F        B♭/F     F
I need a little room to find myself in,
 B♭/F          F          B♭/F      F
I need a little space to work it outÉ
 B♭/F          F       B♭/F F
I need a little room all alone.
 B♭/F
I need a little...
```

```
               F
Chorus 2       You need a little room for your big head,
               B♭        C
               Don't you, don't you?
                   F
               You need a little space for a thousand beds,
               B♭         C
               Won't you, won't you?
               B♭                  C
               Lips that promise, fear the worst,
               F                   Gm
               Tongue so sharp, the bubble burst,
               B♭         C
               Just into un - just.

Instrumental   | Fmaj7  B♭/F | Fmaj7  B♭/F | Fmaj7  B♭/F | Fmaj7  B♭/F |

               | Fmaj7  B♭/F | Fmaj7  B♭/F | Fmaj7  B♭/F ||

               Fmaj7 B♭/F       F        B♭/F     F
Verse 3          I've had a little time to find the truth.
                      B♭/F       F         B♭/F          F
               Now I've had a little room to check what's wrong.
                   B♭/F        F          B♭/F  F
               I've had a little time and I still   love you.
                   B♭/F
               I've had a little...

                   F
Chorus 3       You had a little time and you had a little fun,
               B♭         C
               Didn't you, didn't you?
                     F
               While you had yours do you think I had none,
               B♭      C
               Do you, do you?
                   B♭                 C
               The freedom that you wanted bad
                 F                Gm
               Is yours for good, I hope you're glad.
               B♭         C
               Sad into un - sad.
```

Verse 4

```
                Fmaj7
I had a little time
    Fsus2   Fmaj7
To think it ___ over.
Fsus2        Fmaj7
Had a little room
    Fsus2   Fmaj7
To work it out.
  Fsus2       F
I found a little courage
    Fsus2  Fmaj7
To call it  off.
```

Outro

```
Fmaj7
   I've had a little time,

I've had a little time,

I've had a little time,
                          F
I've had a little time.
```

Missing

Words by Tracey Thorn
Music by Ben Watt

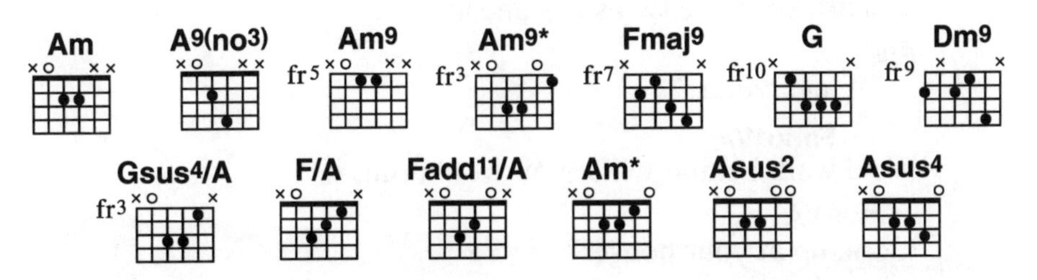

erse 1

Am A9(no3) Am9 A9(no3)
I step off the train

Am A9(no3) Am9 A9(no3)
I'm walking down your street again

Am A9(no3) Am9 A9(no3)
And past your door

Am A9(no3) Am9 A9(no3)
But you don't live there any more.

Am A9(no3) Am9 A9(no3)
It's years since you've been there,

Am A9(no3) Am9 A9(no3) Am A9(no3)
And now you've disappeared some - where

Am9 A9(no3) Am A9(no3) Am9
Like outer space, you've found some better place.

horus 2

A9(no3) Am9* Fmaj9
And I miss you,

G Dm9
(Like the deserts miss the rain)

Am9* Fmaj9
And I miss you oh,

Am9* Dm9
(Like the deserts miss the rain).

Verse 2

Gsus4/A
Could you be dead?

You always were two steps ahead

F/A
Of everyone,

Fadd11/A
We'd walk behind while you would run.

Gsus4/A
I look up at your house

F/A
And I can almost hear you shout

Down to me

Fadd11/A
Where I always used to be.

Chorus 2

Am9* Fmaj9
And I miss you,

G Dm9
(Like the deserts miss the rain)

Am9* Fmaj9
And I miss you oh,

Am9* Dm9
(Like the deserts miss the rain).

Verse 3

Gsus4/A
I'm back on the train,

I ask why did I come again?

F/A Fadd11/A
Can I confess I've been hanging around your old address.

Gsus4/A
And the years have proved

F/A
To offer nothing sinceyou moved,

You're long gone,

Fadd11/A
But I can't move on

Chorus 3 As Chorus 2

```
            Am*
Verse 4       I step off the train
               Asus2
            I'm walking down your street again
            Asus4
              And past your door
                   Asus2
            I guess you don't live there any more.
               Am*
            It's years since you've been there,
            Asus4                                    Am*
              And now you've disappeared some - where
                             Asus2
            Like outer space,      you've found some better place.

                     Am* Asus2
Link        And I miss you, yeah.
                     Am*
            And I miss you.
            Asus2
              You found some better place

                        Am9*  Fmaj9
Outro       ||: And I miss you,
                  G                Dm9
            (Like the deserts miss the rain)
                     Am9*  Fmaj9
            And I miss you    oh,
                   Am9*            Dm9
            (Like the deserts miss the rain). :||  Repeat to fade
```

Mad World

Words & Music by
Roland Orzabal

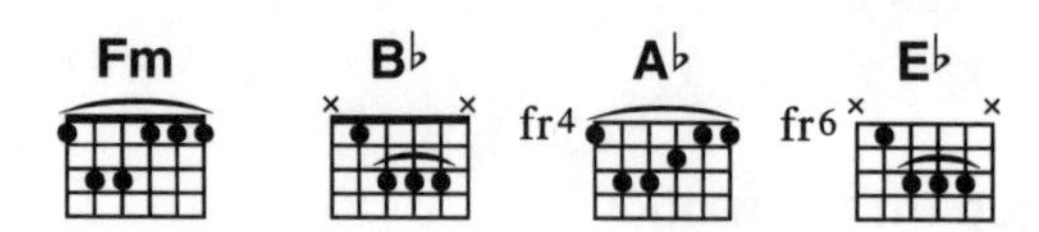

Intro | Fm | B♭ | Fm | B♭ ||

Verse 1

```
Fm                          A♭
   All around me are fa - miliar faces,
E♭                  B♭
   Worn out places, worn out faces.
Fm                             A♭
   Bright and early for their daily races
E♭               B♭
Going nowhere, going nowhere.
```

Verse 2

```
Fm                         A♭
   The tears are filling up their glasses,
E♭                 B♭
No expression, no expression.
Fm                              A♭
   Hide my head I wanna drown my sorrow,
E♭                B♭
No tomorrow, no tomorrow.
```

Chorus 1

```
Fm                          B♭
   And I find it kind of funny,
                     Fm
I find it kind of sad,
                               B♭                              Fm
The dreams in which I'm dying are the best I've ever had.
                    B♭
I find it hard to tell you,
                    Fm
I find it hard to take,
                             B♭
When people run in circles it's a very, very,
Fm           B♭   Fm           B♭
   Mad world,      mad world.
```

```
            Fm                                  A♭
Verse 3       Children waiting for the day they feel good,
            E♭                B♭             Fm
            Happy birthday, happy birth - day,
                                      A♭
            And I feel the way that every child should,
            E♭              B♭          Fm
            Sit and listen, sit and list - en.

                                          A♭
Verse 4     Went to school and I was very nervous
            E♭                  B♭
            No one knew me, no one knew me.
            Fm                             A♭
              Hello teacher tell me what's my lesson,
            E♭                         B♭
            Look right through me, look right through me.


Chorus 2    As Chorus 1

            Fm                 B♭
Outro         Enlargen your world
            Fm     B♭
              Mad   world.
```

Michelle

Words & Music by
John Lennon & Paul McCartney

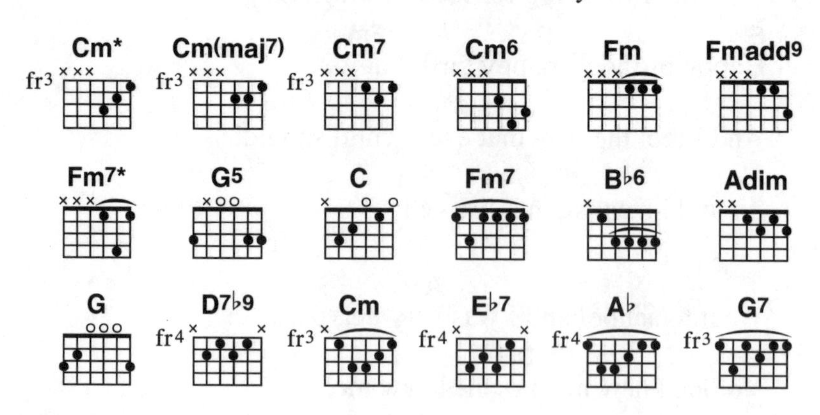

Capo fifth fret

Intro | Cm* Cm(maj7) | Cm7 Cm6 | Fm Fmadd9 Fm Fm7* | G5 ||

Verse 1

C Fm7
Michelle, ma belle,
B♭6 Adim G
These are words that go together well,
D7♭9 G
My Michelle.

Verse 2

C Fm7
Michelle, ma belle,
B♭6 Adim G
Sont les mots qui vont très bien ensemble
D7♭9 G
Très bien ensemble.

Bridge 1

Cm
I love you, I love you, I love you,
E♭7 A♭
That's all I want to say,
G7 Cm
Until I find a way,
Cm* Cm(maj7) Cm7 Cm6
I will say the only words I know
Fm Fmadd9 Fm Fm7* G5
That you'll __ un - der - stand.

Verse 3 As Verse 2

Bridge 2

Cm
I need to, I need to, I need to,
E♭7 A♭
I need to make you see,
G7 Cm
Oh, what you mean to me.
Cm* Cm(maj7) Cm7 Cm6
Until I do I'm hoping you
Fm Fmadd9 Fm Fm7* G5
Will know ______ what I mean.

Solo

Cm Fm7
I love you. _____

| B♭6 | Adim | G D7♭9 | G ||

Bridge 2

Cm
I want you, I want you, I want you,
E♭7 A♭
I think you know by now,
G7 Cm
I'll get to you somehow.
Cm* Cm(maj7) Cm7 Cm6
Until I do I'm telling you,
Fm Fmadd9 Fm Fm7* G5
So you'll ______ un - der - stand.

Verse 4

C Fm7
Michelle, ma belle,
B♭6 Adim G
Sont les mots qui vont très bien ensemble
D7♭9 G
Très bien ensemble.
Cm* Cm(maj7) Cm7 Cm6
And I will say the only words I know
Fm Fmadd9 Fm Fm7* G5
That you'll ______ un - der - stand,
C
My Michelle.

Solo

| Fm7 | B♭6 | Adim | G D7♭9 |

| Fm7 | B♭6 | *Fade out*

Missing Man

Words & Music by
Gary Clark & Julia Fordham

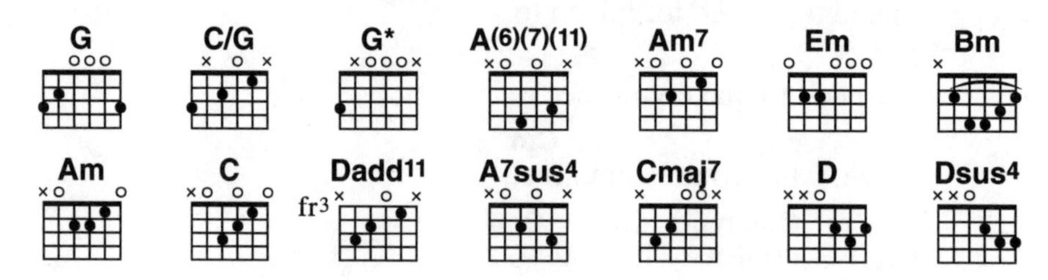

Capo first fret

Intro | G G C/G G* C/G | A(6)(7)(11) | Am7 |
| G G C/G G* C/G | A(6)(7)(11) | Am7 | Em ||

Verse 1
```
Bm                             Am
   Yet another day slides into midnight
Bm                                    Am
From your camp there's not a single word.
Bm                               Am  Bm  C                  G  G  C/G  G*  C/G
   Seemingly you have for - gotten    I'm still your girl.
```

Chorus 1
```
Dsus4  G                      Am
   Hell,    people tell me I am strong,
C                                Em
   And I'd have to prove 'em wrong,
G                             A7sus4
   As the cracks begin to show
Cmaj7                     A7sus4                  G  G  C/G  G*  C/G
   I'm tryin' to find the strength to let you go,
A(6)(7)(11)  Am7  Em
   Missing man.
```

Verse 2
```
Bm                               Am
   Hope turned out to be a dangerous lesson,
Bm                          Am
Faith a shallow river in disguise,
Bm                                     Am  Bm
   Running through my patient spirit,
C                 G  G  C/G  G*  C/G
Drowning my pride.
```

Chorus 2 As Chorus 1

```
             Bm
Bridge       Missing man,
             Am
             Missing man,
             C                  D  Dsus4 D
             Do you miss me missing man?
             Bm
             Missing man,
             Am
             Missing man,
             C                  D  Dsus4 D
             Do you miss me missing man?

             G             Am
Chorus 3       People tell me I am strong,
             C                       Em
               And I'd have to prove 'em wrong,
             G                        A7sus4
               As the cracks begin to show
             Cmaj7                    A7sus4                G  G  C/G  G*  C/G
               I'm tryin' to find the strength to let you go,
             A(6)(7)(11)   Am7  G  G  C/G  G*  C/G  A(6)(7)(11)  Am7  Em
               Missing man.

                   Bm
Outro        ||: Missing man,
             Am
             Missing man,
             C                  D  Dsus4 D
             Do you miss me missing man?
             Bm
             Missing man,
             Am
             Missing man,
             C                  D  Dsus4 D
             Do you miss me missing man?     :||  Repeat to fade
```

Moonshadow

Words & Music by
Cat Stevens

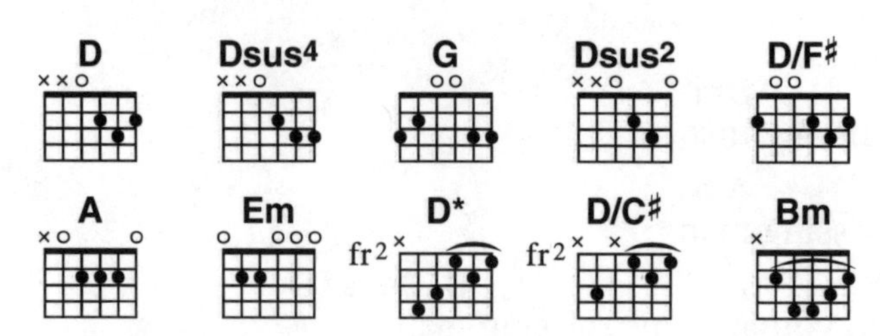

Intro | D | Dsus4 D | G | D Dsus2 D ||

Chorus 1

```
   D                         Dsus4  D       D/F♯
Yes, I'm bein' followed by a moon - shadow,
          G              A        D        Dsus2 D
          moonshadow, moon - shadow
D                        Dsus4  D       D/F♯
Leapin and hoppin' on a moon - shadow,
         G              A        D        Dsus2 D
         moonshadow, moon - shadow
```

Verse 1

```
    G  D   G          D      G            D        Em      A
And if I ever lose my hands, lose my plough, lose my land,
   G  D   G           D
Oh if I ever lose my hands,
   Em      A     D* D/C♯   Bm
Oh i - i - i - i - i - i  -  if,
  Em              A       D
I won't have to work no more.
```

Verse 2

```
    G  D   G          D    G       D           Em    A
And if I ever lose my eyes, if my colours all run dry,
    G  D   G          D
Yes if I ever lose my eyes,
   Em      A     D* D/C♯   Bm
Oh i - i - i - i - i - i  -  if,
  Em              A     D
I won't have to cry no more.
```

Chorus 2 As Chorus 1

Verse 3

    G D G D G D Em A
And if I ever lose my legs, I won't moan, and I won't beg,

    G D G D
Oh if I ever lose my legs,

    Em A D* D/C♯ Bm
Oh i - i - i - i - i - i - i - if,

    Em A D
I won't have to walk no more.

Verse 4

    G D G D G D Em A
And if I ever lose my mouth, all my teeth, north and south,

    G D G D
Yes if I ever lose my mouth,

    Em A D* D/C♯ Bm
Oh i - i - i - i - i - i - i - if,

    Em A D
I won't have to talk.

Instr. ‖: D | Dsus4 D D/F♯ | G A | D Dsus2 D :‖

Bridge

    E A E A
Did it take long to find me? I asked the faithful light.

    E A E A G
Oh did it take long to find me? And are you gonna stay the night?

Chorus 3

    D Dsus4 D D/F♯
I'm bein' followed by a moon - shadow,

    G A D Dsus2 D
moonshadow, moon - shadow

    D Dsus4 D D/F♯
Leapin and hoppin' on a moon - shadow,

    G A D Dsus2 D
moonshadow, moon - shadow

    G A D
Moonshadow, moon - shadow

    G A D
Moonshadow, moon - shadow.

Mr. Writer

Words & Music by
Kelly Jones & Marshall Bird

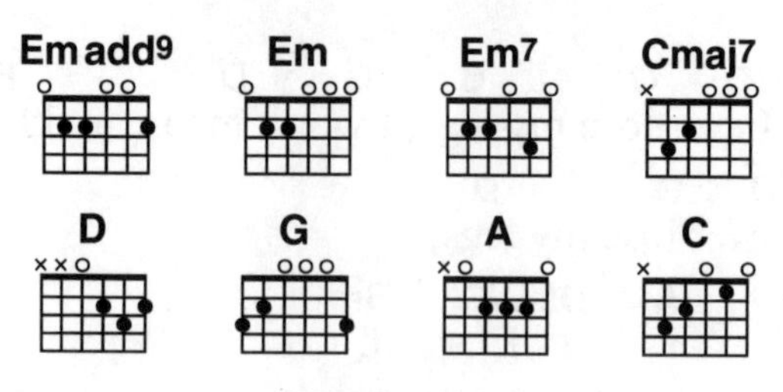

Capo first fret

Intro **Drums fade in** || **Emadd9** | **Emadd9** |
| **Em Em7** | **Cmaj7** | **Em Em7** | **Cmaj7** ||

Verse 1
```
Em     Em7                 Cmaj7
  You line 'em up, look at your shoes,
                             Em       Em7              Cmaj7
You hang names on your wall and you shoot them all.
Em          Em7                      Cmaj7
   You fly around in planes that bring you down to meet me.
              Em       Em7
Who loves you like me,
                 Cmaj7
Crashing to the ground?
```

Pre-chorus 1
```
              D
Are you so lonely?
                  Cmaj7
You don't even know me,
                      D
But you'd like to stone me.
```

Chorus 1
```
Em                                        G
Mister Writer, why don't you tell it like it is?
                                   A
Why don't you tell it like it really is
                         C
Before you go on home?
```

Link | **Em Em7** | **Cmaj7** | **Em Em7** | **Cmaj7** ||

Verse 2

```
Em             Em7                  Cmaj7
   I used to treat you right, give you my time,
                               Em
But when I turned my back on you,
             Em7           Cmaj7
Then you do what you do.
Em         Em7              Cmaj7
   You've just enough, in my own view,
                   Em
Education to perform.
             Em7        Cmaj7
I'd like to shoot you all.
```

Pre-chorus 2

```
                 D
And then you go home
              Cmaj7
With you on your own.
                D
What do you really know?
```

Chorus 2 As Chorus 1

Solo | Em Em7 | Cmaj7 | Em Em7 | Cmaj7 ||

Pre-chorus 3

```
                 D
And then you go home
              Cmaj7
With you on your own.
                D
What do you even know?
```

Chorus 3 As Chorus 1

Chorus 4

```
    Em                                                 G
||: Mister Writer, why don't you tell it like it really is?
                                      A
Why don't you tell it like it always is
                      C
Before you go on home?   :||
```

Coda | Emadd9 | Emadd9 | Emadd9 | Emadd9 |

| Emadd9 | Emadd9 | Em ||

Ms. Jackson

Words & Music by
André Benjamin, Antwan Patton & David Sheats

Cmaj7 D Em

Intro | Cmaj7 | Cmaj7 | Cmaj7 | D |
| Em | Em | D | D ||

Chorus 1

Cmaj7
I'm sorry Ms. Jackson
D
I am for real,
Em
Never meant to make your daughter cry
D
I apologize a trillion times.
Cmaj7
I'm sorry Ms. Jackson
D
I am for real
Em
Never meant to make your daughter cry
D
I apologize a trillion times.

Link 1 | Cmaj7 | Cmaj7 | Cmaj7 | D |
| Em | Em | D | D ||

Chorus 2 As Chorus 1

Verse 1

Cmaj7
Me and your daughter

D
Got a special thing go - ing on

Em
You say it's puppy love

D
We say it's fully grown.

Cmaj7
Hope that we feel this,

D
Feel this way forev - er

Em
You can plan a pretty picnic

D
But you can't predict the weather.

Link 2

| Cmaj7 | Cmaj7 | Cmaj7 | D | Em | Em | D | D ||

Can't predict the weather...

Chorus 3 As Chorus 1

Verse 2 As Verse 1

Outro

Cmaj7
Hope that we feel this,

D
Feel this way forev - er,

Em
You can plan a pretty picnic

D
But you can't predict the weather...

| Cmaj7 | Cmaj7 | Cmaj7 | D | Em | Em | D | D ||

Can't predict the weather...

Cmaj7
I'm sorry Ms. Jackson...

Nothing Compares 2 U

Words & Music by
Prince

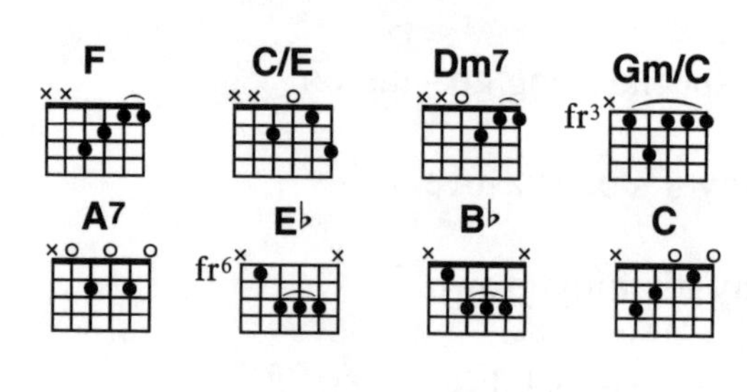

Intro | F | F |

Verse 1

```
F                                   C/E
   It's been seven hours and fifteen days
Dm7                                       F     Gm/C
   Since U took your love away.
F                                C/E
   I go out every night and sleep all day
Dm7                                       F     Gm/C
   Since U took your love away.
F                                              C/E
   Since U been gone I can do whatever I want,
Dm7                                       F     Gm/C
   I can see whomever I choose.
```

Chorus 1

```
F                                         C/E
   I can eat my dinner in a fancy restaurant
   Dm7
But nothing,
                                  A7
I said nothing can take away these blues,
      E♭        B♭
'Cause nothing compares,
E♭            B♭      C
   Nothing compares 2 U. ___
```

Verse 2

```
F                                C/E
   It's been so lonely without U here
Dm7                                       F     Gm/C
   Like a bird without a song.
F                                             C/E
   Nothing can stop these lonely tears from falling,
      Dm7                      B♭
Tell me baby where did I go wrong?
```

cont.

```
        F
           I could put my arms
                          C/E
        Around every boy I see
        Dm7                                          F       Gm/C
           But they'd only remind me of U.
```

Chorus 2

```
        F                                      C/E
           I went 2 the doctor guess what he told me

        Guess what he told me?
                   Dm7
        He said "Girl U better try 2 have fun
                    A7
        No matter what U do."

        But he's a fool
             E♭              B♭
        'Cause nothing compares
        Dm7                  C
           Nothing compares 2 U.
```

Instrumental ‖: F | C/E | Dm7 | F Gm/C :‖

Verse 3

```
        F
        All the flowers that U planted, mama
        C/E
           In the back yard,
        Dm7                              F        Gm/C
           All died when U went away.
```

Chorus 3

```
        F                                          C/E
           I know that living with U, baby, was sometimes hard
        Dm7                                     A7
           But I'm willing 2 give it another try.

           E♭           B♭
        ‖: Nothing compares,
        Dm7             C          x3
           Nothing compares 2 U.   :‖
```

Outro ‖: E♭ B♭ | Dm7 C | C :‖ *Repeat to fade*

Oliver's Army

Words & Music by
Elvis Costello

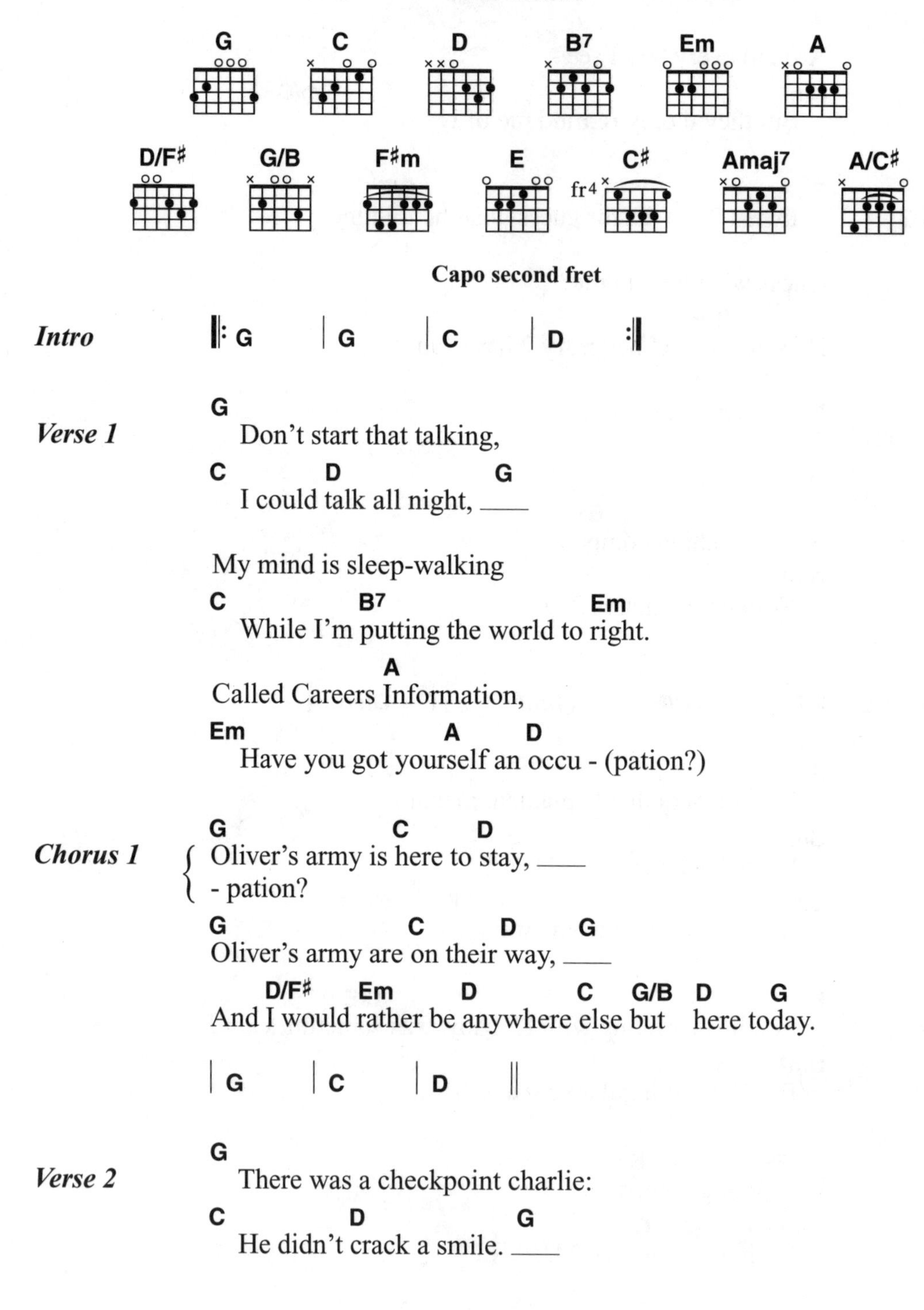
G C D B7 Em A

D/F# G/B F#m E C# Amaj7 A/C#

fr4

Capo second fret

Intro | G | G | C | D :|

Verse 1

G
Don't start that talking,
C D G
I could talk all night, ___

My mind is sleep-walking
C B7 Em
While I'm putting the world to right.
A
Called Careers Information,
Em A D
Have you got yourself an occu - (pation?)

Chorus 1

G C D
Oliver's army is here to stay, ___
- pation?
G C D G
Oliver's army are on their way, ___
D/F# Em D C G/B D G
And I would rather be anywhere else but here today.

| G | C | D ||

Verse 2

G
There was a checkpoint charlie:
C D G
He didn't crack a smile. ___

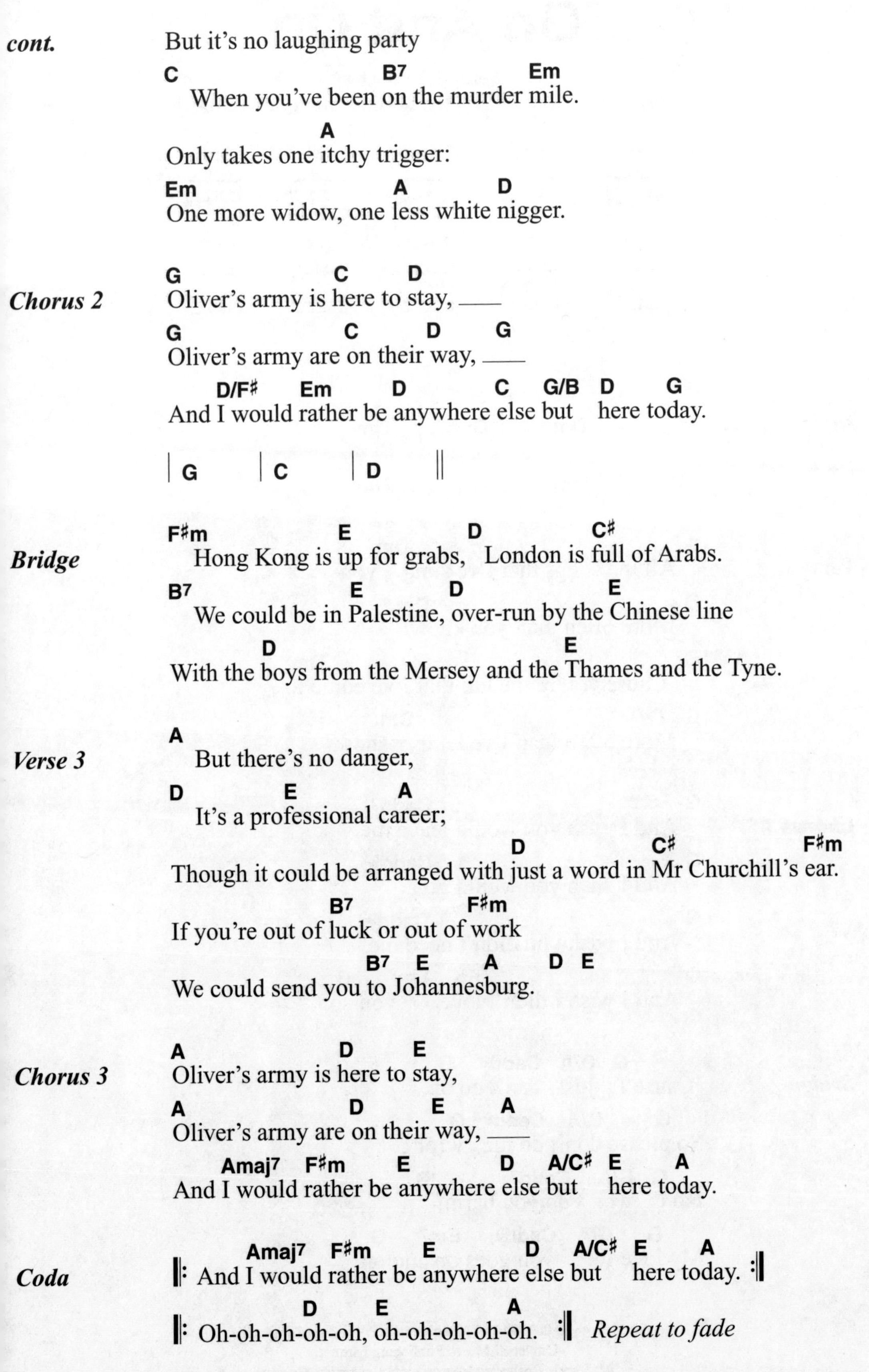

cont.

But it's no laughing party

C B7 Em
When you've been on the murder mile.

A
Only takes one itchy trigger:

Em A D
One more widow, one less white nigger.

Chorus 2

G C D
Oliver's army is here to stay, ___

G C D G
Oliver's army are on their way, ___

D/F♯ Em D C G/B D G
And I would rather be anywhere else but here today.

| G | C | D ||

Bridge

F♯m E D C♯
Hong Kong is up for grabs, London is full of Arabs.

B7 E D E
We could be in Palestine, over-run by the Chinese line

D E
With the boys from the Mersey and the Thames and the Tyne.

Verse 3

A
But there's no danger,

D E A
It's a professional career;

D C♯ F♯m
Though it could be arranged with just a word in Mr Churchill's ear.

B7 F♯m
If you're out of luck or out of work

B7 E A D E
We could send you to Johannesburg.

Chorus 3

A D E
Oliver's army is here to stay,

A D E A
Oliver's army are on their way, ___

Amaj7 F♯m E D A/C♯ E A
And I would rather be anywhere else but here today.

Coda

Amaj7 F♯m E D A/C♯ E A
𝄆 And I would rather be anywhere else but here today. 𝄇

D E A
𝄆 Oh-oh-oh-oh-oh, oh-oh-oh-oh-oh. 𝄇 *Repeat to fade*

On And On

Words & Music by
Crispin Hunt, Richard Hawley, Simon Stafford & Dee Boyle

G Dm Cadd9 F% Em7
G/A D Em7* G7 Em7/A

Intro

| G | Dm | G | Dm |
| G | Dm | G | Dm ||

Verse 1

```
G                               Dm
   All the songs that I've sung    you
G                             Dm
   More often than you know,
G                                        Dm
   'Cause you're the lull that I've come to
G                              Dm
   More often than I've let it     show.
```

Chorus 1

```
G                            Cadd9
   And I wish you would leave me,
G                            Cadd9
   And I wish you would go,
G                             Cadd9
   And I wish you didn't need me,
G                         F%    Em7     G
   And I wish I didn't love        you so.
```

Bridge

```
          G   G/A    Cadd9    G
'Cause I    just   can't go on,
    G        G/A    Cadd9  G
So please don't do me    wrong,
    G  G/A     Cadd9            D
No I    won't do you harm,
     G     G/A    Cadd9      Em7*    G
My love for     you goes on and on.
```

Instrumental | Dm | G7 | Dm | G7 ||

Verse 3

G7   Dm
There's no one else I want, be - side you
G7   Dm
Give me your cold shoulder to cry upon.
G7   Dm
You're never anywhere I find you,
G7   Dm
You're never anything I rely upon.

Chorus 2

G   Em7/A   Cadd9   D
And I wish you would leave me,
G   Em7/A   Cadd9 D
And I wish you would go,
G   Em7/A   Cadd9   D
And I wish you didn't need me,
G   Em7/A   Cadd9
And I wish I didn't know

Outro

          D   G   Em7/A
||: That I just can't go on,
Cadd9 D   G   Em7/A
So   please don't do me wrong,
Cadd9 D   G   Em7/A
No   I won't do you harm,
Cadd9 D   G   Em7/A   Cadd9
My   love for you goes on and on and on and on and on.
    D   G   Em7/A
No I just can't go on
Cadd9 D   G   Em7/A
So   please don't do me wrong,
Cadd9 D   G   Em7/A
No   I won't do you harm,
Cadd9 D   G   Em7/A   Cadd9
My   love____________________
D   G   Em7/A   Cadd9
Goes on and on and on and on and on and on...:||

Repeat ad lib. to fade

One Horse Town

Words by Conor Deasy
Music by Conor Deasy, Kevin Horan, Pádraic McMahon,
Daniel Ryan & Ben Carrigan

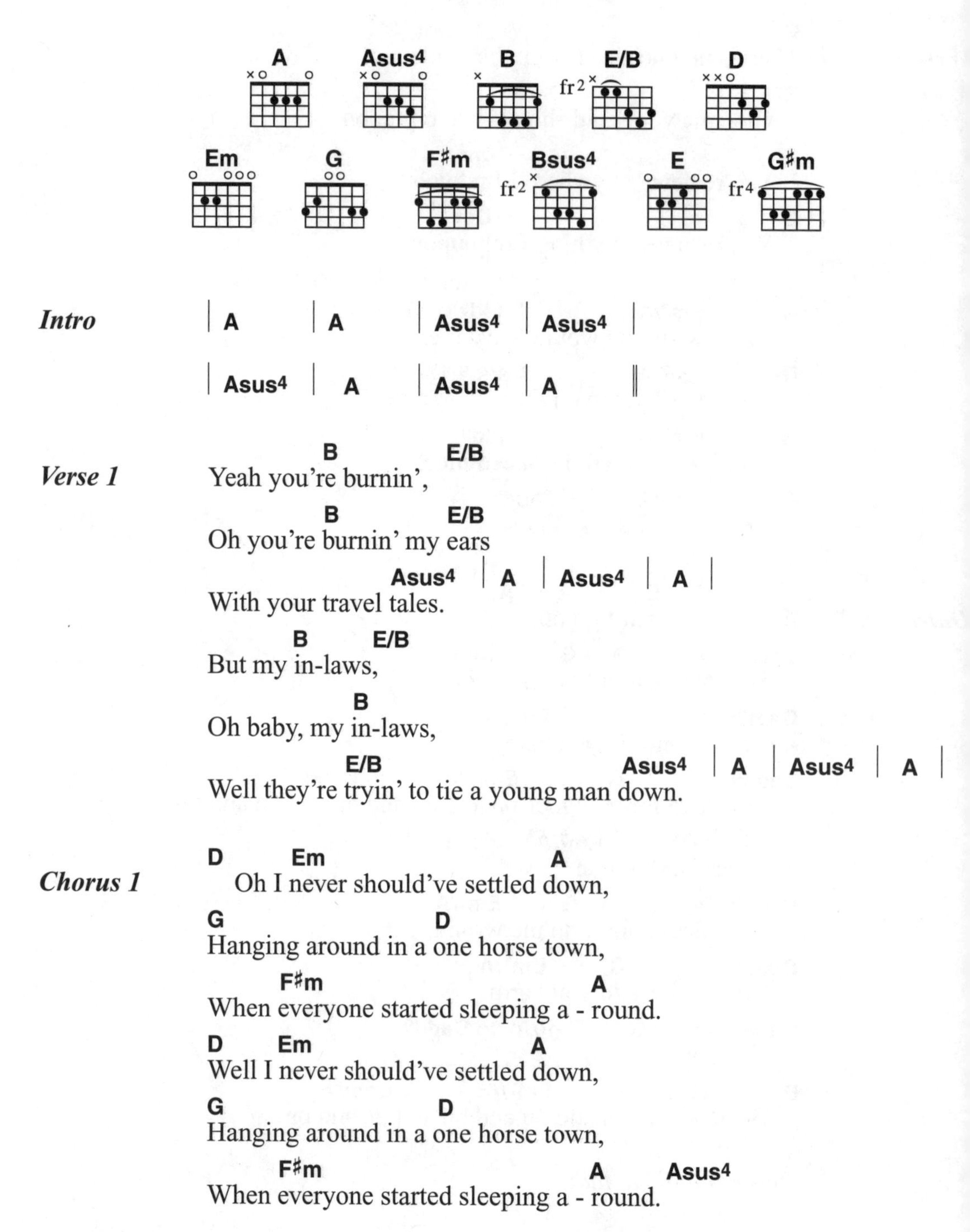

Intro

| A | A | Asus4 | Asus4 |
| Asus4 | A | Asus4 | A ||

Verse 1

```
                B              E/B
Yeah you're burnin',
                B              E/B
Oh you're burnin' my ears
                      Asus4 | A | Asus4 | A |
With your travel tales.
            B        E/B
But my in-laws,
                 B
Oh baby, my in-laws,
                  E/B                         Asus4 | A | Asus4 | A |
Well they're tryin' to tie a young man down.
```

Chorus 1

```
D          Em                        A
   Oh I never should've settled down,
G                        D
Hanging around in a one horse town,
         F♯m                            A
When everyone started sleeping a - round.
D        Em                          A
Well I never should've settled down,
G                         D
Hanging around in a one horse town,
         F♯m                            A         Asus4
When everyone started sleeping a - round.
```

```
Link 1        | Asus4  | A  | Asus4  | A  ||

                     B        E/B
Verse 2       But this feeling
                  B
              Oh, that I'm feeling,
                 E/B                      Asus4  | A  | Asus4  | A |
              You're praying on a tender heart
                  B       E/B
              So this evening
                       B
              Oh baby, I'm leaving
                 E/B                   Asus4  | A  | Asus4  | A |
              On a one way ticket to - night.

Chorus 2      As Chorus 1

Link 2        As Link 1

Link 3        | Bsus4  | B        | Bsus4  | B      ||
                                           Oh, oh, oh!

              E            F#m                   B
Chorus 4        Well my friends oh don't go settle down,
              A                    E
              Hanging around in a one horse town
                   G#m                      B
              When everyone started sleeping a - round.
              E          F#m                  B
                'Guess I never should've settled down,
                     A                     E
              You see, hanging around in a one horse town
                   G#m                   B      E
              Does nothing for your state of mind.
```

One Last Love Song

Words & Music by
Paul Heaton & David Rotheray

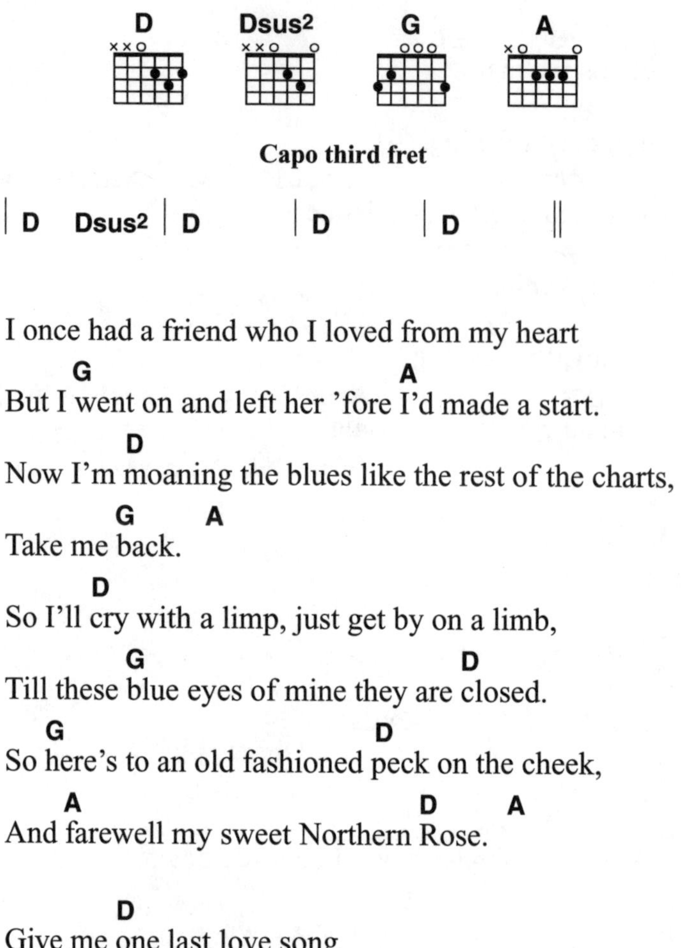

Capo third fret

Intro

| D Dsus2 | D | D | D ||

Verse 1

```
I once had a friend who I loved from my heart
       G                        A
But I went on and left her 'fore I'd made a start.
           D
Now I'm moaning the blues like the rest of the charts,
           G      A
Take me back.
        D
So I'll cry with a limp, just get by on a limb,
          G                         D
Till these blue eyes of mine they are closed.
    G                         D
So here's to an old fashioned peck on the cheek,
    A                         D      A
And farewell my sweet Northern Rose.
```

Chorus 1

```
        D
Give me one last love song
    G                A
To bring you back, bring you back,
        D                   G
Give me one last video, just dressed in black,
         A
Dressed in black.
G                        D
Give him a chorus and that bit at the end,
          G                         D
Where he wails on and on 'bout the loss of a friend.
```

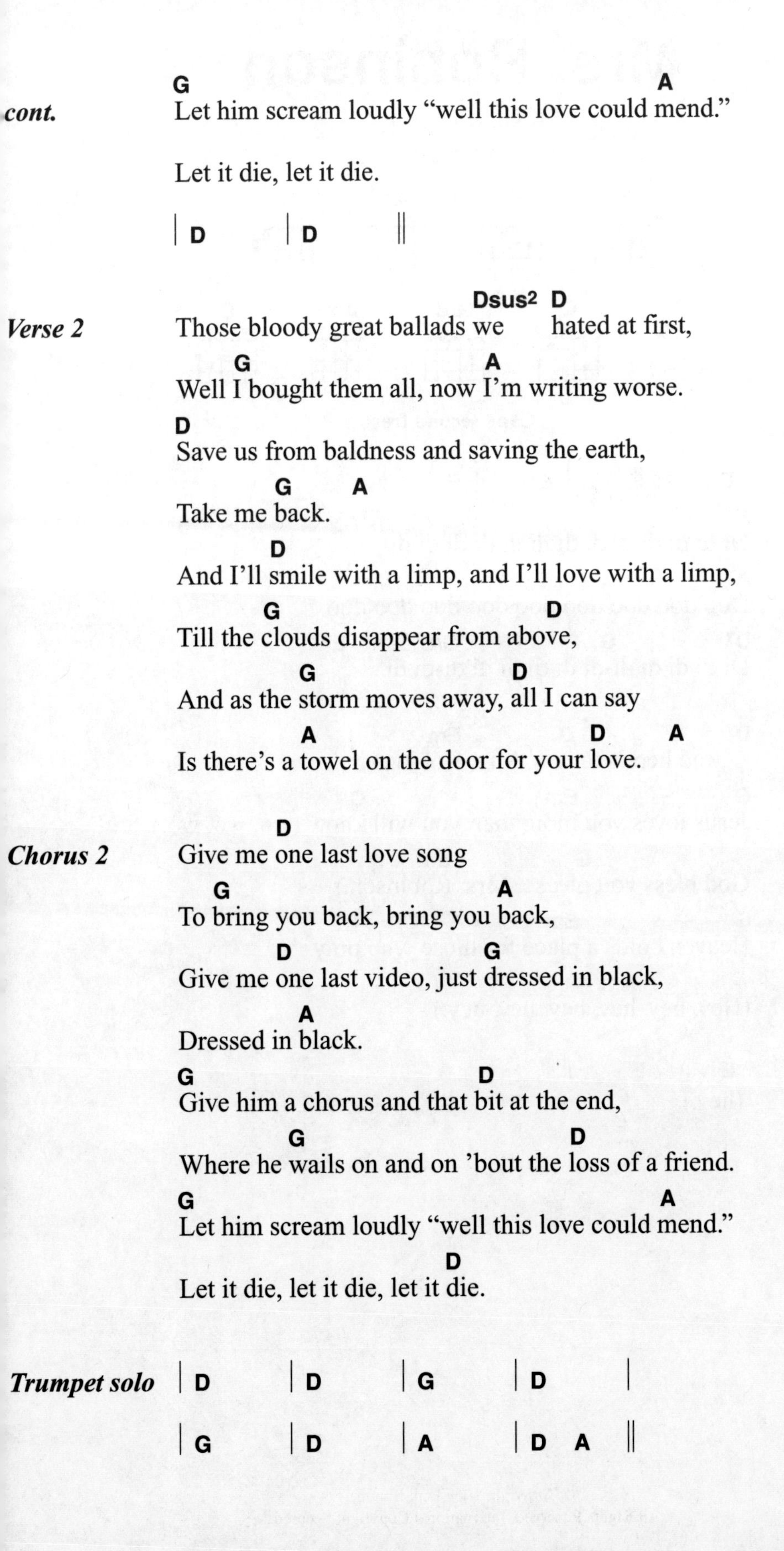

cont.
G A
Let him scream loudly "well this love could mend."

Let it die, let it die.

| D | D ||

Verse 2
Dsus2 D
Those bloody great ballads we hated at first,
G A
Well I bought them all, now I'm writing worse.
D
Save us from baldness and saving the earth,
G A
Take me back.
D
And I'll smile with a limp, and I'll love with a limp,
G D
Till the clouds disappear from above,
G D
And as the storm moves away, all I can say
A D A
Is there's a towel on the door for your love.

Chorus 2
D
Give me one last love song
G A
To bring you back, bring you back,
D G
Give me one last video, just dressed in black,
A
Dressed in black.
G D
Give him a chorus and that bit at the end,
G D
Where he wails on and on 'bout the loss of a friend.
G A
Let him scream loudly "well this love could mend."
D
Let it die, let it die, let it die.

Trumpet solo
| D | D | G | D |

| G | D | A | D A ||

Mrs. Robinson

Words & Music by
Paul Simon

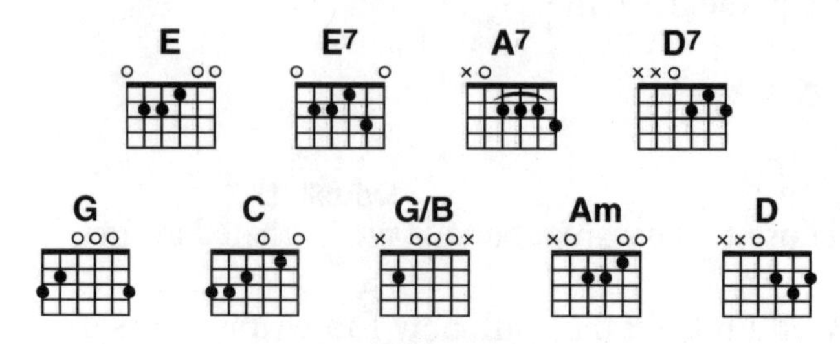

Capo second fret

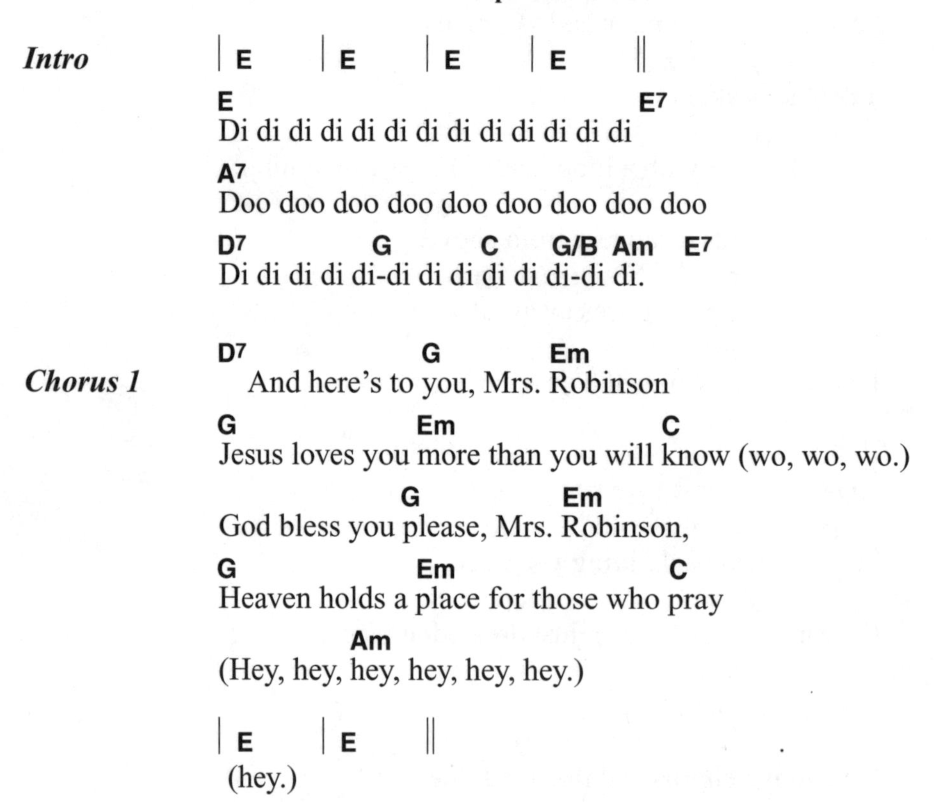

Intro

| E | E | E | E ||

E   E7
Di di di di di di di di di di di di di

A7
Doo doo doo doo doo doo doo doo doo

D7   G   C   G/B Am   E7
Di di di di di-di di di di di di-di di.

Chorus 1

D7   G   Em
   And here's to you, Mrs. Robinson

G   Em   C
Jesus loves you more than you will know (wo, wo, wo.)

                          G   Em
God bless you please, Mrs. Robinson,

G   Em   C
Heaven holds a place for those who pray

            Am
(Hey, hey, hey, hey, hey, hey.)

| E | E ||
(hey.)

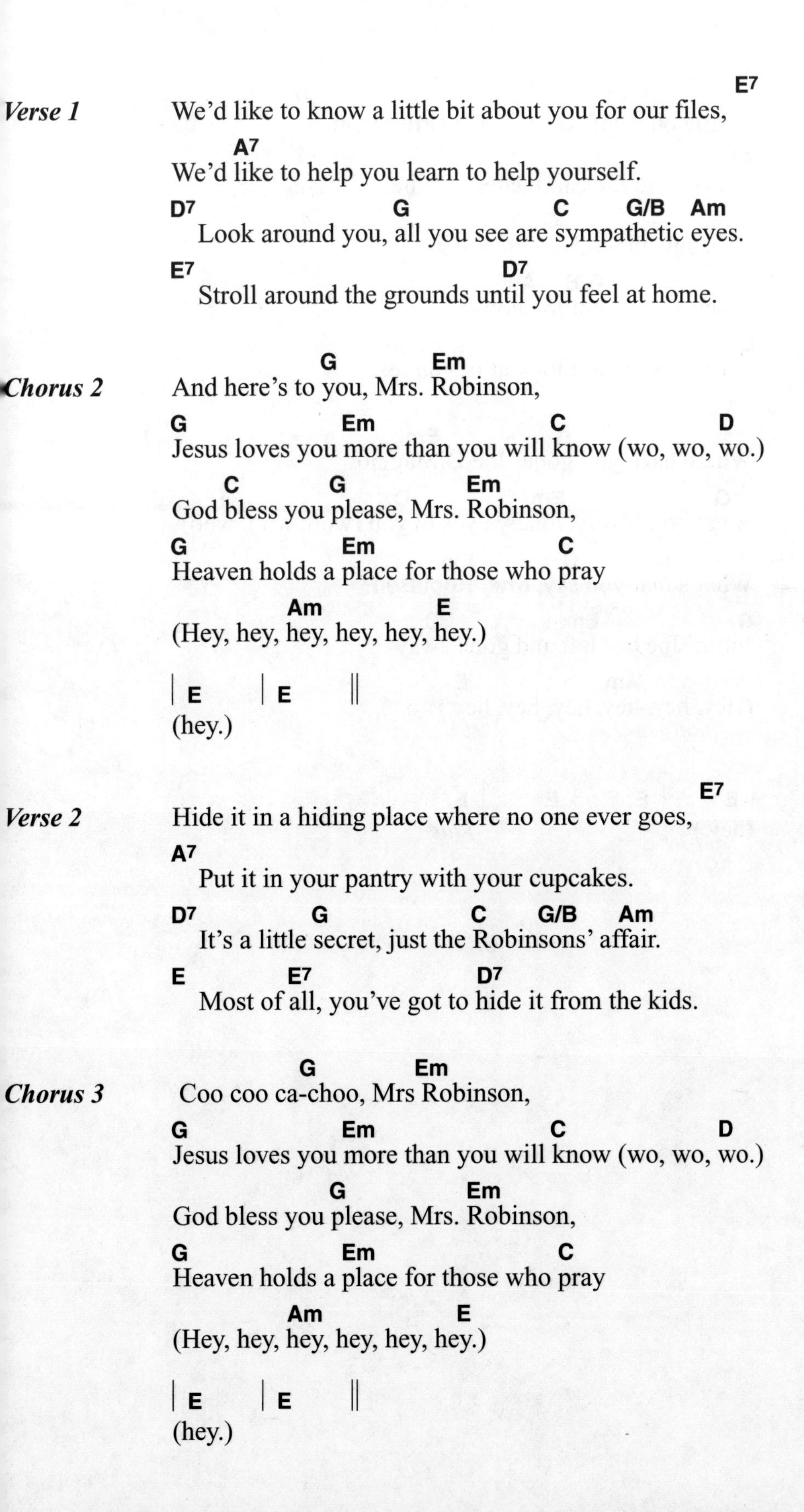

Verse 1

E7
We'd like to know a little bit about you for our files,
A7
We'd like to help you learn to help yourself.
D7 G C G/B Am
Look around you, all you see are sympathetic eyes.
E7 D7
Stroll around the grounds until you feel at home.

Chorus 2

G Em
And here's to you, Mrs. Robinson,
G Em C D
Jesus loves you more than you will know (wo, wo, wo.)
C G Em
God bless you please, Mrs. Robinson,
G Em C
Heaven holds a place for those who pray
Am E
(Hey, hey, hey, hey, hey, hey.)

| E | E ||
(hey.)

Verse 2

E7
Hide it in a hiding place where no one ever goes,
A7
Put it in your pantry with your cupcakes.
D7 G C G/B Am
It's a little secret, just the Robinsons' affair.
E E7 D7
Most of all, you've got to hide it from the kids.

Chorus 3

G Em
Coo coo ca-choo, Mrs Robinson,
G Em C D
Jesus loves you more than you will know (wo, wo, wo.)
G Em
God bless you please, Mrs. Robinson,
G Em C
Heaven holds a place for those who pray
Am E
(Hey, hey, hey, hey, hey, hey.)

| E | E ||
(hey.)

Verse 3

```
                                               E7
Sitting on a sofa on a Sunday afternoon,
A7
   Going to the candidates' debate.
D7               G
   Laugh about it, shout about it
C                 G/B   Am
When you've got to choose.
E7                                      D7
   Ev'ry way you look at it, you lose.
```

Chorus 4

```
                      G             Em
Where have you gone, Joe DiMaggio?
  G                  Em              C                  D
A nation turns its lonely eyes to you (woo, woo, woo)
        C        G           Em
What's that you say, Mrs. Robinson?
G                Em          C
Joltin' Joe has left and gone away
               Am             E
(Hey, hey, hey, hey, hey, hey.)
```

Coda

```
| E      | E      | E      | E      ||
(hey.)                     fade
```

Part Of The Process

Words & Music by
Paul Godfrey, Ross Godfrey & Skye Edwards

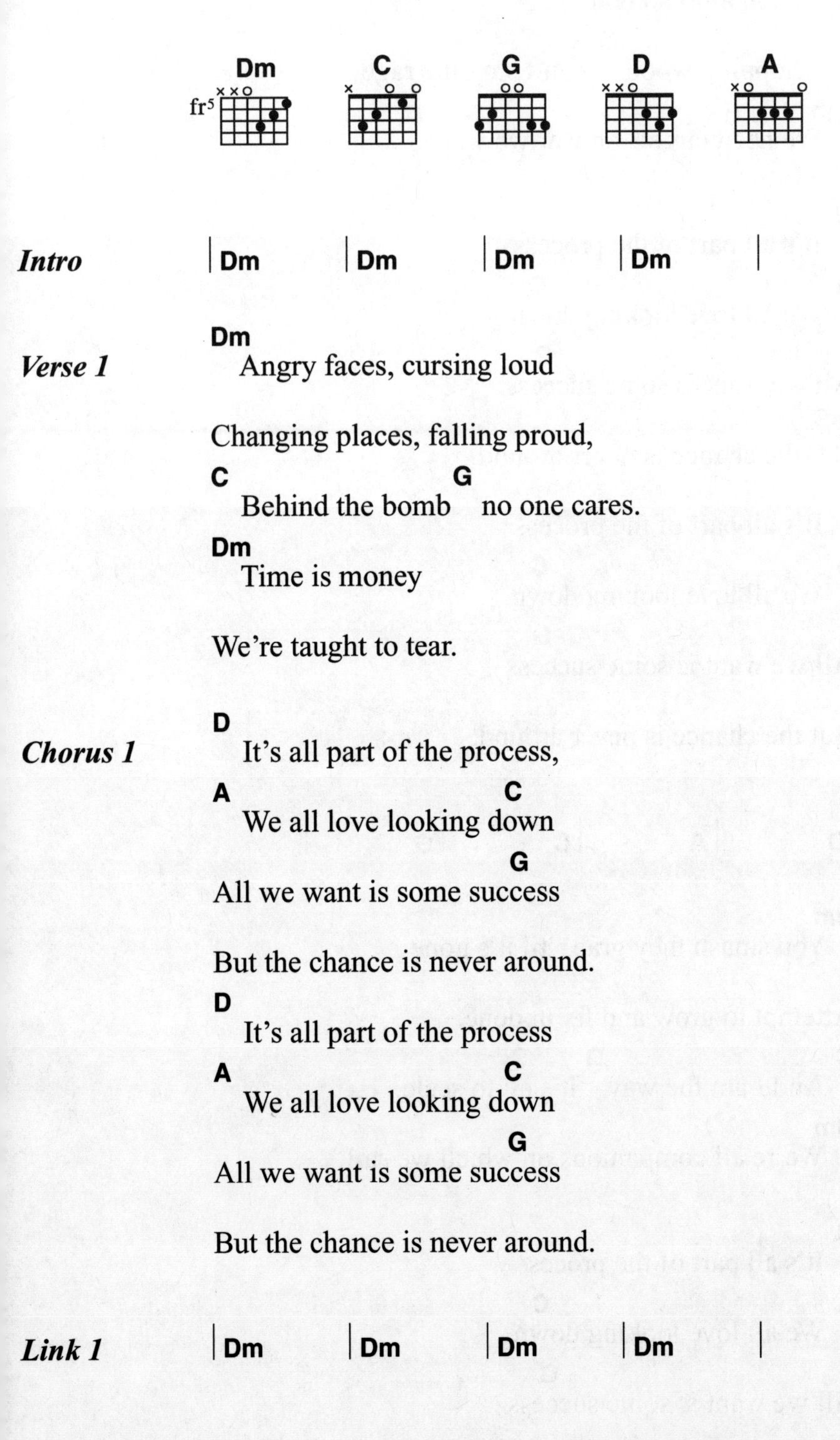

Intro | Dm | Dm | Dm | Dm |

Verse 1

Dm
Angry faces, cursing loud

Changing places, falling proud,
C G
Behind the bomb no one cares.
Dm
Time is money

We're taught to tear.

Chorus 1

D
It's all part of the process,
A C
We all love looking down
G
All we want is some success

But the chance is never around.
D
It's all part of the process
A C
We all love looking down
G
All we want is some success

But the chance is never around.

Link 1 | Dm | Dm | Dm | Dm |

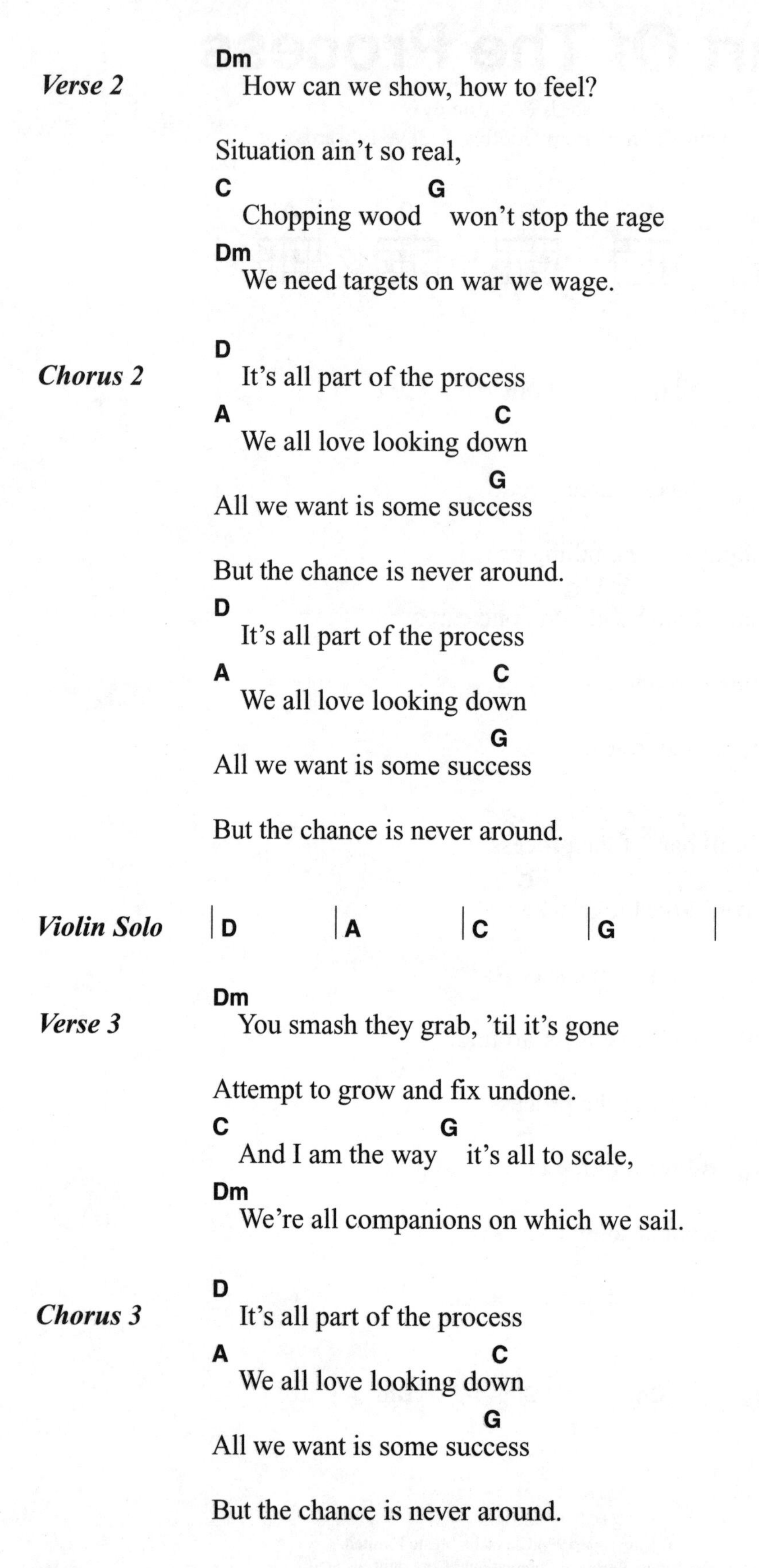

Verse 2

Dm
How can we show, how to feel?

Situation ain't so real,

C **G**
Chopping wood won't stop the rage

Dm
We need targets on war we wage.

Chorus 2

D
It's all part of the process

A **C**
We all love looking down

G
All we want is some success

But the chance is never around.

D
It's all part of the process

A **C**
We all love looking down

G
All we want is some success

But the chance is never around.

Violin Solo | **D** | **A** | **C** | **G** |

Verse 3

Dm
You smash they grab, 'til it's gone

Attempt to grow and fix undone.

C **G**
And I am the way it's all to scale,

Dm
We're all companions on which we sail.

Chorus 3

D
It's all part of the process

A **C**
We all love looking down

G
All we want is some success

But the chance is never around.

cont.

```
D
   It's all part of the process
A                         C
   We all love looking down
                          G
All we want is some success

But the chance is never around.
```

Chorus 4

```
D
   And it's all part of the process
A                         C
   We all love looking down
                          G
All we want is some success

But the chance is never around.
D
   And it's all part of the process
A                         C
   We all love looking down
                          G
All we want it some success

And the chance . . .
```

Outro

```
| D      | A      | C      | G      | D      ||
```

Queen Of The Underworld

Words & Music by
Jesse Malin

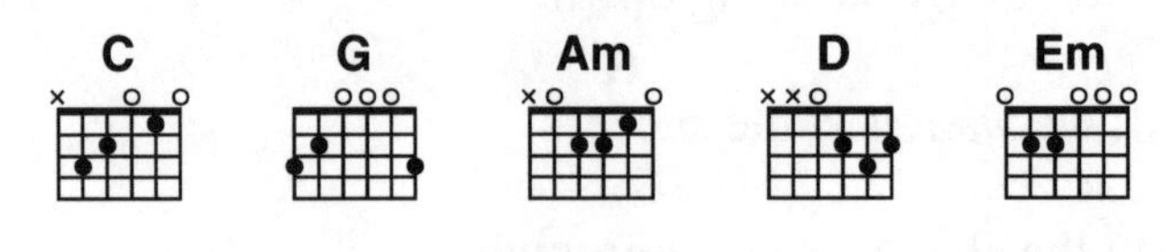

Capo first fret

Verse 1

```
C                         G
  You say you want a revolution,
C                         G
  Something you can touch.
C                G
  Like an age old contradiction,
C                  G
  With alcohol and lust.
Am                                G
  And all the things you have are broken,
Am                               D
  And you can't go back if they move.
Am                          G         Em
  From disfunction to disfunction,
Am                C               D
  You know I'm singing just for you.
```

Chorus 1

```
C                D
  Queen of the Underworld,
C                      D
  Took a ride on the tilt-a-whirl.
C                 D
  Meanwhile another girl's,
```

Bridge 1

```
Am                                  G
  Out on the street, you hear their laughter,
Am                                D
  And pretty green must turn to blue.
Am                                  G      Em
  Everything you heard I've gotten,
Am     C               D
  Persecution's nothing new.
```

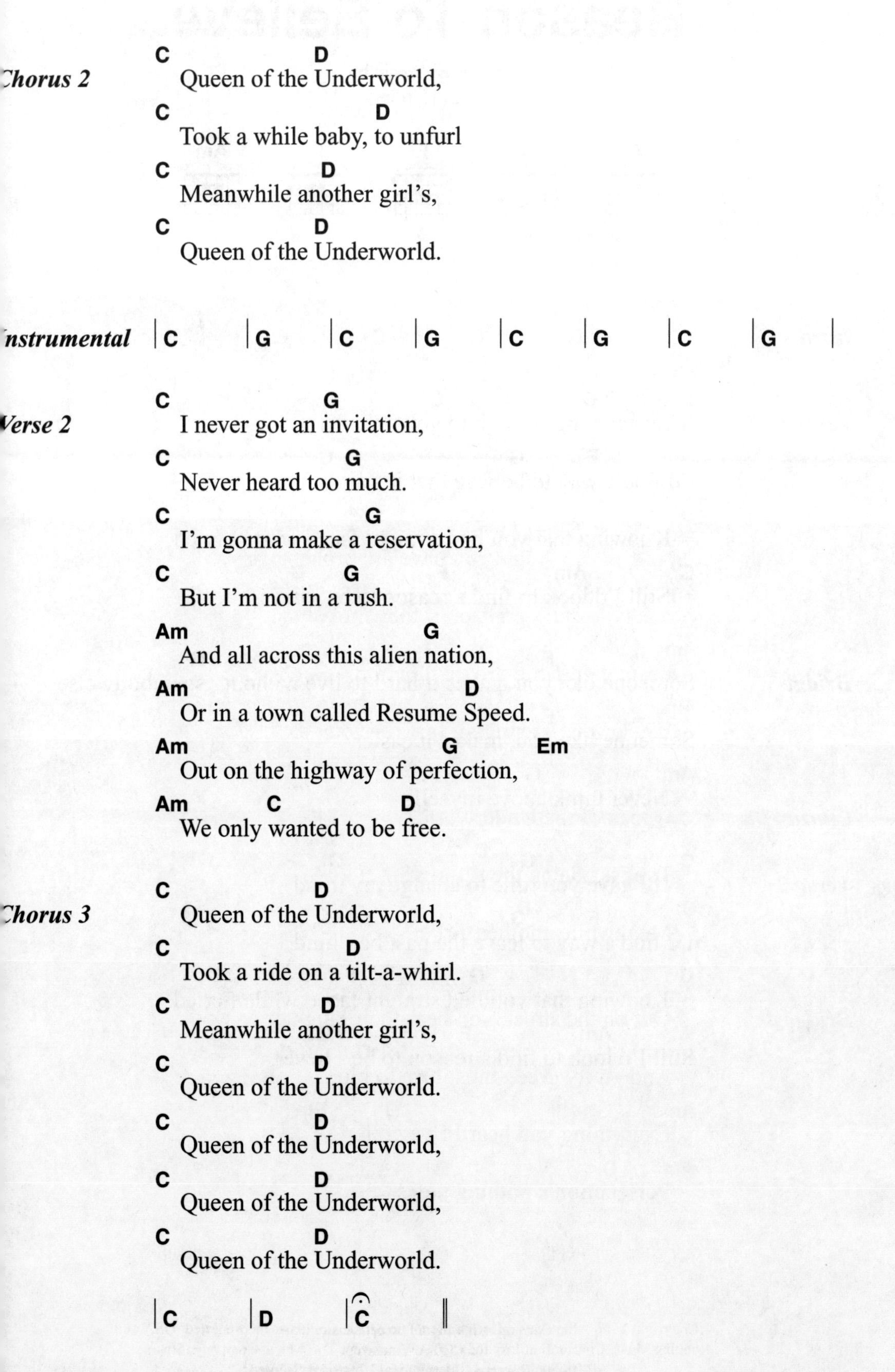

```
            C                  D
Chorus 2       Queen of the Underworld,
            C                          D
               Took a while baby, to unfurl
            C                    D
               Meanwhile another girl's,
            C                  D
               Queen of the Underworld.

Instrumental | C    | G    | C    | G    | C    | G    | C    | G    |

            C                   G
Verse 2        I never got an invitation,
            C                 G
               Never heard too much.
            C                           G
               I'm gonna make a reservation,
            C                      G
               But I'm not in a rush.
            Am                            G
               And all across this alien nation,
            Am                                D
               Or in a town called Resume Speed.
            Am                              G           Em
               Out on the highway of perfection,
            Am            C              D
               We only wanted to be free.

            C                  D
Chorus 3       Queen of the Underworld,
            C                     D
               Took a ride on a tilt-a-whirl.
            C                    D
               Meanwhile another girl's,
            C                  D
               Queen of the Underworld.
            C                  D
               Queen of the Underworld,
            C                  D
               Queen of the Underworld,
            C                  D
               Queen of the Underworld.

            | C      | D      | C (fermata)  ||
```

Reason To Believe

Words & Music by
Tim Hardin

C G F D Am

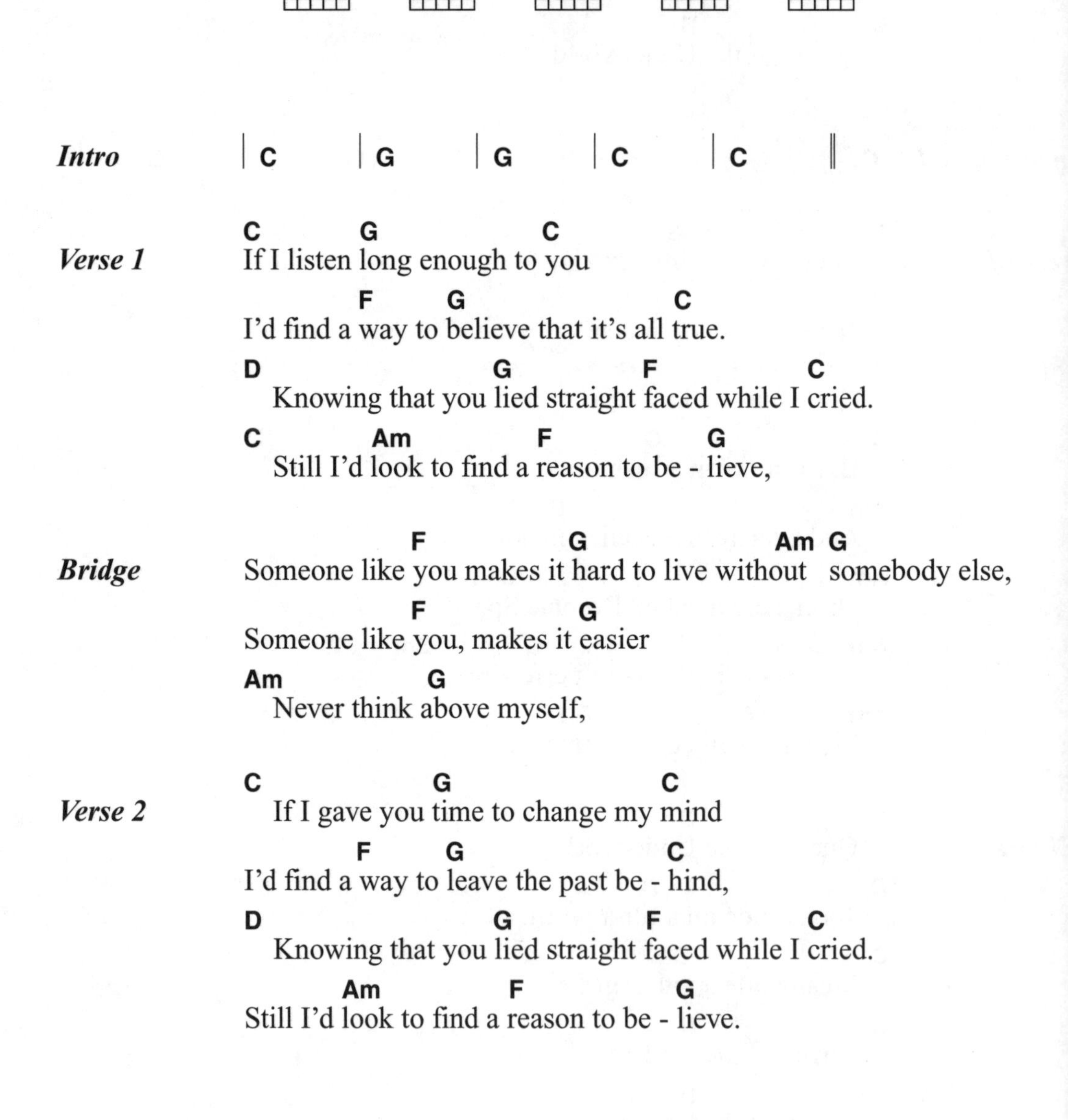

Intro | C | G | G | C | C ||

Verse 1

C G C
If I listen long enough to you
F G C
I'd find a way to believe that it's all true.
D G F C
Knowing that you lied straight faced while I cried.
C Am F G
Still I'd look to find a reason to be - lieve,

Bridge

F G Am G
Someone like you makes it hard to live without somebody else,
F G
Someone like you, makes it easier
Am G
Never think above myself,

Verse 2

C G C
If I gave you time to change my mind
F G C
I'd find a way to leave the past be - hind,
D G F C
Knowing that you lied straight faced while I cried.
Am F G
Still I'd look to find a reason to be - lieve.

Instrumental ‖: F | G | Am | G :‖ G ‖

```
              C          G                 C
*Verse 3*     If I listen long enough to you
                    F       G             C
              I'd find a way to believe it's all true.
              D                    G           F             C
                 Knowing that you lied straight faced while I cried.
                        Am               F              G
              Still I'd look to find a reason to be - lieve.
```

Return To Sender

Words & Music by
Otis Blackwell & Winfield Scott

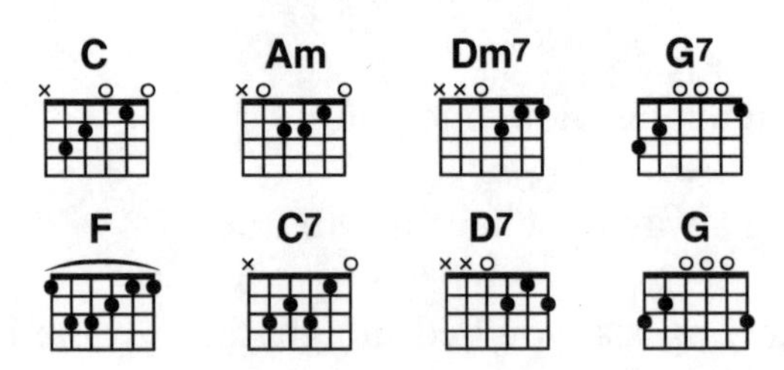

Capo third fret

Intro

C Am
Return to sender,
Dm7 G7
Return to sender.

Verse 1

C Am
I gave a letter to the postman,
Dm7 G7
He put it in his sack.
C Am
Bright and early next morning
Dm7 G7 C
He brought my letter back.
N.C.
(She wrote upon it:)

Chorus 1

F G7
Return to sender,
F G7
Address unknown,
F G7
No such number,
C C7
No such zone.
F G7
We had a quarrel,
F G7
A lovers' spat.
D7 G
I write I'm sorry but my letter keeps coming back.

```
                C                                  Am
Verse 2            So then I dropped it in the mailbox,
                Dm7                 G7
                And sent it special D
                C                              Am
                   Bright and early next morning
                   Dm7           G7    C
                It came right back to me.
                N.C.
                (She wrote upon it:)

                F             G7
Chorus 2           Return to sender,
                F               G7
                   Address unknown,
                F             G7
                   No such person,
                C             C7
                   No such zone.

                F
Bridge             This time I'm gonna take it myself
                     C
                And put it right in her hand,
                     D7
                And if it comes back the very next day
                G
                Then I'll understand.
                N.C.
                (The writing in it.)

                F             G7
Chorus 3           Return to sender,
                F               G7
                   Address unknown,
                F             G7
                   No such number,
                C             C7
                   No such zone.

                   F            G7
Chorus 4        ||: Return to sender. :||   Repeat to fade
```

Run

Words & Music by Gary Lightbody, Jonathan Quinn,
Mark McClelland, Nathan Connolly & Iain Archer

Am F/A G5 Gsus4 C G F

Intro |: Am F/A | G5 Gsus4 G5 | Am F/A | G5 Gsus4 G5 :|

Verse 1

Am F/A G5 Gsus4 G5
I'll sing it one last time for you
Am F/A G5 Gsus4 G5
Then we really have to go
Am F/A G5 Gsus4 G5
You've been the only thing that's right
Am F/A G5 Gsus4 G5
In all I've done.

Verse 2

Am F/A G5 Gsus4 G5
And I can barely look at you
Am F/A G5 Gsus4 G5
But every single time I do
Am F/A G5 Gsus4 G5
I know we'll make it an - y - where
Am F/A G5 Gsus4 G5
Away from here.

Chorus 1

C
Light up, light up
G
As if you have a choice
Am
Even if you cannot hear my voice
F | F |
I'll be right beside you dear
C
Louder, louder
G
And we'll run for our lives
Am
I can hardly speak I understand
F | F |
Why you can't raise your voice to say.

Link | Am F/A | G5 Gsus4 G5 | Am F/A | G5 Gsus4 G5 ||

Verse 3
```
                Am              F/A            G5     Gsus4   G5
To think I might not see those eyes
                Am               F/A        G5  Gsus4   G5
It makes it so hard not to    cry
                Am              F/A              G5  Gsus4   G5
And as we say our long good - byes
            Am        F/A   G5      Gsus4    G5
I nearly do.
```

Chorus 2 As Chorus 1

Chorus 3
```
C
   Slower, slower
                G
We don't have time for that
                            Am
All I want is to find an easier way
                            F
To get out of our little heads.
C
   Have heart my dear
                 G
We're bound to be afraid
                          Am
Even if it's just for a   few days
                            F    | F   |
Making up for all this mess.
```

Solo |: C | C | G | G | Am | Am | F | F :|

Outro
```
C
   Light up, light up
          G
As if you have a choice
                             Am
Even if you cannot hear my voice
                         G   F  | F  | C  ||
I'll be right beside you dear.
```

San Francisco (Be Sure To Wear Some Flowers In Your Hair)

Words & Music by
John Phillips

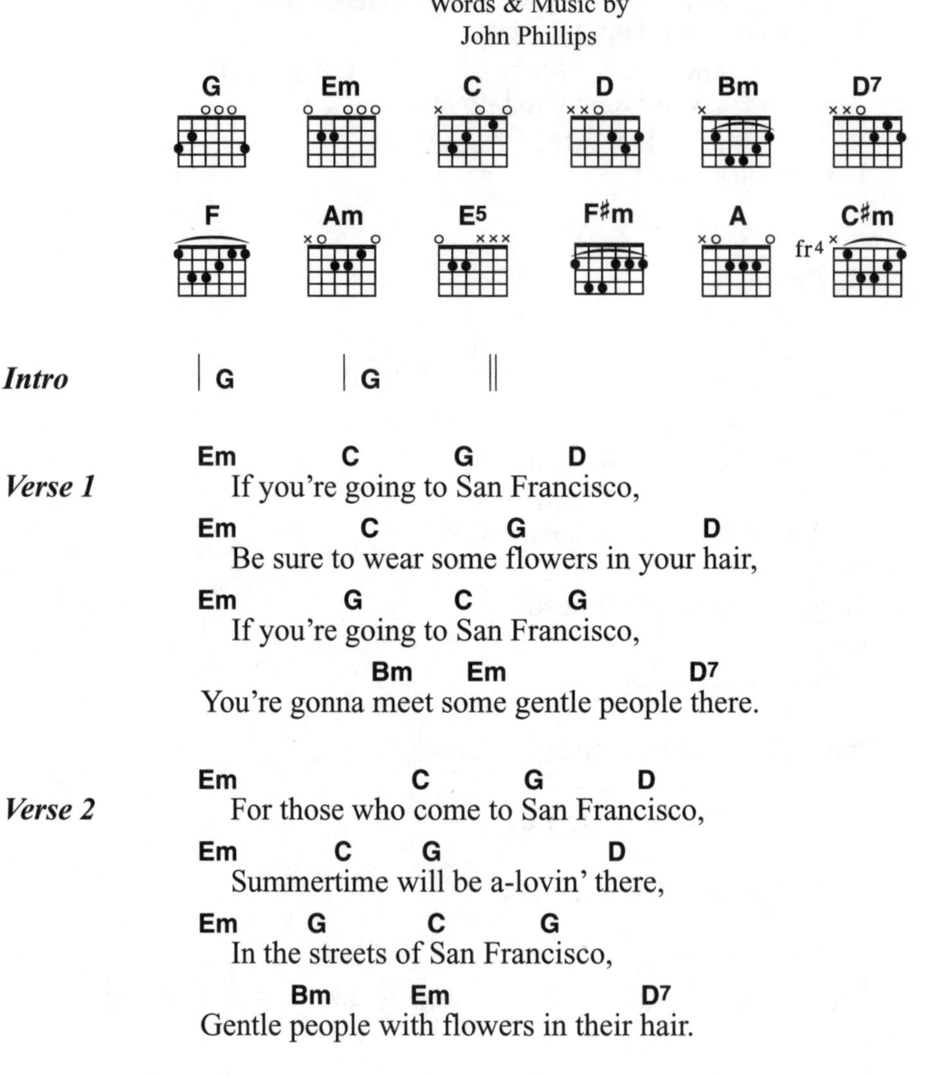


```
Intro      | G        | G        ||

           Em         C        G        D
Verse 1       If you're going to San Francisco,
           Em           C          G              D
              Be sure to wear some flowers in your hair,
           Em          G        C        G
              If you're going to San Francisco,
                           Bm      Em                 D7
           You're gonna meet some gentle people there.

           Em                 C        G        D
Verse 2       For those who come to San Francisco,
           Em           C      G              D
              Summertime will be a-lovin' there,
           Em      G        C        G
              In the streets of San Francisco,
                     Bm        Em              D7
           Gentle people with flowers in their hair.
```

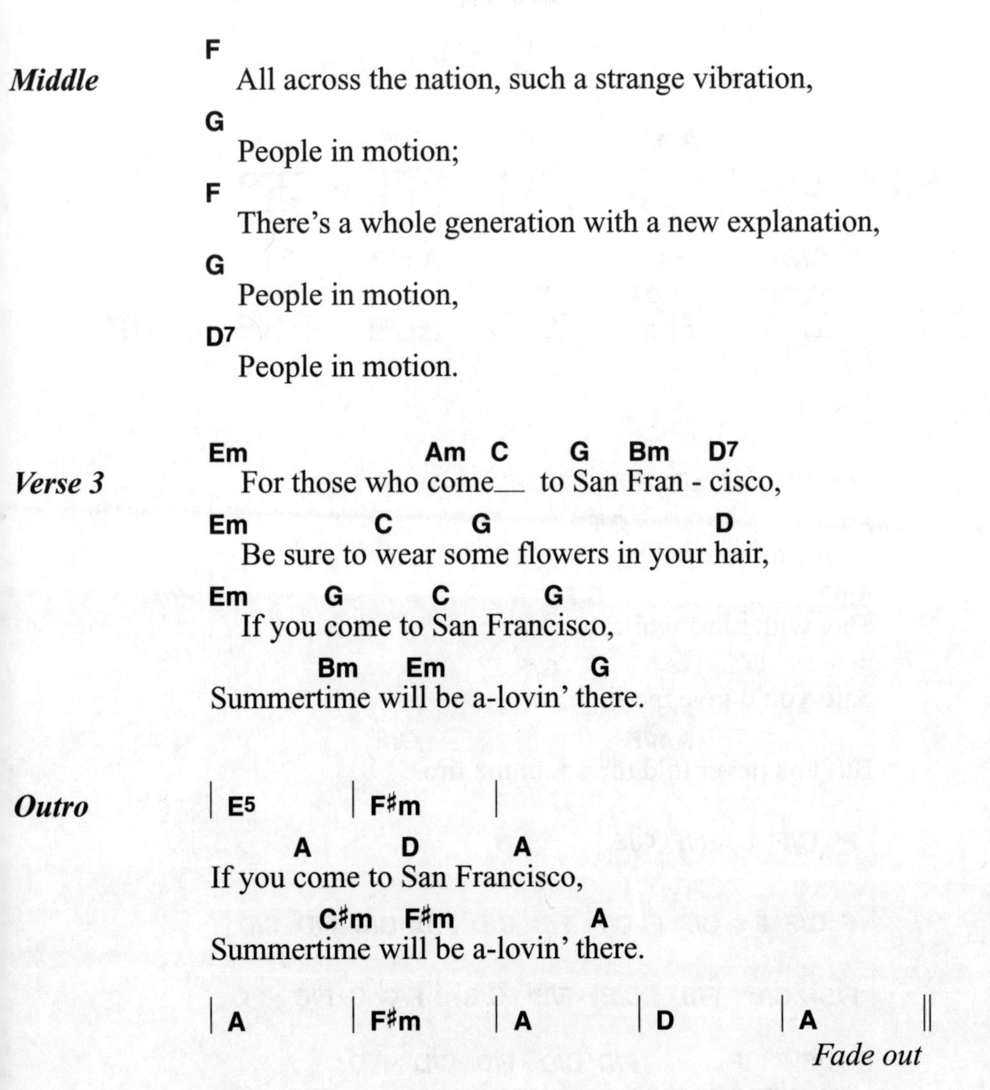

Middle

F
All across the nation, such a strange vibration,
G
People in motion;
F
There's a whole generation with a new explanation,
G
People in motion,
D7
People in motion.

Verse 3

Em Am C G Bm D7
For those who come__ to San Fran - cisco,
Em C G D
Be sure to wear some flowers in your hair,
Em G C G
If you come to San Francisco,
Bm Em G
Summertime will be a-lovin' there.

Outro

| E5 | F♯m |

A D A
If you come to San Francisco,
C♯m F♯m A
Summertime will be a-lovin' there.

| A | F♯m | A | D | A ||

Fade out

Sara

Words & Music by
Stevie Nicks

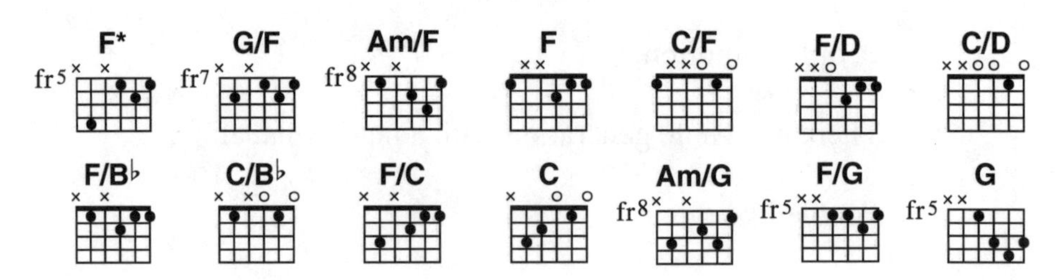

Intro | F* G/F | Am/F G/F | F* G/F | Am/F G/F ||

F* G/F
Wait a minute baby,

Am/F G/F
Stay with me a while,

F* G/F
Said you'd give me light,

Am/F G/F
But you never told me about the fire.

| F* G/F | Am/F G/F |

Link 1 | F C/F F | C/F F C/F | F/D C/D F/D | C/D F/D C/D |

| F/B♭ C/B♭ F/B♭ | C/B♭ F/B♭ C/B♭ | F/C C F/C | C ||

Verse 1

F C/F F F/D C/D F/D C/D F/D
Drowning in the sea of love,

C/D F/B♭ C/B♭ F/B♭ C/B♭ F/B♭ C/B♭ F/C C F/C C
Where every - one would love to drown.

F C/F F C/F F
But now it's gone

C/F F/D C/D F/D C/D F/D
It doesn't matter what for,

C/D F/B♭ C/B♭ F/B♭ C/B♭ F/B♭
When you build your house,

C/B♭ F/C C F/C C
Then call me home.

| F* G/F Am/F | F* G/F Am/F | F/G G Am/G | F/G G Am/G |

Chorus 1

Ooh,_______

F* G/F Am/F
And he was just like
F* G/F Am/F
A great dark wing,
F/G G Am/G | F/G G Am/G
Within the wings of a storm.
F* G/F Am/F | F* G/F Am/F
I think I have met my match,
F/G G Am/G | F/G G Am/G
He was singing.
F* G/F Am/F | F* G/F Am/F
And un - doing,
F/G G Am/G | F/G G Am/G
And undoing
F* G/F Am/F | F* G/F Am/F
The laces,
F/G G Am/G
Undoing the laces.
F/G G Am/G
Ooh, ooh.

Verse 2

F C/F F F/D C/D F/D C/D F/D
In the sea of love,
C/D F/B♭ C/B♭ F/B♭ C/B♭ F/B♭ C/B♭ F/C C F/C C
Where every - one would love to drown,
F C/F F C/F F
But now it's gone,
C/F F/D C/D F/D C/D F/D
They say it doesn't matter anymore,
C/D F/B♭ C/B♭ F/B♭ C/B♭ F/B♭
If you build your house,
C/B♭ F/C C F/C C F/C C
Then please call me, oh,

Verse 3

```
     F  C/F  F  C/F  F
Said Sara,
C/F            F/D   C/D  F/D   C/D  F/D  C/D
You're the poet in my heart,
F/B♭  C/B♭  F/B♭  C/B♭  F/B♭  C/B♭   F/C  C  F/C  C  F/C  C
Never change,         and don't you ever stop.
    F  C/F   F  C/F  F
But now it's gone,      no
 C/F      F/D  C/D  F/D   C/D  F/D
It doesn't matter anymore,
C/D            F/B♭  C/B♭  F/B♭   C/B♭  F/B♭
When you build your house,
C/B♭  F/C  C  F/C  C
I'll come by.
```

Outro

```
   F  C/F   F  C/F  F
𝄆 Sara...
C/F F/D  C/D  F/D   C/D  F/D  C/D
Oh Sara...

F/B♭  C/B♭  F/B♭  C/B♭  F/B♭  C/B♭

F/C  C  F/C  C  𝄇
```

Repeat to fade

Since I Told You It's Over

Words & Music by
Kelly Jones, Richard Jones & Stuart Cable

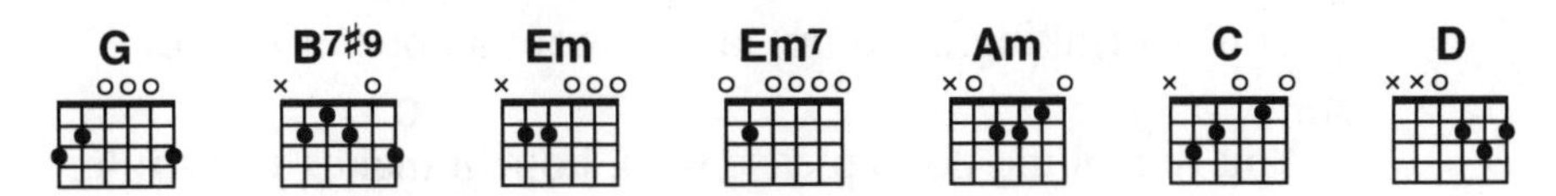

Capo sixth fret

Verse 1

G B7♯9
I'm black and blue from the wind and the rain
Em Em7
Said I'm sorry for the lies and the pain,
Am C
I never ever meant to make you cry
D
If I could take it back, you know, I would

I wanna burn up and die.

Chorus 1

G
So take a look at me now
B7♯9
Since I told you it's over
Em
You got a hole in your heart
Em7
I found a four leaf clover
Am
You can't tell me this now,
C
This far down the line
D
That you're never, ever gonna get over me.

Verse 2

```
G                                B7#9
   You send a cross, it's a cross I bear,
Em                                          Em7
   You're drinking, hard up, late without a hope or a care
Am                                         C
   You're making do to please who, hope it makes you smile,
             D
You're not a - round for long, you gotta savour what's gone

And move your life right along.
```

Chorus 2

As Chorus 1

Bridge

```
Am
   I'm lost, I'm cold
          B7#9
And getting old
                             Em     | Em7  | C    | C    |
My head is full of lies I told.
Am
   I've been down, been around
                 B7#9
But I've fallen on my own two feet,
                             Em   Em7               C   D | D   |
And I've left you out to drown,   I never meant for that.
```

Verse 3

```
G                             B7#9
   I look around, sometimes I stare
Em                                       Em7
   I think back now and then, I hope you know I care,
Am                            C
   I walked away that day, time to treat you right,
             D
But you were on your track, it was me turning back,

I left you freezing outside.
```

Chorus 3

G
So take a look at me now

B7#9
Since I told you it's over

Em
You got a hole in your heart

Em7
I found a four leaf clover.

Am
You can't tell me this now

C
This far down the line

D
That you're never, ever gonna get over me. Ah___

Verse 4

G B7#9
(ah)_ a ma ma_

Em
You never get over me

Em7
A - na - na - na,_ na_

Am C
Na, you never get over me

D
But you were on your track, it was me turning back

I left you freezing outside.

Outro chorus

G
So take a look at me now

B7#9
Since I told you it's over

Em
You got a hole in your heart

Em7
I found a four leaf clover.

Am
You can't tell me this now

C
This far down the line... *(to fade)*

Sing

Words & Music by
Fran Healy

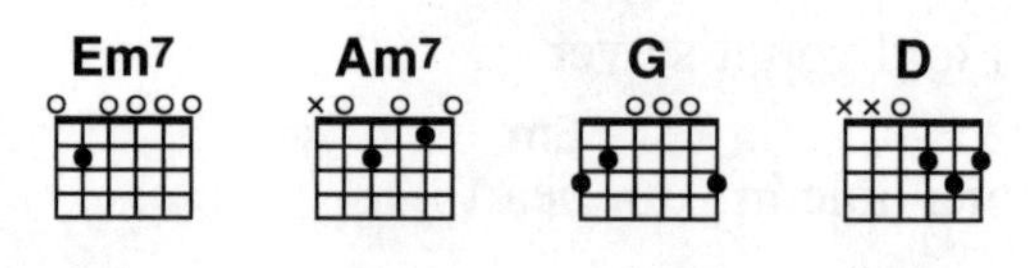

Capo second fret

Intro ‖: Em7 | Am7 | Am7 | Em7 :‖

```
            Em7                         Am7
*Verse 1*   Baby, you've been going so crazy,
                                        Em7
            Lately, nothing seems to be going right.
                                              Am7
            So low, why do you have to get so low?
                                                      Em7
            You're so, you've been waiting in the sun too long.

                         G     D      Am7
*Chorus 1*  But if you sing, sing,
                                G
            Sing, sing, sing, sing.
                                      D                 Am7
            For the love you bring won't mean a thing
                                          G
            Unless you sing, sing, sing, sing.

            Em7                      Am7
*Verse 2*   Colder, crying over your shoulder,
                                               Em7
            Hold her, tell her everything's gonna be fine.
                                              Am7
            Surely, you've been going too hurry,
                                                  Em7
            Hurry, 'cause no one's gonna be stopped, now, now, now, now, now,
```

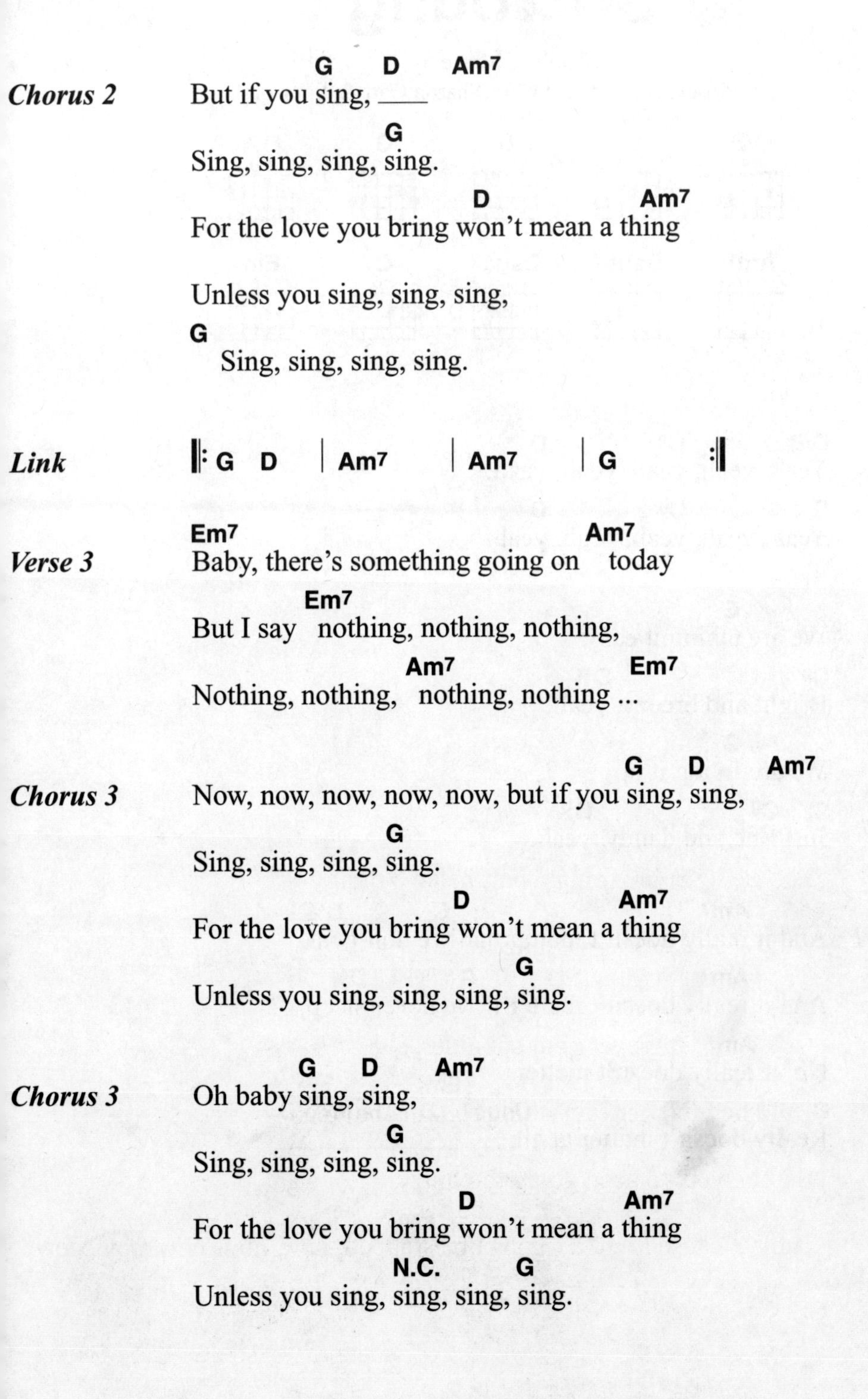

Chorus 2

G D Am7
But if you sing, ___

G
Sing, sing, sing, sing.

D Am7
For the love you bring won't mean a thing

Unless you sing, sing, sing,

G
Sing, sing, sing, sing.

Link

𝄆 G D | Am7 | Am7 | G 𝄇

Verse 3

Em7 Am7
Baby, there's something going on today

Em7
But I say nothing, nothing, nothing,

Am7 Em7
Nothing, nothing, nothing, nothing ...

Chorus 3

G D Am7
Now, now, now, now, now, but if you sing, sing,

G
Sing, sing, sing, sing.

D Am7
For the love you bring won't mean a thing

G
Unless you sing, sing, sing, sing.

Chorus 3

G D Am7
Oh baby sing, sing,

G
Sing, sing, sing, sing.

D Am7
For the love you bring won't mean a thing

N.C. G
Unless you sing, sing, sing, sing.

So Young

Words & Music by
Andrea Corr, Caroline Corr, Sharon Corr & Jim Corr

G/B C9 D G D4/9 fr4

Am7 Dsus4 Dsus2 C Em

```
             G/B         C9         D
Intro        Yeah, yeah, yeah, yeah, yeah.
             G           C9         D
             Yeah, yeah, yeah, yeah, yeah.

                       G
Verse 1      We are taking it easy.
             C9                  D4/9
             Bright and breezy, yeah.
                       G
             We are living it up
                C9                D4/9
             Just fine and dandy, yeah.

                      Am7                        C       D4/9
Pre-chorus 1 And it really doesn't matter that we don't eat,
                      Am7                     C       D4/9
             And it really doesn't matter if we never sleep,
                     Am7
             No, it really doesn't matter.
             C                      Dsus4  D  Dsus2  D
             Really doesn't matter at all.________________
```

Chorus 1

G
'Cos we are so young now,
C9 D
We are so young, so young now.
G
And when tomorrow comes
C9 D
We can do it all again.

Verse 2

G
We are chasing the moon,
C D6/9
Just running wild and free.
G
We are following through
C9 D6/9
Every dream and every need.

Pre-chorus 2

Am7 C D6/9
And it really doesn't matter that we don't eat,
Am7 C D6/9
And it really doesn't matter if we never sleep,
Am7
No, it really doesn't matter.
C Dsus4 D Dsus2 D
Really doesn't matter at all.________________

Chorus 2

G
'Cos we are so young now,
C9 D
We are so young, so young now.
G
And when tomorrow comes
C9 D
We can do it all again.

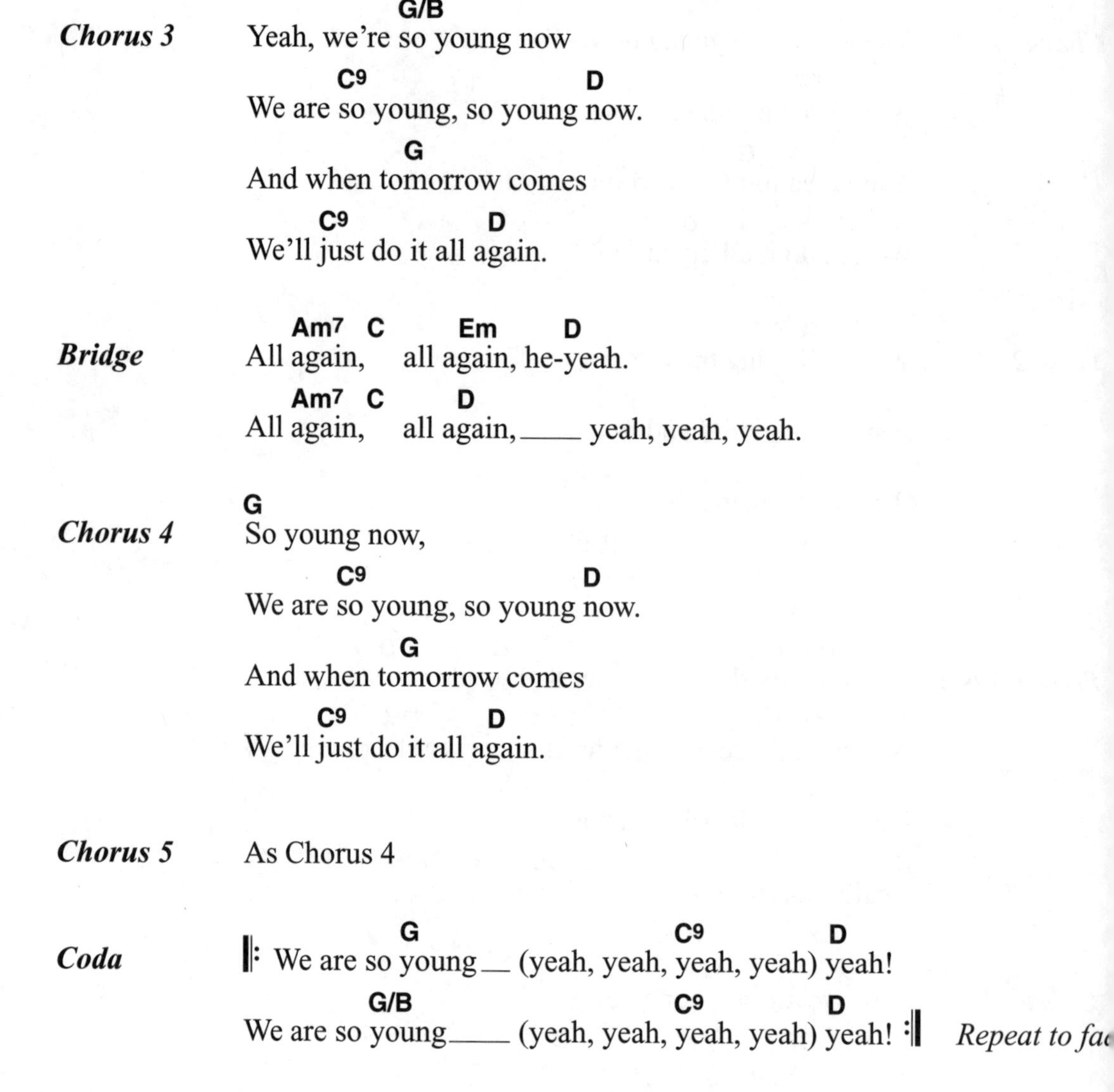
Chorus 3
G/B
Yeah, we're so young now
C9 D
We are so young, so young now.
G
And when tomorrow comes
C9 D
We'll just do it all again.
Bridge
Am7 C Em D
All again, all again, he-yeah.
Am7 C D
All again, all again, ___ yeah, yeah, yeah.
Chorus 4
G
So young now,
C9 D
We are so young, so young now.
G
And when tomorrow comes
C9 D
We'll just do it all again.
Chorus 5
As Chorus 4
Coda
G C9 D
𝄆 We are so young ___ (yeah, yeah, yeah, yeah) yeah!
G/B C9 D
We are so young ___ (yeah, yeah, yeah, yeah) yeah! 𝄇
Repeat to fa

Solid Air

Words & Music by
John Martyn

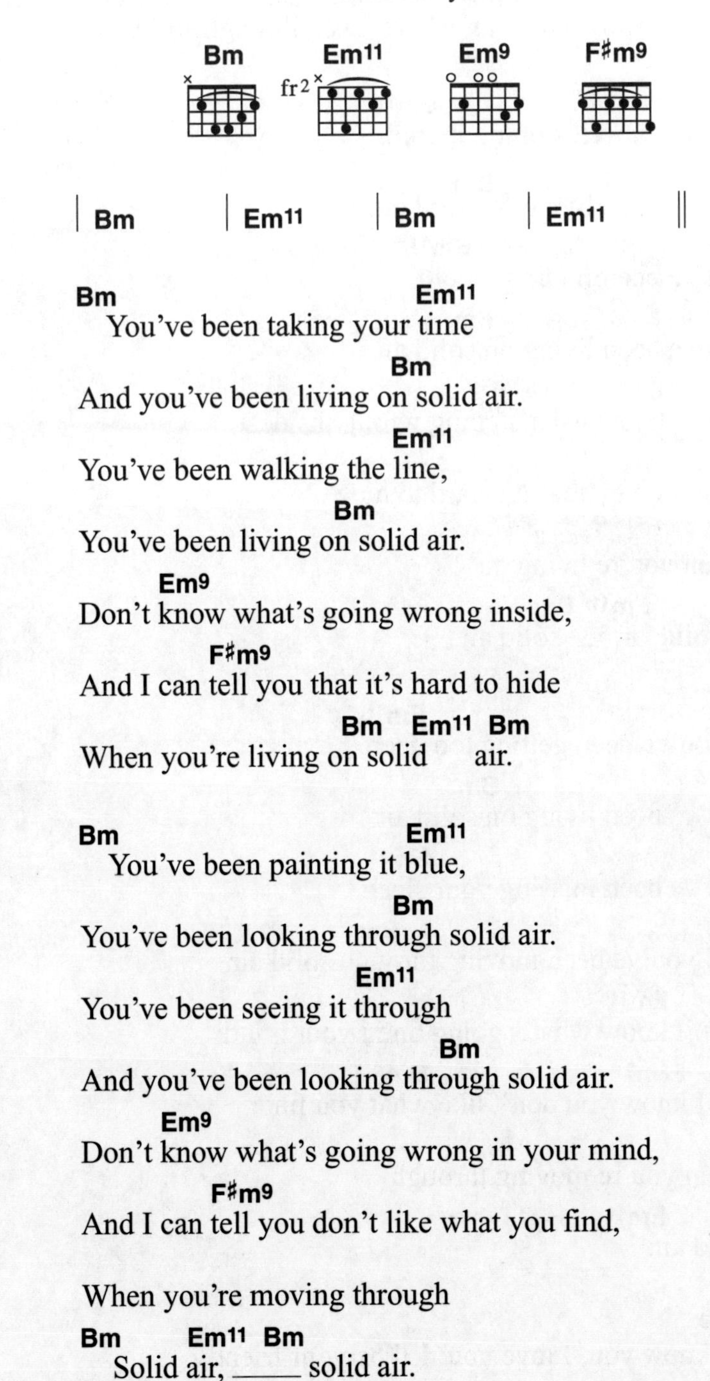

Intro | Bm | Em11 | Bm | Em11 ||

Verse 1

```
Bm                              Em11
   You've been taking your time
                            Bm
And you've been living on solid air.
                            Em11
You've been walking the line,
                       Bm
You've been living on solid air.
        Em9
Don't know what's going wrong inside,
           F♯m9
And I can tell you that it's hard to hide
                        Bm   Em11  Bm
When you're living on solid      air.
```

Verse 2

```
Bm                             Em11
   You've been painting it blue,
                            Bm
You've been looking through solid air.
                         Em11
You've been seeing it through
                                  Bm
And you've been looking through solid air.
        Em9
Don't know what's going wrong in your mind,
           F♯m9
And I can tell you don't like what you find,

When you're moving through
Bm        Em11  Bm
   Solid air, ____ solid air.
```

Chorus 1

F#m9
I know you, I love you; and I can be your friend.
Em11 Bm Em11 Bm
I could follow you anywhere, even through solid air.

Verse 3

Bm Em11
You've been stoning it cold,
Bm
You've been living on solid air.
Em11
You've been finding it cold,
Bm
You've been living on solid air.
Em9
I don't know what's going wrong inside,
F#m9
I can tell you that it's hard to hide

When you're living on
Bm Em11 Bm
Solid air, ___ solid air.

Verse 4

Bm Em11
You've been getting too deep,
Bm
You've been living on solid air.
Em11
You've been missing your sleep
Bm
And you've been moving through solid air.
Em11
I don't know what's going on in your mind;
F#m9 Bm
But I know you don't like what you find

When you're moving through
Em11
Solid air.

Chorus 2

F#m9
I know you, I love you; I'll be your friend.
Em11 Bm Em11 Bm
I could follow you anywhere, even through solid air.

Verse 5

Bm   Em11
You've been walking your line,
                              Bm
You've been walking on solid air.
                              Em11
You've been taking your time
                                          Bm
'Cause you've been walking on solid air.
        Em9
Don't know what's going wrong inside;
            F♯m9
But I can tell you that it's hard to hide

When you're living on
Bm   Em11 Bm
Solid air,   solid air.

Verse 6

Bm   Em11
You've been painting it blue,
                           Bm
You've been living on solid air.
                          Em11
You've been seeing it through
                                  Bm
And you've been living on solid air.
        Em9
I don't know what's going on in your mind;
            F♯m9
But I can tell you don't like what you find

When you're living on
Bm   Em11 Bm
Solid air,   solid air.

Chorus 3

F♯m9
I know you, I love you; and I'll be your friend,
                     Em11   Bm   Em11   Bm
I could follow you   anywhere, even through solid air.

Outro

Em11 Bm   Em11
Ice   blue solid air,
Em11 Bm   Em11 Bm   Em11 Bm Em11
Ice ____ blue   so - lid air. ____

|: Bm9 | Bm9 :| Bm ||

Play 3 times

Somewhere Only We Know

Words & Music by
Tim Rice-Oxley, Tom Chaplin & Richard Hughes

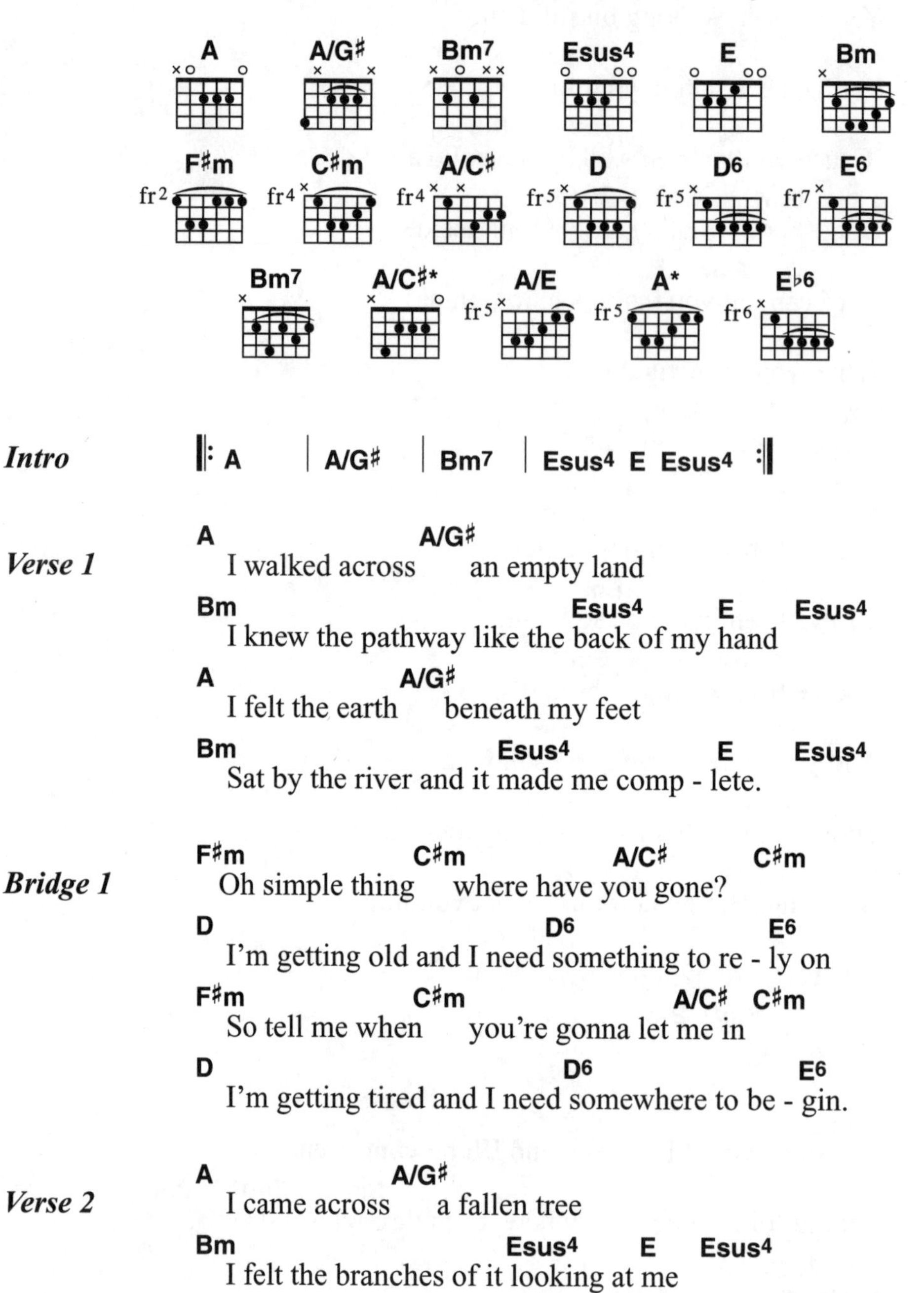

Intro | |: A | A/G♯ | Bm7 | Esus4 E Esus4 :| |

Verse 1

A A/G♯
I walked across an empty land
Bm Esus4 E Esus4
I knew the pathway like the back of my hand
A A/G♯
I felt the earth beneath my feet
Bm Esus4 E Esus4
Sat by the river and it made me comp - lete.

Bridge 1

F♯m C♯m A/C♯ C♯m
Oh simple thing where have you gone?
D D6 E6
I'm getting old and I need something to re - ly on
F♯m C♯m A/C♯ C♯m
So tell me when you're gonna let me in
D D6 E6
I'm getting tired and I need somewhere to be - gin.

Verse 2

A A/G♯
I came across a fallen tree
Bm Esus4 E Esus4
I felt the branches of it looking at me
A A/G♯
Is this the place we used to love
Bm Esus4 E Esus4
Is this the place that I've been dreaming of?

Bridge 2 As Bridge 1

Chorus 1

Bm7 A/C#* A/E
And if you have a minute why don't we go
Bm7 A/C#* A/E
Talk about it somewhere only we know
Bm7 A/C#* A/E
This could be the end of every - thing
D6
So why don't we go
D6 A*
Somewhere only we know.

Link 1

D6 E6 D6 E6 Bm7/E E6
Somewhere only we know.___

Bridge 3 As Bridge 1

Chorus 2

Bm7 A/C#* A/E
And if you have a minute why don't we go
Bm7 A/C#* A/E
Talk about it somewhere only we know
Bm7 A/C#* A/E
This could be the end of every - thing
D6
So why don't we go
D6 A*
So why don't we go.

Outro

| Bm7 | A/C#* A/E | Bm7 | A/C#* A/E ||
Bm7 A/C#* A/E
This could be the end of every - thing
D6
So why don't we go
E6 A*
Somewhere only we know
D6 E6 E♭6 D6
Somewhere only we kno - ow
E6 D6 D A*
Somewhere only we know.__

Starman

Words & Music by
David Bowie

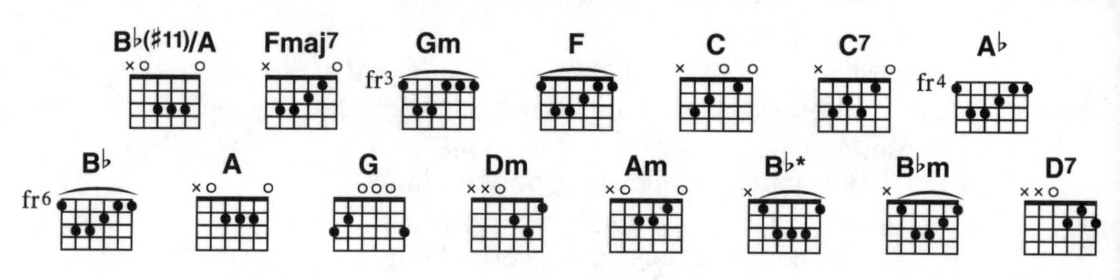

Intro ‖: B♭(♯11)/A | B♭(♯11)/A | Fmaj7 | Fmaj7 :‖

Verse 1

Gm
Didn't know what time it was,

The lights were low-ow-ow.

F
I lean back on my radio-o-o,

C C7
Some cat was laying down some rock'n'roll,

F A♭ B♭
"Lotta soul", he said.

Verse 2

Gm
Then the loud sound did seem to fa-a-ade

F
Came back like a slow voice on a wave of pha-a-ase

C C7 A G
That weren't no D.J. that was hazy cosmic jive.

Chorus 1

```
              F           Dm
There's a starman waiting in the sky Ð
     Am                    C
He'd like to come and meet us
       C7
But he thinks he'd blow our minds.
              F           Dm
There's a starman waiting in the sky
     Am              C
He's told us not to blow it
             C7
'Cause he knows it's all worthwhile,

He told me:
B♭*         B♭m              F          D7
   "Let the children lose it, let the children use it,
Gm             C
   Let all the children boogie."
```

Link 1

| B♭* | F | C | F | B♭* | F | C ‖

Verse 3

```
Gm
   Well I had to phone someone so I picked on you-ou-ou,
F
   Hey that's far out! so you heard him too-oo-oo.
C                                C7                     F A♭ B♭
   Switch on the T.V. we may pick him up on Channel 2.
```

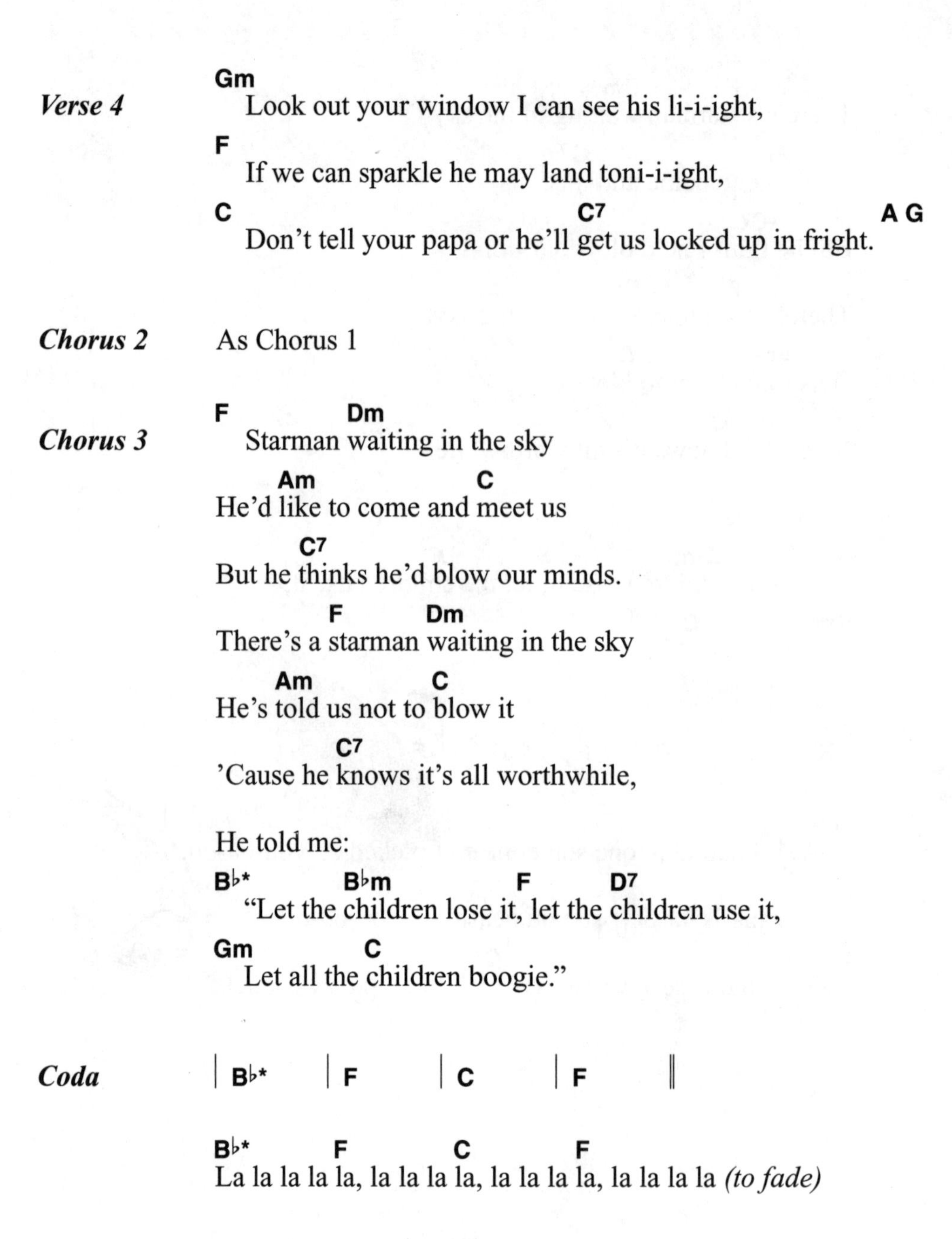

Verse 4

Gm
Look out your window I can see his li-i-ight,

F
If we can sparkle he may land toni-i-ight,

C   C7   A G
Don't tell your papa or he'll get us locked up in fright.

Chorus 2

As Chorus 1

Chorus 3

F   Dm
Starman waiting in the sky

Am   C
He'd like to come and meet us

C7
But he thinks he'd blow our minds.

F   Dm
There's a starman waiting in the sky

Am   C
He's told us not to blow it

C7
'Cause he knows it's all worthwhile,

He told me:

B♭*   B♭m   F   D7
"Let the children lose it, let the children use it,

Gm   C
Let all the children boogie."

Coda

| B♭* | F | C | F ||

B♭*   F   C   F
La la la la la, la la la la, la la la la, la la la la *(to fade)*

Stop Crying Your Heart Out

Words & Music by
Noel Gallagher

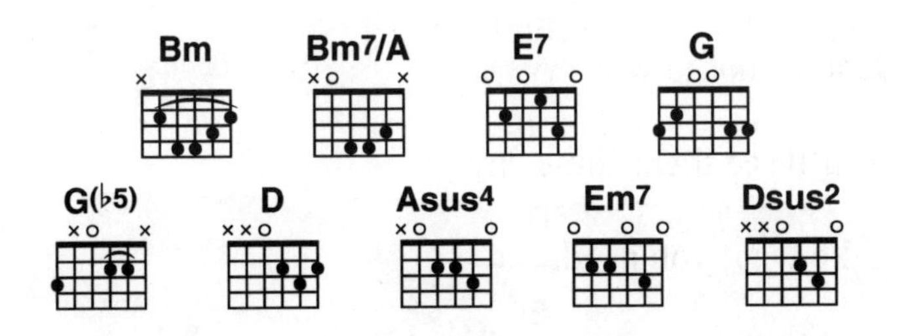

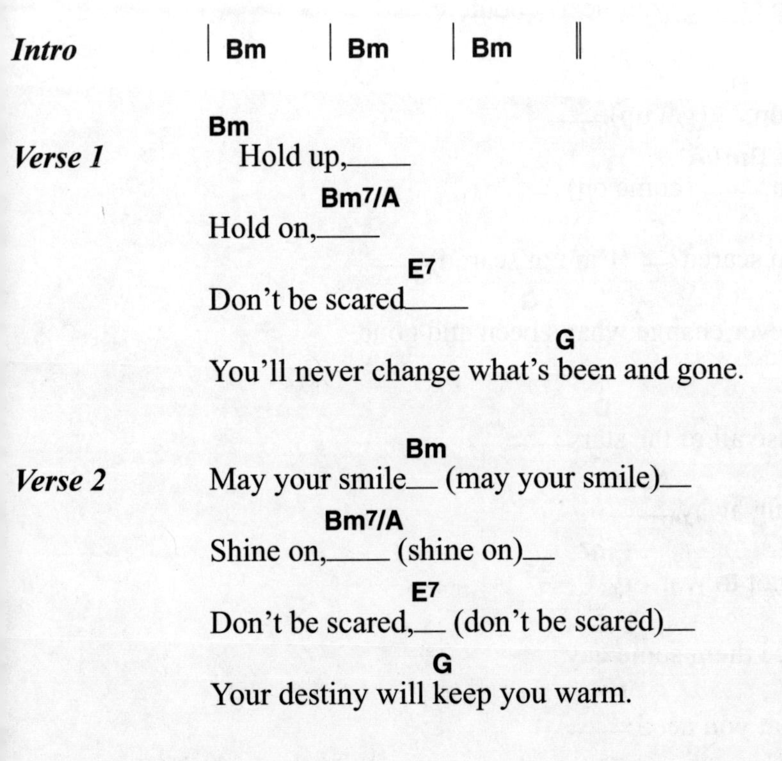

Intro | Bm | Bm | Bm ||

Verse 1

Bm
Hold up,___
Bm7/A
Hold on,___
E7
Don't be scared___
G
You'll never change what's been and gone.

Verse 2

Bm
May your smile__ (may your smile)__
Bm7/A
Shine on,___ (shine on)__
E7
Don't be scared,__ (don't be scared)__
G
Your destiny will keep you warm.

Chorus 1

G(♭5) D
'Cause all of the stars___
Asus4
Are fading away,___
Em7
Just try not to wor - ry,
G
You'll see them some day.
D
Take what you need,___
E7
And be on your way___
G
And stop crying your heart___ out.

Verse 3

G(♭5) Bm
Get up,___ (get up)___
Bm7/A
Come on,___ (come on)___
E7
Why you scared?___ (I'm not scared)___
G
You'll never change what's been and gone.

Chorus 2

G(♭5) D
'Cause all of the stars___
Asus4
Are fading away,___
Em7
Just try not to wor - ry,
G
You'll see them some day.
D
Take what you need,___
E7
And be on your way___
G | G(♭5) |
And stop crying your heart___ out.

Middle

| D | Asus4 | Em7 | G | D |
Ah,___
| E7 | G ||
Ah.___

Chorus 3

```
                                   D
'Cause all of the stars___
                           Asus4
Are fading away,___
                              Em7
Just try not to wor - ry,
                              G
You'll see them some day.
                              D
Take what you need,___
                                   Asus4
And be on your way___
                                      Em7
And stop crying your heart__ out.
```

Chorus 4

```
G                           D
   Where all of us stars___
                           Asus4
Were fading away,___
                              Em7
Just try not to worry,
                              G
You'll see us some day.
                              D
Take what you need,___
                              Asus4
And be on your way___
                                   Em7
And stop crying your heart___ out.
G                             Em7
   Stop crying your heart___ out,
G                             Em7
   Stop crying your heart___ out,
G                             Em7    | G |
   Stop crying your heart___ out.
```

Outro 3

```
| Em7 | G      | Em7 | G   |
                       𝄐
| Em7 | G      | Em7 | G   ||
| Dsus2 | Asus4 | Em7 | G  |
                                 𝄐
| D Dsus2 | Asus4 | Em7 | G | D  ||
```

Streets Of Your Town

Words & Music by
Robert Forster & Grant McLennan

G6 (fr3) Fmaj7 C Am G/B

Capo third fret

Intro ‖: G6 Fmaj7 | G6 Fmaj7 | G6 Fmaj7 | G6 Fmaj7 :‖

Chorus 1

```
G6               Fmaj7   G6            Fmaj7
   Round and round,     up and down,
G6                  Fmaj7      G6              Fmaj7
   Through the streets of your town. ___
G6          Fmaj7   G6       Fmaj7
   Everyday     I,  make my way
G6                  Fmaj7      G6              Fmaj7
   Through the streets of your town. ___
```

Verse 1

```
C                  G6                  Fmaj7
   And don't the sun look good today,       (shine)
C             G6             Fmaj7
   But the rain is on its way.     (shine)
C                G6                 Fmaj7
   Watch the butcher shine his knives,   (shine)
C               G6                Fmaj7
   And this town is full of battered wives.
```

Chorus 2 As Chorus 1

Verse 2

```
C             G6            Fmaj7
   And I ride your river under the bridge, (shine)
C             G6                 Fmaj7
   And I take your boat out to the ridge  (shine)
C                G6               Fmaj7
   'Cause I love that engine roar       (shine)
C              G6                    Fmaj7
    But I still don't know what I'm here for.
```

Chorus 3

```
G6               Fmaj7   G6         Fmaj7
   Round and round,     up and down,
G6                Fmaj7     G6             Fmaj7
   Through the streets of your town. ___
G6          Fmaj7   G6       Fmaj7
   Everyday    I,  make my way
G6                Fmaj7     G6             Fmaj7
   Through the streets of your town. ___
```

Bridge

```
Fmaj7   Am
   They shut it down,
Fmaj7   Am
   They closed it down,
Fmaj7   Am
   They shut it down,
Fmaj7   Am
   They pulled it down.
```

Guitar solo

```
|: C         | G/B        | Fmaj7      | Fmaj7      :|
```

Play 4 times

Chorus 4

```
     G6               Fmaj7   G6         Fmaj7
|:     Round and round,     up and down,
G6                Fmaj7  G6               Fmaj7
   Through the streets of your town. ___
G6          Fmaj7   G6       Fmaj7
   Everyday    I   make my way
G6                Fmaj7     G6             Fmaj7
   Through the streets of your town. ___          :|
```

Repeat to fade

Summer Breeze

Words & Music by
James Seals & Darrell Crofts

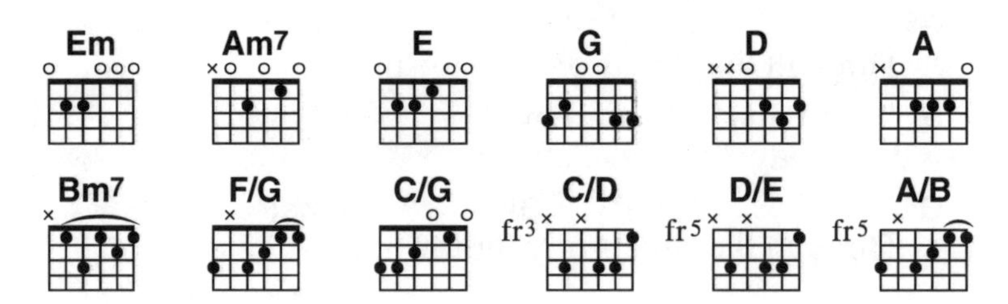

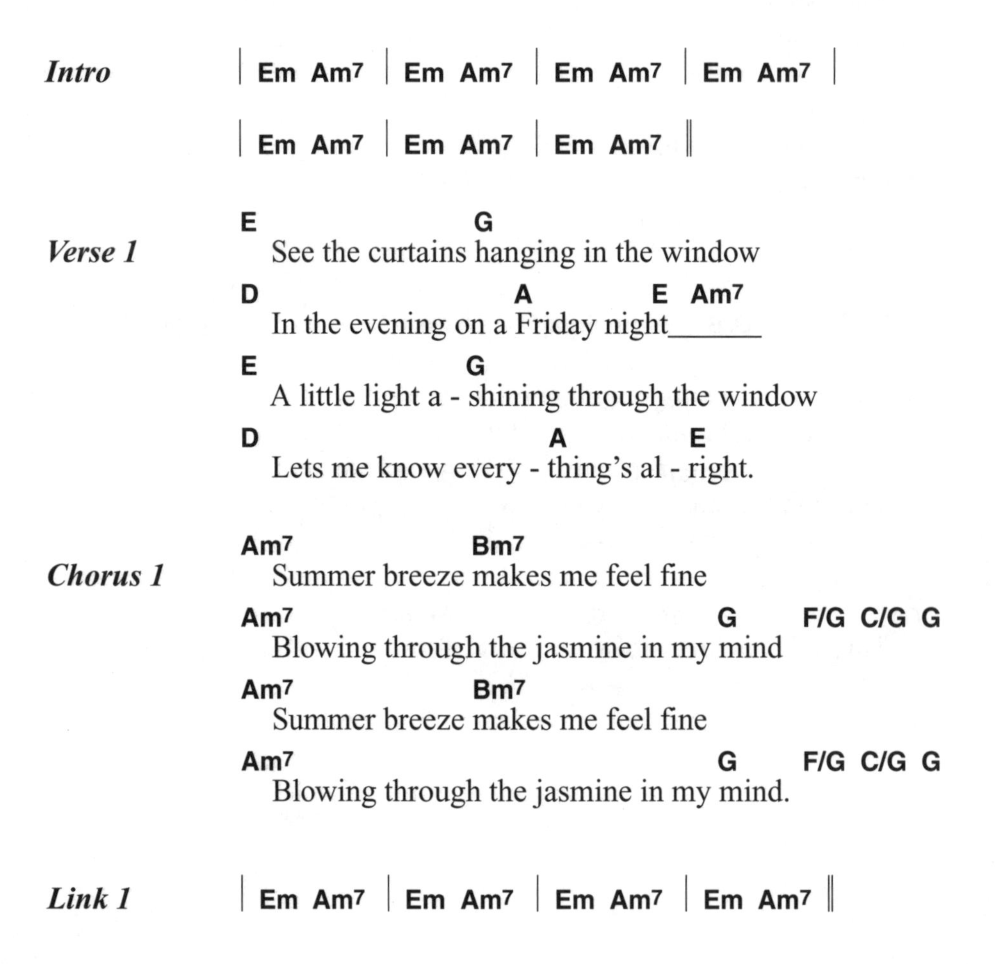

Intro

| Em Am7 | Em Am7 | Em Am7 | Em Am7 |
| Em Am7 | Em Am7 | Em Am7 ||

Verse 1

```
E                        G
   See the curtains hanging in the window
D                       A            E  Am7
   In the evening on a Friday night______
E                     G
   A little light a - shining through the window
D                            A            E
   Lets me know every - thing's al - right.
```

Chorus 1

```
Am7                      Bm7
   Summer breeze makes me feel fine
Am7                                         G      F/G C/G G
   Blowing through the jasmine in my mind
Am7                      Bm7
   Summer breeze makes me feel fine
Am7                                         G      F/G C/G G
   Blowing through the jasmine in my mind.
```

Link 1

| Em Am7 | Em Am7 | Em Am7 | Em Am7 ||

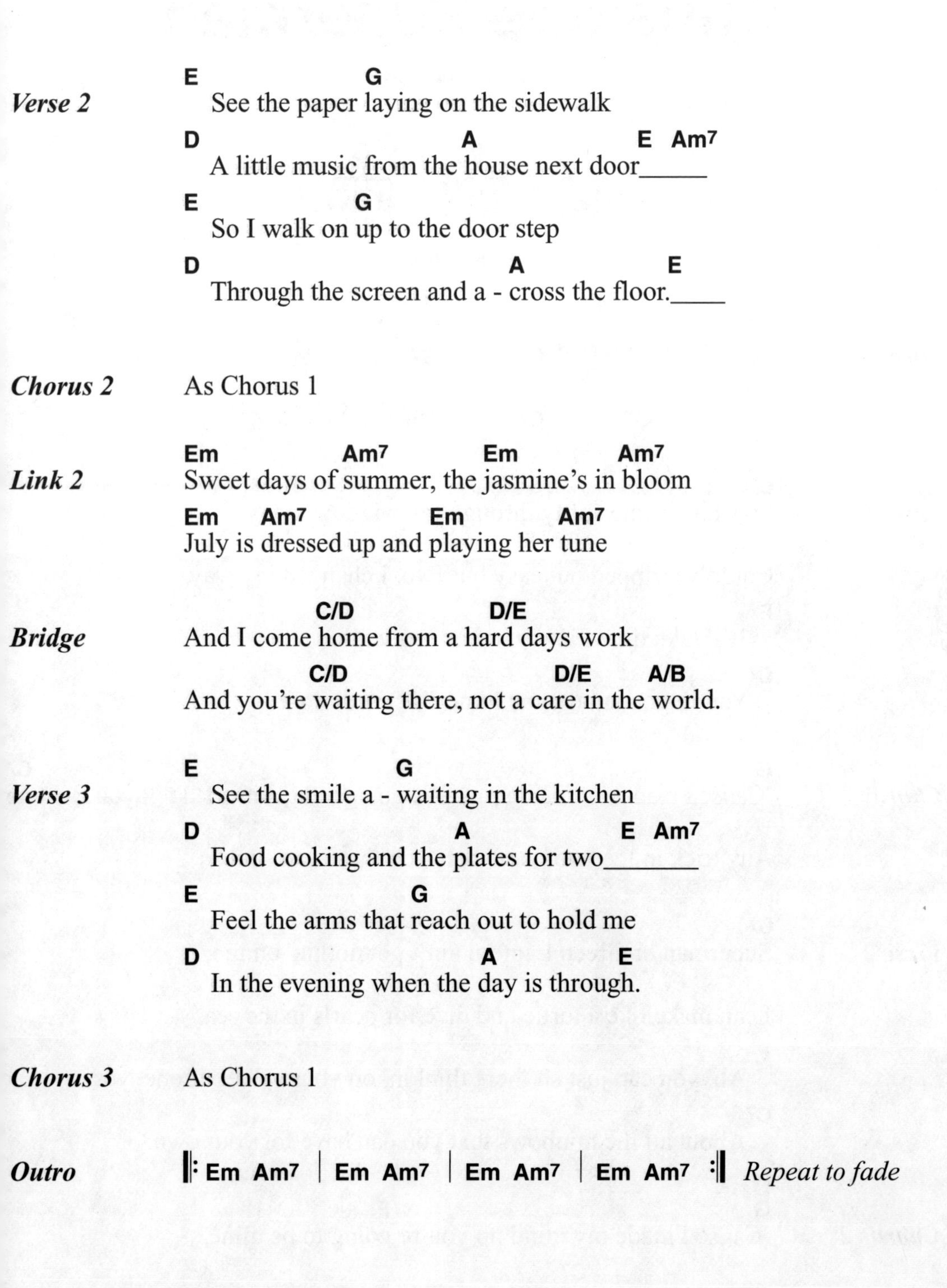

Verse 2

E G
See the paper laying on the sidewalk
D A E Am7
A little music from the house next door_____
E G
So I walk on up to the door step
D A E
Through the screen and a - cross the floor.____

Chorus 2

As Chorus 1

Link 2

Em Am7 Em Am7
Sweet days of summer, the jasmine's in bloom
Em Am7 Em Am7
July is dressed up and playing her tune

Bridge

C/D D/E
And I come home from a hard days work
C/D D/E A/B
And you're waiting there, not a care in the world.

Verse 3

E G
See the smile a - waiting in the kitchen
D A E Am7
Food cooking and the plates for two_______
E G
Feel the arms that reach out to hold me
D A E
In the evening when the day is through.

Chorus 3

As Chorus 1

Outro

𝄆 Em Am7 | Em Am7 | Em Am7 | Em Am7 𝄇 *Repeat to fade*

Sunshine Superman

Words & Music by
Donovan Leitch

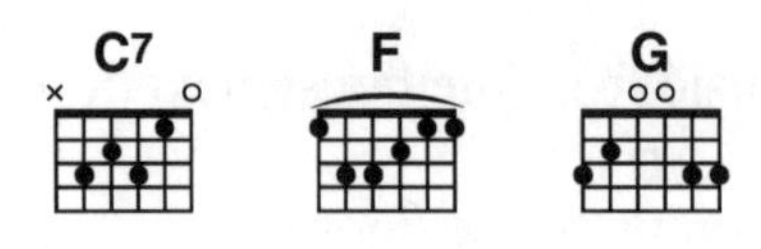

Capo first fret

Intro | C7 | C7 | C7 | C7 |
| C7 | C7 | C7 | C7 ||

Verse 1

C7
Sunshine came softly through my window today.

Could've tripped out easy but I've, I changed my way.

F
It'll take time I know it, but in a while

C7
You're gonna be mine I know it, we'll do it in style.

Chorus 1

G F C7
'Cause I made my mind up you're going to be mine, I'll tell you right no

Any trick in the book now baby, oh that I can find.

Verse 2

C7
Superman or Green Lantern ain't got nothin' on me,

I can make like a turtle and dive for pearls in the sea.

F
Ah, you can just sit there thinkin' on your velvet throne, yes,

C7
About all the rainbows that you can have for your own.

Chorus 2

G F
'Cause I made my mind up you're going to be mine,

C7
I'll tell you right now

Any trick in the book now baby, oh that I can find.

Verse 3

```
C7
Everybody's hustlin' just to have a little scene.

When I say we'll be cool, I think that you know what I mean.
F
   We stood on a beach at sunset, do you remember when?
C7
   I know a beach where baby oh, it never ends.
```

Chorus 3

```
G                                          F
When you've made your mind up, for - ever to be mine,
                          C7
Mm - mm - mm - mm,

I'll pick up your hand and slowly blow your little mind.
G                                      F
'Cause I made my mind up, you're going to be mine,
                         C7
I'll tell you right now,

Any trick in the book now baby, oh that I can find.
```

Guitar solo

```
| C7   | C7   | C7   | C7   |
| C7   | C7   | C7   | C7   |
| F    | F    | F    | F    |
| C7   | C7   | C7   | C7   |
| G    | G    | F    | F    |
| C7   | C7   | C7   | C7   ||
```

Verse 4

C7
Superman or Green Lantern ain't got a nothin' on me.

I can make like a turtle and dive for your pearls in the sea, yep.

F
Ah you, you, you, can just sit there well thinkin' on your velvet thron

C7
About all the rainbows a-you can a-have for your own.

Chorus 4

G F
When you've made your mind up for - ever to be mine,

C7
Mm - mm - mm - mm,

I'll pick up your hand and slowly blow your little mind.

G F
When you've made your mind up, for - ever to be mine,

C7
I'll pick up your hand,

I'll pick up your hand and slowly blow your little mind,

Blow your little mind...

Outro | C7 | C7 | C7 | C7 ‖ *To fade*

Thank You For Loving Me

Words & Music by
Jon Bon Jovi & Richie Sambora

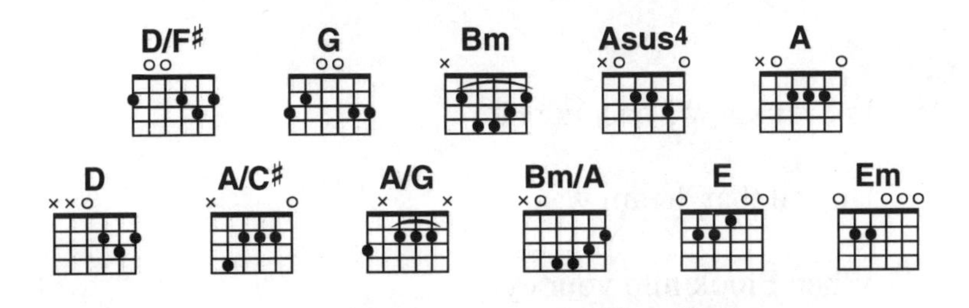

Intro ‖: D/F♯ | G | Bm | Asus4 A :‖

Verse 1

G
It's hard for me to say the things
D
I wanna say sometimes
G
There's no one here but you and me
D
And that broken old street light.

Pre-chorus 1

A/C♯ Bm
Lock the doors
G A A/G
We'll leave the world out - side
D/F♯ G
All I've got to give to you
Asus4 A
Are these five words and I _

Chorus 1

D G
Thank you for loving me
A
For being my eyes
D
When I couldn't see
A/C♯ Bm Bm/A
For parting my lips
E A
When I couldn't breathe__

cont.

D G A
Thank you for loving me
D/F♯ G Asus4 A
Thank you for loving me.

Verse 2

G
I never knew I had a dream
D
Un - til that dream was you
G
When I look into your eyes
D
The sky's a different blue.

Pre-chorus 2

A/C♯ Bm
Cross my heart
G A A/G
I wear no dis - guise
D G
If I tried, you'd make believe
Asus4 A
That you believed my lies.

Chorus 2

D G
Thank you for loving me
A
For being my eyes
D
When I couldn't see
A/C♯ Bm Bm/A
For parting my lips
E A
When I couldn't breathe_
D/F♯ G A
Thank you for loving me.

Bridge

G
You pick me up when I fall down
A
You ring the bell before they count me out
Em D/F♯ G
If I was drowning you would part the sea
C D Em
And risk your own life to rescue me
A
Yeah, yeah, yeah, yeah, yeah, yeah, yeah,

Solo | D | G | A | D A/C♯ ‖
Lock the

Pre-chorus 3

```
Bm
Doors
G                    A
Leave the world out - side
D/F♯          G
All I've got to give to you
   Asus4              A
Are these five words and I
```

Chorus 3

```
    D         G
Thank you for loving me
          A
For being my eyes
        D
Oh when I couldn't see
  A/C♯     Bm    Bm/A
For parting my    lips
           E    A
When I couldn't breathe__
   D/F♯       G
Thank you for loving me
           A
When I couldn't fly
  D
Oh, you gave me wings
  A/C♯     Bm
You parted my    lips
   Bm/A     E    A
When I couldn't breathe__
    D     G    A
Thank you for loving me
    D/F♯  G    A
Thank you for loving  me
    D     G    Asus4
Thank you for loving me
A             D/F♯ | G    | Bm    | Asus4 A A/G ‖
Oh, for loving me.
```

Outro | D/F♯ | G | Bm | Asus4 A | D ‖

Ten Storey Love Song

Words & Music by
John Squire

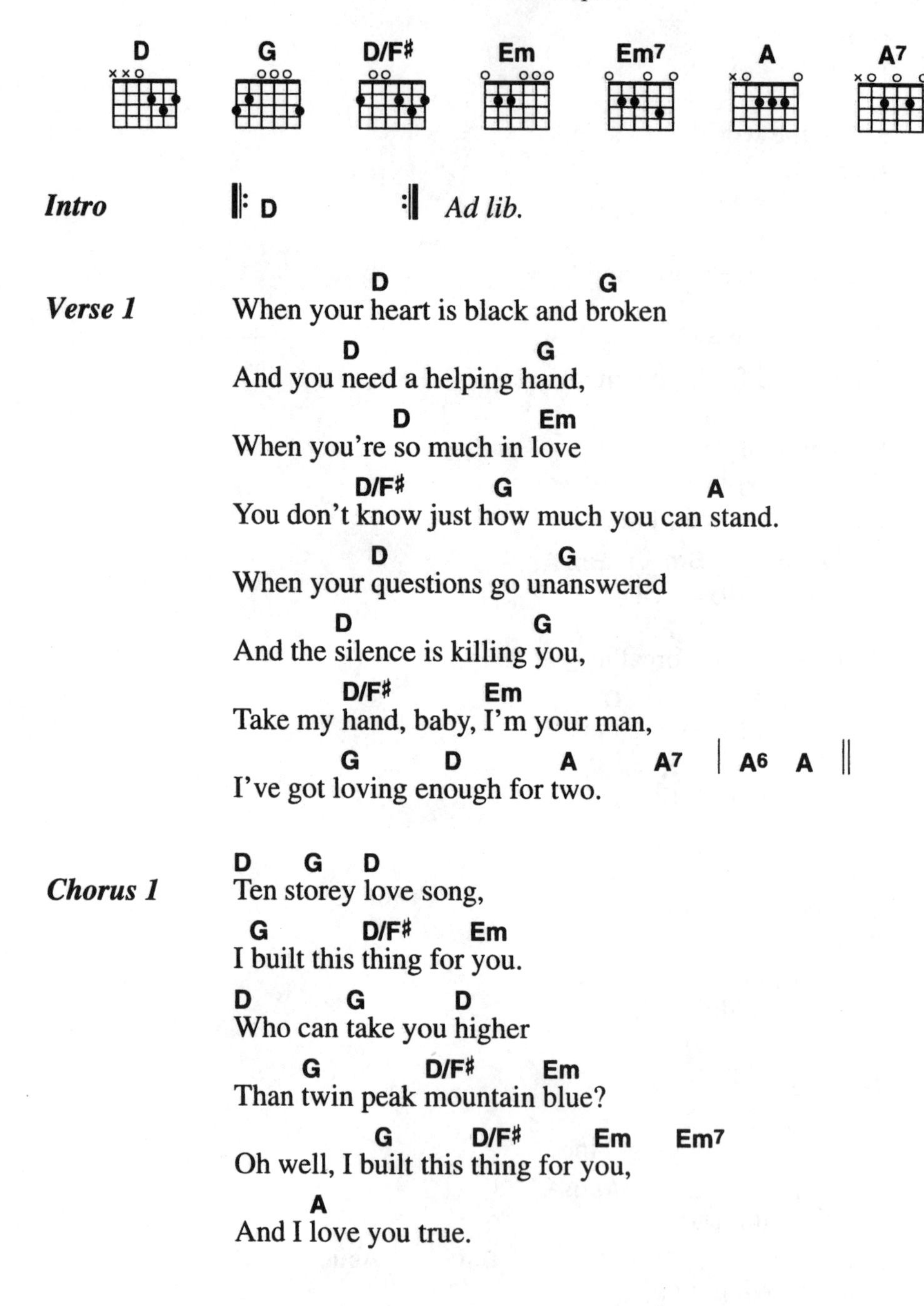

Intro 𝄆 D 𝄇 *Ad lib.*

Verse 1

D G
When your heart is black and broken
D G
And you need a helping hand,
D Em
When you're so much in love
D/F# G A
You don't know just how much you can stand.
D G
When your questions go unanswered
D G
And the silence is killing you,
D/F# Em
Take my hand, baby, I'm your man,
G D A A7 | A6 A ||
I've got loving enough for two.

Chorus 1

D G D
Ten storey love song,
G D/F# Em
I built this thing for you.
D G D
Who can take you higher
G D/F# Em
Than twin peak mountain blue?
G D/F# Em Em7
Oh well, I built this thing for you,
A
And I love you true.

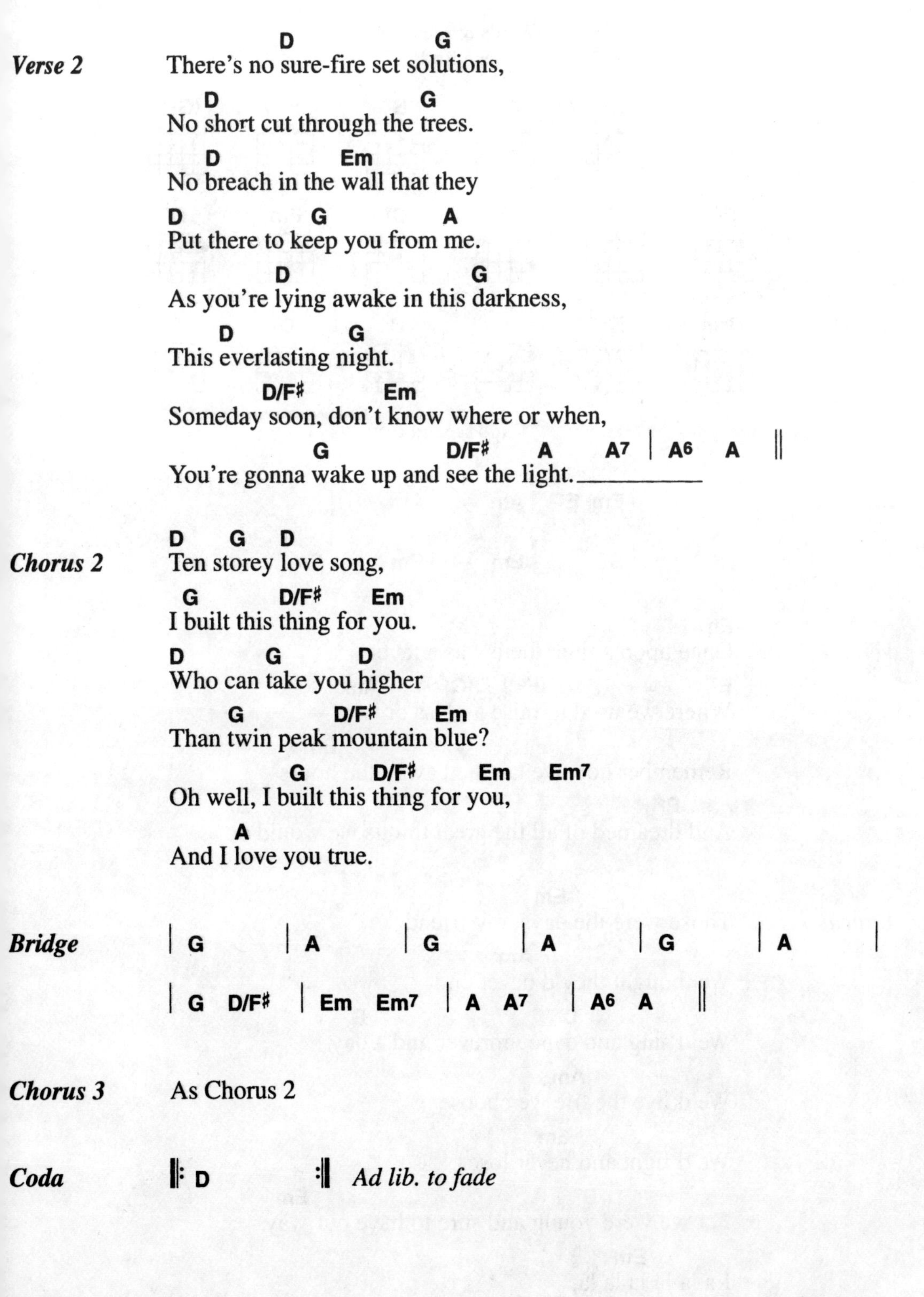

Verse 2

D G
There's no sure-fire set solutions,
D G
No short cut through the trees.
D Em
No breach in the wall that they
D G A
Put there to keep you from me.
D G
As you're lying awake in this darkness,
D G
This everlasting night.
D/F# Em
Someday soon, don't know where or when,
G D/F# A A7 | A6 A ||
You're gonna wake up and see the light. __________

Chorus 2

D G D
Ten storey love song,
G D/F# Em
I built this thing for you.
D G D
Who can take you higher
G D/F# Em
Than twin peak mountain blue?
G D/F# Em Em7
Oh well, I built this thing for you,
A
And I love you true.

Bridge

| G | A | G | A | G | A |

| G D/F# | Em Em7 | A A7 | A6 A ||

Chorus 3 As Chorus 2

Coda |: D :| *Ad lib. to fade*

Those Were The Days

Words & Music by
Gene Raskin

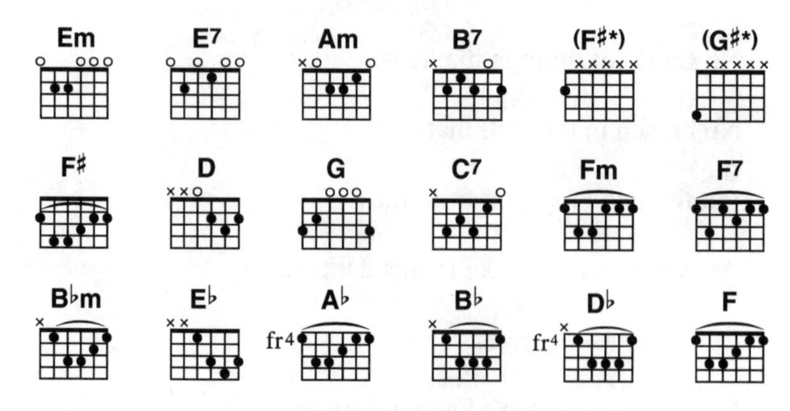

Capo second fret

Intro | Em | Em E7 | Am | Am |

| B7 | B7 || Em | Em | Em | Em |

Verse 1

Em
Once upon a time there was a tavern,
E7 (F♯*) (G♯*) Am
Where we used to raise a glass or two
Em
Remember how we laughed away the hours
F♯ B7
And dreamed of all the great things we would do.

Chorus 1

Em
Those were the days, my friend
Am
We thought they'd never end,
D G
We'd sing and dance forever and a day.
Am
We'd live the life we choose
Em
We'd fight and never lose,
B7 Em
For we were young and sure to have our way.
Em
La la la la la la,

cont.

Am
La la la la la la,
B7
La la la la,
Em | Em |
La la la la la la.

Verse 2

Em
Then the busy years went rushing by us,
E7 (F#*)(G#*) Am
We lost our starry notions on the way,
Em
If by chance I'd see you in the tavern
F# B7
We'd smile at one another and we'd say:

Chorus 2

Em
Those were the days, my friend
Am
We thought they'd never end,
D G
We'd sing and dance forever and a day.
Am
We'd live the life we choose
Em
We'd fight and never lose,
B7
Those were the days,
Em
Oh yes those were the days.
Em
La la la la la la,
Am
La la la la la la,
B7
La la la la,
Em | Em |
La la la la la la.

Verse 3

Em
Just tonight I stood before the tavern,
E7 (F#*) (G#*) Am
Nothing seemed the way it used to be,
Em
In the glass I saw a strange reflection
F# B7
Was that lonely woman really me?

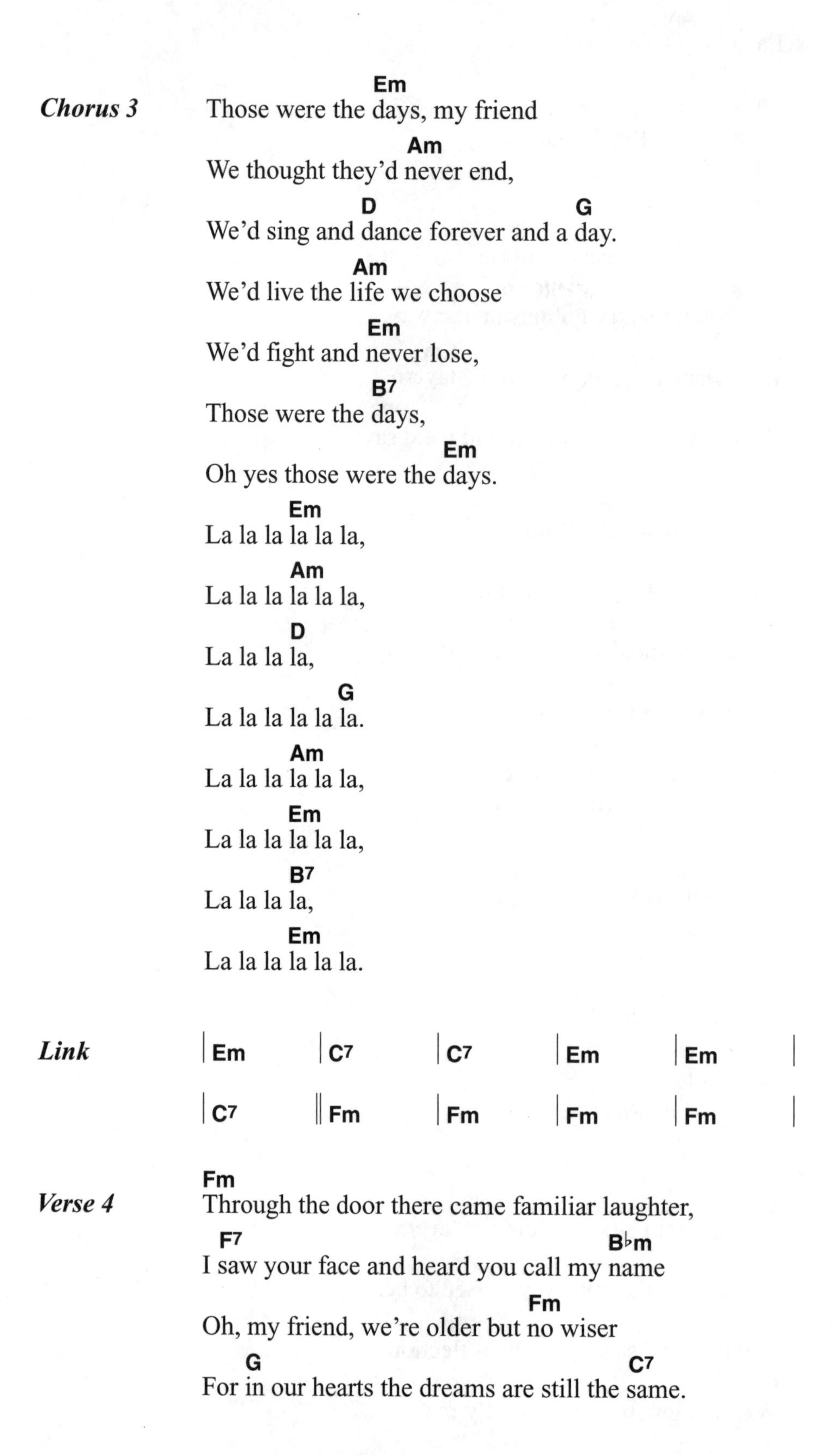

Chorus 3

Em
Those were the days, my friend
Am
We thought they'd never end,
D G
We'd sing and dance forever and a day.
Am
We'd live the life we choose
Em
We'd fight and never lose,
B7
Those were the days,
Em
Oh yes those were the days.
Em
La la la la la la,
Am
La la la la la la,
D
La la la la,
G
La la la la la la.
Am
La la la la la la,
Em
La la la la la la,
B7
La la la la,
Em
La la la la la la.

Link

| Em | C7 | C7 | Em | Em |
| C7 || Fm | Fm | Fm | Fm |

Verse 4

Fm
Through the door there came familiar laughter,
F7 B♭m
I saw your face and heard you call my name
Fm
Oh, my friend, we're older but no wiser
G C7
For in our hearts the dreams are still the same.

Chorus 4

```
                     Fm
Those were the days, my friend
                          B♭m
We thought they'd never end,
                    E♭                    A♭
We'd sing and dance forever and a day.
                   B♭m
We'd live the life we choose
                    Fm
We'd fight and never lose,
                     C7
Those were the days,
                              Fm
Oh yes those were the days.
             Fm
La la la la la la,
             B♭m
La la la la la la,
             E♭
La la la la,
                A♭
La la la la la la.
             B♭m
La la la la la la,
             Fm
La la la la la la,
             C7
La la la la,
             Fm
La la la la la la.
```

Outro | Fm | A♭ | A♭ | B♭ | D♭ | F ‖

Time After Time

Words & Music by
Cyndi Lauper & Robert Hyman

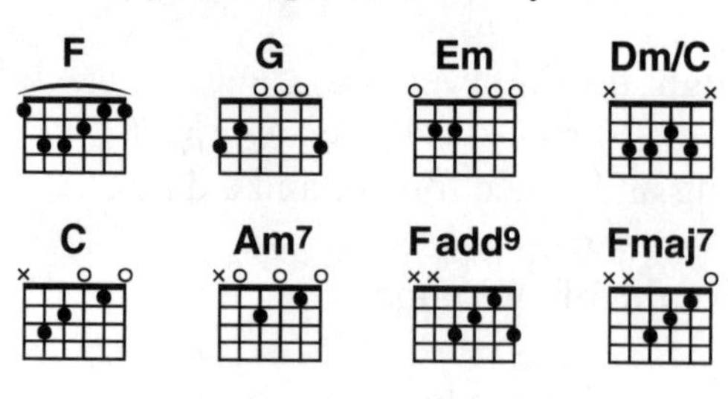

Intro |: F | G | Em | F :|

Verse 1

Dm/C C Dm/C C Dm/C C Dm/C C
Lying in my bed, I hear the clock tick and think of you.
Dm/C C Dm/C C Dm/C C Dm/C C
Caught up in circ - les, confu - sion is nothing new.
F G Em F G Em
Flash back, warm nights, almost left behind.
F G Em F
Suitcase of memories,
G
Time after...

Verse 2

Dm/C C Dm/C C Dm/C C Dm/C C
Some - times you picture me, I'm walk - ing too far ahead.
Dm/C C Dm/C C Dm/C C Dm/C C
You're calling to me, I can't hear what you've said.
F G Em F G Em
Then you say, "Go slow," - I fall behind.
F G Em F
The second hand unwinds.

Chorus 1

G Am7
|: If you're lost, you can look and you will find me
Fadd9 G C
Time after time.
G Am7
If you fall I will catch you, I'll be waiting
Fadd9 G C
Time after time. :|

Link |: F | G | Em | F :|

```
               Dm/C   C       Dm/C  C          Dm/C   C        Dm/C     C
Verse 3        Af  -  ter my picture fades and dark - ness has turned to grey,
               Dm/C   C              Dm/C  C               Dm/C  C    Dm/C   C
               Watch - ing through win - dows, you're wondering if I'm ok - ay.
               F  G  Em  F        G      Em
               Secrets stol - en from deep inside,
               F      G          Em    F
                  The drum beats out of time.

Chorus 2       As Chorus 1 (no repeat)

Instrumental  ||: G        | Am7        | Fadd9  G | C        :||

               F    G   Em  F        G     Em
Verse 4        You say, "Go  slow," - I fall behind.
               F      G         Em      F
                  The second hand unwinds.

Chorus 3       As Chorus 1 (with repeat)

                     Fadd9  G    C
Coda          ||:    Time after time.  :||  Repeat to fade
```

Tropicalia

Words & Music by
Beck Hansen

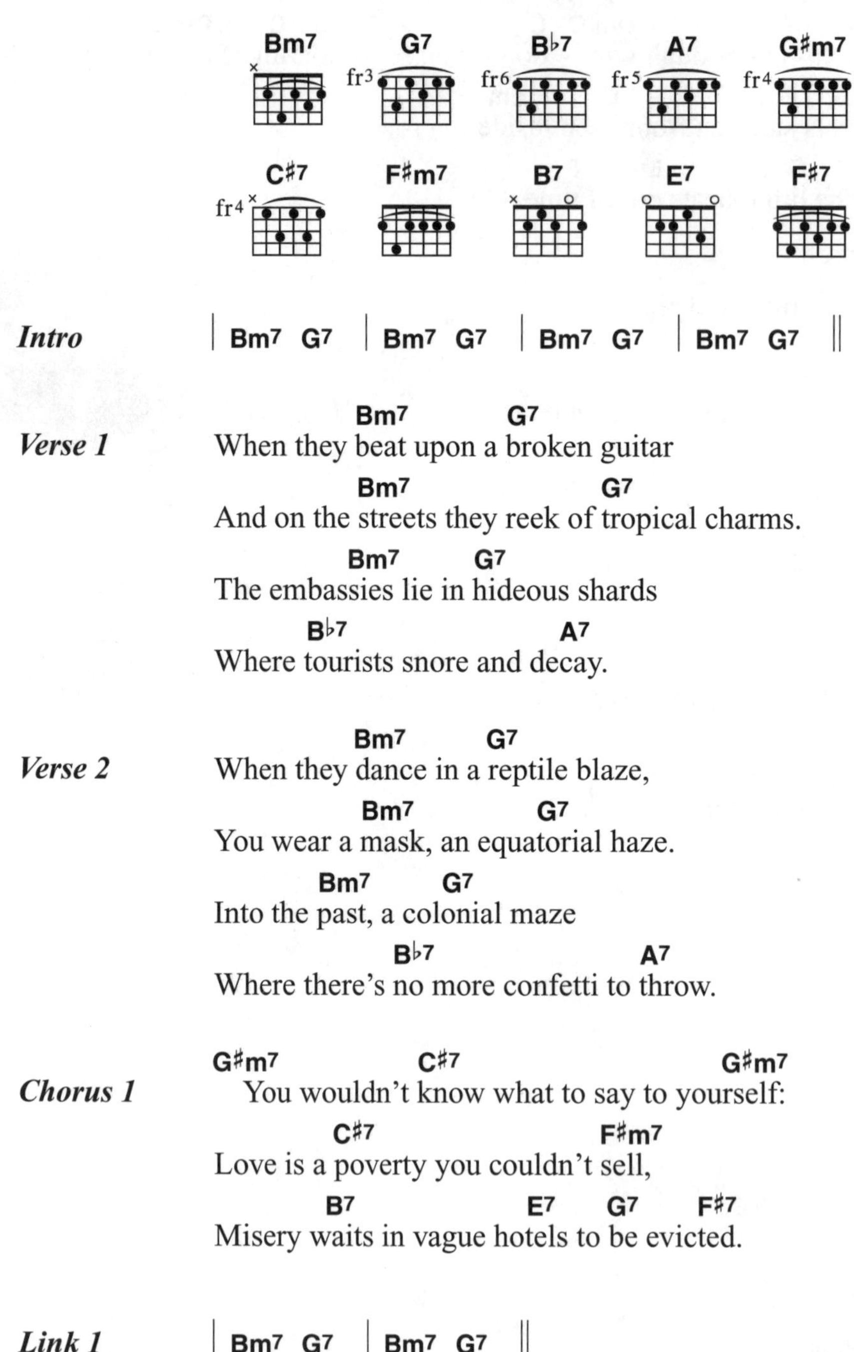

Intro | Bm7 G7 | Bm7 G7 | Bm7 G7 | Bm7 G7 ||

Verse 1

Bm7 G7
When they beat upon a broken guitar
Bm7 G7
And on the streets they reek of tropical charms.
Bm7 G7
The embassies lie in hideous shards
B♭7 A7
Where tourists snore and decay.

Verse 2

Bm7 G7
When they dance in a reptile blaze,
Bm7 G7
You wear a mask, an equatorial haze.
Bm7 G7
Into the past, a colonial maze
B♭7 A7
Where there's no more confetti to throw.

Chorus 1

G♯m7 C♯7 G♯m7
You wouldn't know what to say to yourself:
C♯7 F♯m7
Love is a poverty you couldn't sell,
B7 E7 G7 F♯7
Misery waits in vague hotels to be evicted.

Link 1 | Bm7 G7 | Bm7 G7 ||

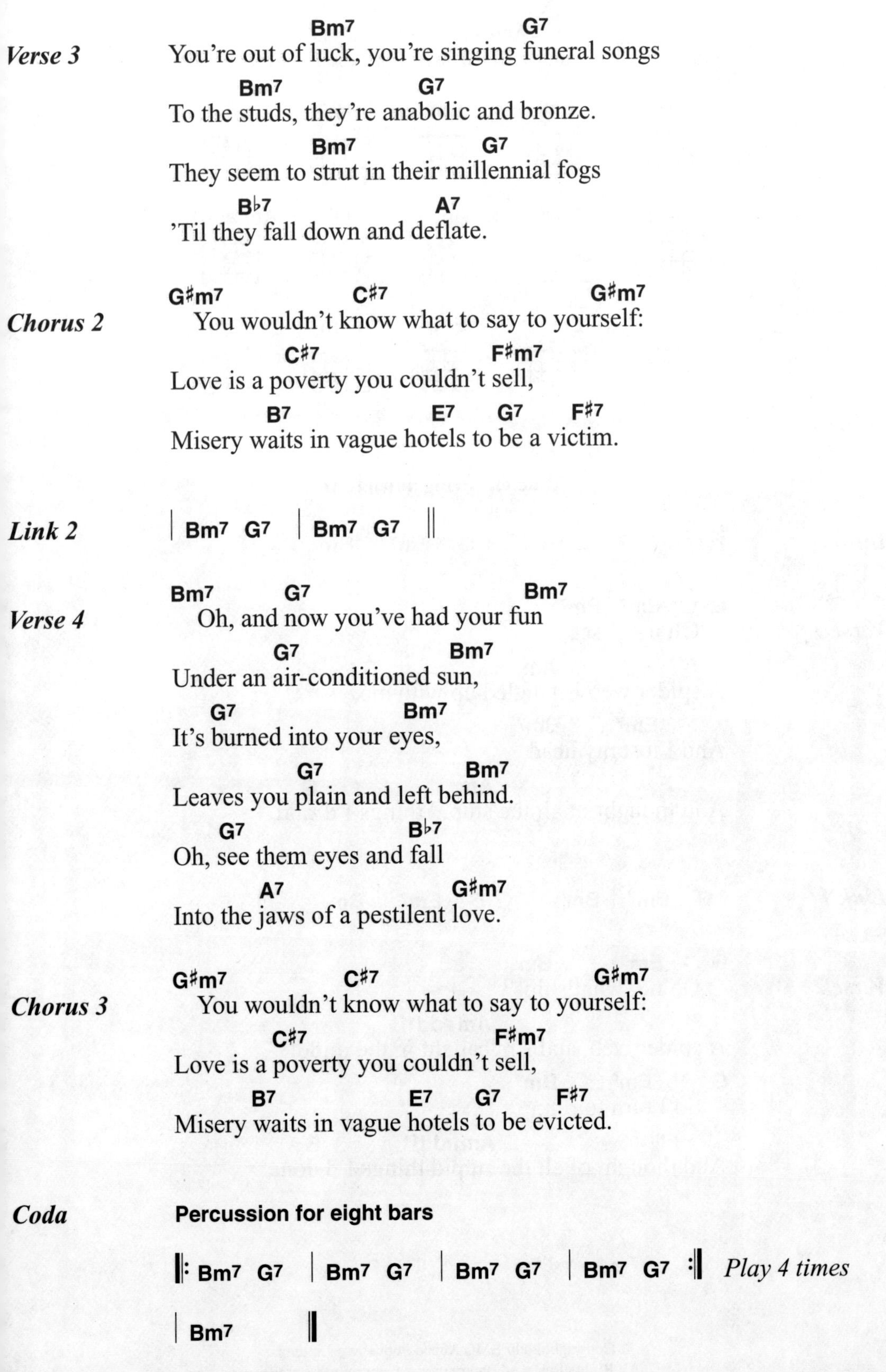

Verse 3

Bm7 G7
You're out of luck, you're singing funeral songs
Bm7 G7
To the studs, they're anabolic and bronze.
Bm7 G7
They seem to strut in their millennial fogs
B♭7 A7
'Til they fall down and deflate.

Chorus 2

G♯m7 C♯7 G♯m7
You wouldn't know what to say to yourself:
C♯7 F♯m7
Love is a poverty you couldn't sell,
B7 E7 G7 F♯7
Misery waits in vague hotels to be a victim.

Link 2

| Bm7 G7 | Bm7 G7 ||

Verse 4

Bm7 G7 Bm7
Oh, and now you've had your fun
G7 Bm7
Under an air-conditioned sun,
G7 Bm7
It's burned into your eyes,
G7 Bm7
Leaves you plain and left behind.
G7 B♭7
Oh, see them eyes and fall
A7 G♯m7
Into the jaws of a pestilent love.

Chorus 3

G♯m7 C♯7 G♯m7
You wouldn't know what to say to yourself:
C♯7 F♯m7
Love is a poverty you couldn't sell,
B7 E7 G7 F♯7
Misery waits in vague hotels to be evicted.

Coda

Percussion for eight bars

|: Bm7 G7 | Bm7 G7 | Bm7 G7 | Bm7 G7 :| *Play 4 times*

| Bm7 ||

Trouble

Words & Music by
Guy Berryman, Jon Buckland, Will Champion & Chris Martin

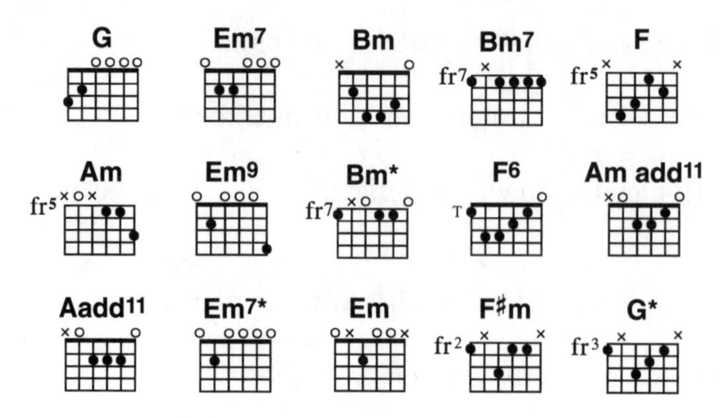

Tune top string down to D

Intro ‖: G Em7 | Bm | G Em7 | Bm :‖

Verse 1

```
G       Em7  Bm7
   Oh no,  I see,
   F             Am            G
A spider web is tangled up with me,
       Em7      Bm7
And I lost my head,
     F                 Am            G
And thought of all the stupid things I'd said.
```

Link 1 | G Em7 | Bm | G Em7 | Bm ‖

Verse 2

```
G       Em9          Bm*
   Oh no, what's this?
   F6                      Amadd11
A spider web, and I'm caught in the middle,
G         Em9       Bm*
   So I turn to run,
     F6                Amadd11         G
And thought of all the stupid things I'd done.
```

Chorus 1

```
           Aadd11                          Em7
And ah, I never meant to cause you trouble,
           Aadd11                        Em7
And ah, I never meant to do you wrong,
           Aadd11                         Em7
And ah, well if I ever caused you trouble,
         Aadd11                         Em7
Then oh, I never meant to do you harm.
```

Link 2

| G Em7 | Bm | G Em7 | Bm ||

Verse 3

```
G      Em9  Bm*
   Oh no,  I see,
   F6                    Amadd11
A spider web and it's me in the middle,
G     Em7       Bm*
   So I twist and turn,
     F6              Amadd11          G
But here I am in my little bubble.
```

Chorus 2

```
                  Aadd11                                Em7
Singing out ah, I never meant to cause you trouble,
       Aadd11                        Em7
And ah, I never meant to do you wrong,
       Aadd11                        Em7
And ah, well if I ever caused you trouble,
        Aadd11                              Em7
Then oh no I never meant to do you harm.
```

Link 3

||: G Em9 | Bm* | G Em9 | Bm* :||

Coda

```
Em             F♯m     G*  F♯m     Em
   And they spun a web for me,
           F♯m        G*  F♯m    Em
And they spun a web for me,
           F♯m        G*  F♯m    Em      | Em    |
And they spun a web for me.
```

||: G Em7 | Bm* | G Em7 | Bm* :||

Try A Little Tenderness

Words & Music by
Harry Woods, Jimmy Campbell & Reg Connelly

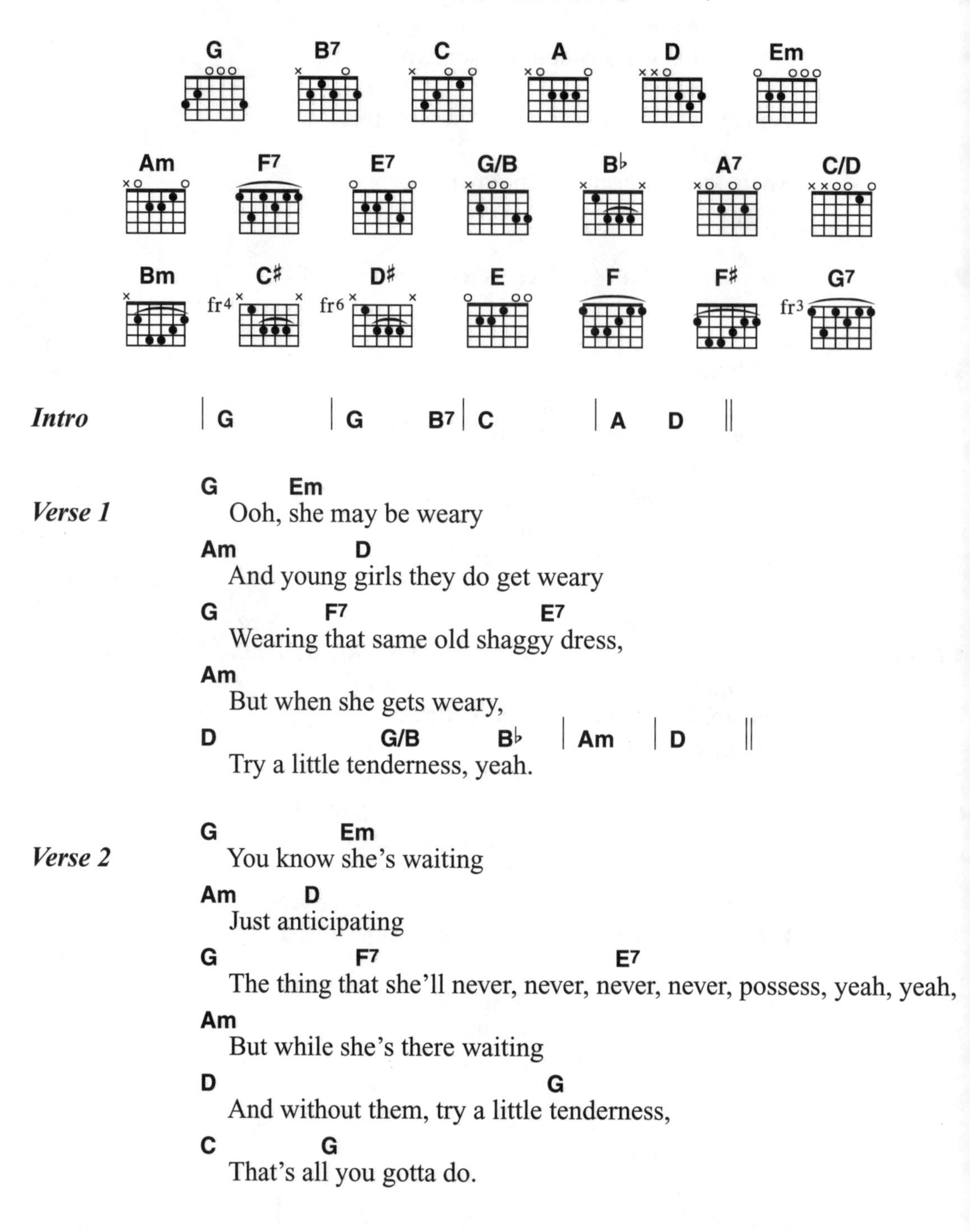

Intro | G | G B7 | C | A D ||

Verse 1

```
G         Em
  Ooh, she may be weary
Am              D
  And young girls they do get weary
G             F7                 E7
  Wearing that same old shaggy dress,
Am
  But when she gets weary,
D                   G/B       B♭   | Am   | D    ||
  Try a little tenderness, yeah.
```

Verse 2

```
G               Em
  You know she's waiting
Am        D
  Just anticipating
G                F7                         E7
  The thing that she'll never, never, never, never, possess, yeah, yeah,
Am
  But while she's there waiting
D                                       G
  And without them, try a little tenderness,
C               G
  That's all you gotta do.
```

```
                C              B7
*Bridge*            It's not just sentimental, no, no, no,
                Em                        A7
                    She has her griefs and care,
                C                                B7
                    But the soft words they are spoke so gentle, yeah,
                A7                             C/D      D
                    It makes it easier,   easier to bear.

                G        Em
Verse 3             You won't regret it, no, no,
                Am                  D
                    Young girls they don't forget it,
                G                      F7            E7
                Love is their whole happiness, yeah, yeah, yeah,
                Am
                    But it's all so easy
                D
                    All you gotta do is try,
                                  G/B
                Try a little tenderness, yeah.
                                            E7
                Oh, you gotta   do it now,

                Hold her where you wanna.

                      Am                  Bm            C
Outro           ||:   Squeeze her,   don't tease her,
                   C#                   D                  D#
                Never leave her,   make love to her,
                        E             F      F#    G7
                Just,   just, just try a little tenderness, yeah, yeah, yeah,
                F7                                              E7
                     You've gotta know how to love her, man.  :||    Repeat to fade
                                                                    with vocal ad lib.
```

Things Have Changed

Words & Music by
Bob Dylan

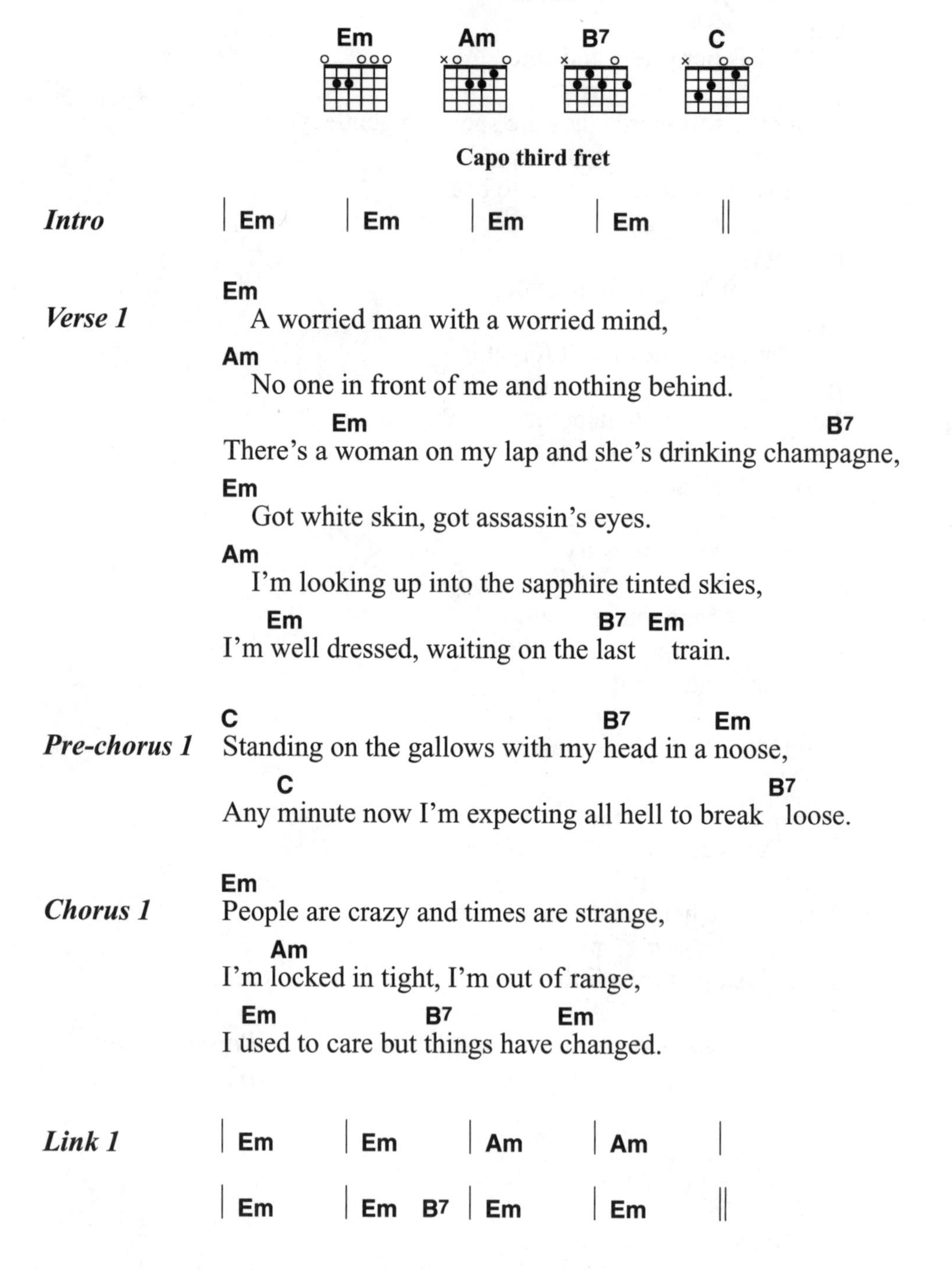

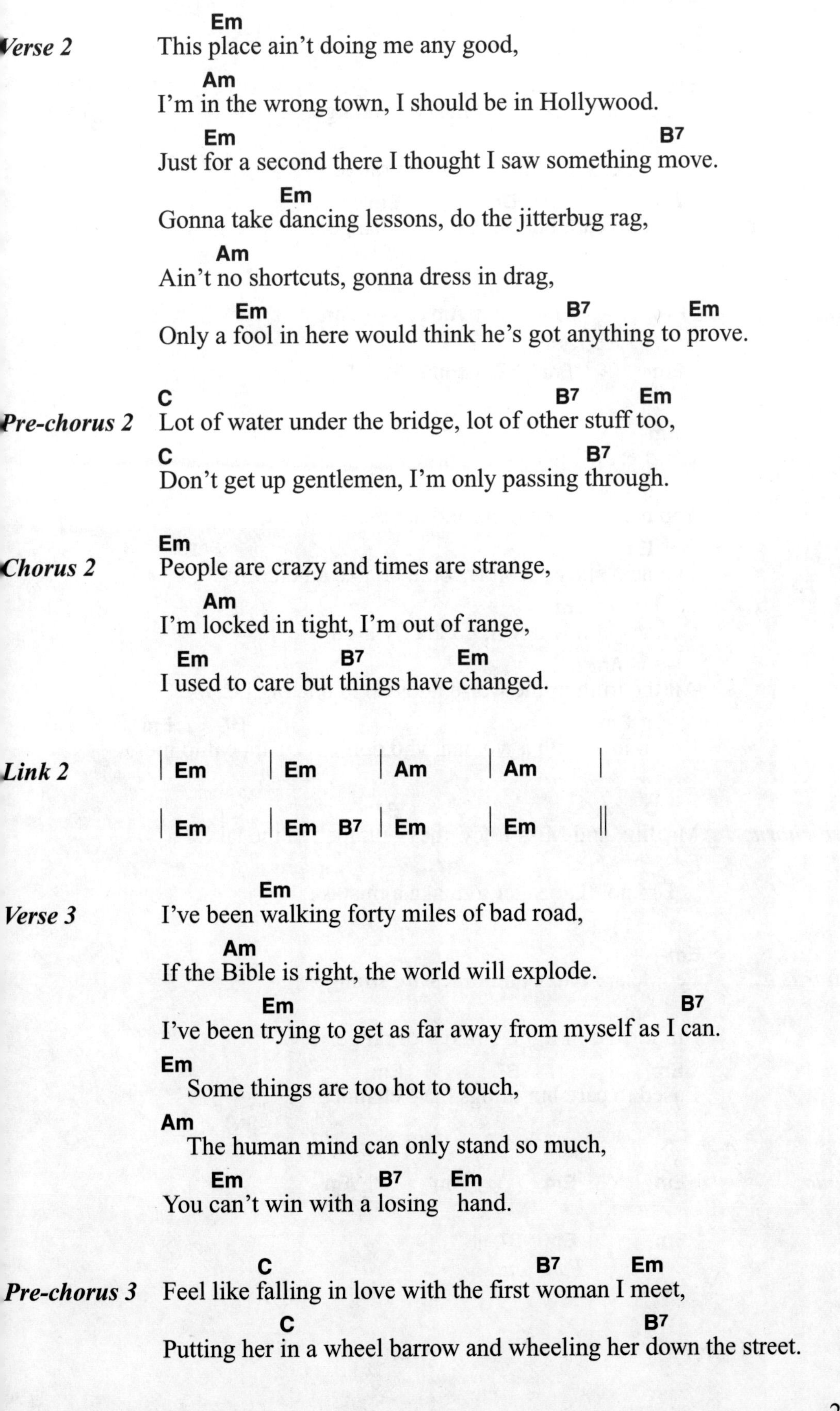

Verse 2

Em
This place ain't doing me any good,
Am
I'm in the wrong town, I should be in Hollywood.
Em B7
Just for a second there I thought I saw something move.
Em
Gonna take dancing lessons, do the jitterbug rag,
Am
Ain't no shortcuts, gonna dress in drag,
Em B7 Em
Only a fool in here would think he's got anything to prove.

Pre-chorus 2

C B7 Em
Lot of water under the bridge, lot of other stuff too,
C B7
Don't get up gentlemen, I'm only passing through.

Chorus 2

Em
People are crazy and times are strange,
Am
I'm locked in tight, I'm out of range,
Em B7 Em
I used to care but things have changed.

Link 2

| Em | Em | Am | Am |
| Em | Em B7 | Em | Em ||

Verse 3

Em
I've been walking forty miles of bad road,
Am
If the Bible is right, the world will explode.
Em B7
I've been trying to get as far away from myself as I can.
Em
Some things are too hot to touch,
Am
The human mind can only stand so much,
Em B7 Em
You can't win with a losing hand.

Pre-chorus 3

C B7 Em
Feel like falling in love with the first woman I meet,
C B7
Putting her in a wheel barrow and wheeling her down the street.

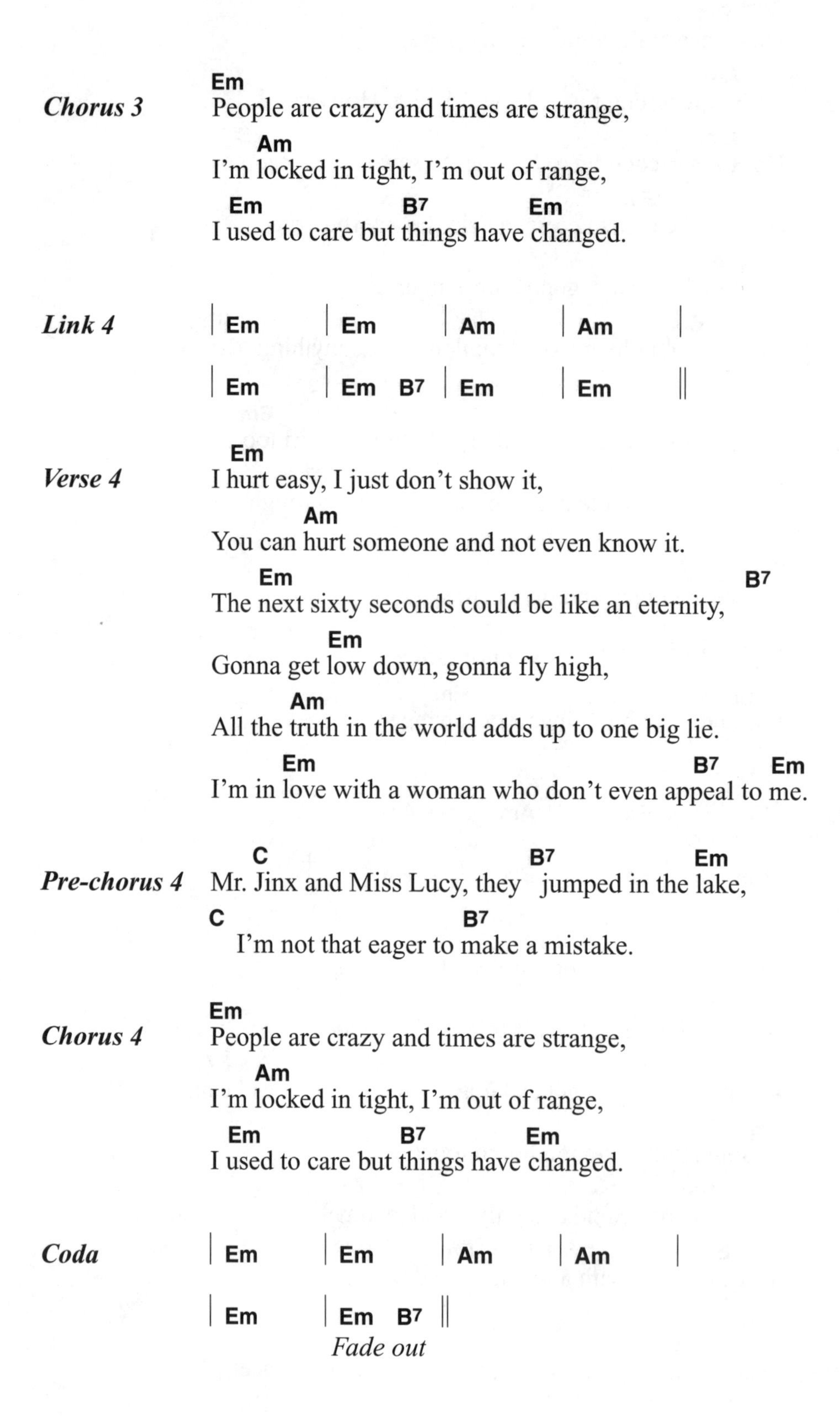

Chorus 3

Em
People are crazy and times are strange,
Am
I'm locked in tight, I'm out of range,
Em B7 Em
I used to care but things have changed.

Link 4

| Em | Em | Am | Am |
| Em | Em B7 | Em | Em ||

Verse 4

Em
I hurt easy, I just don't show it,
Am
You can hurt someone and not even know it.
Em B7
The next sixty seconds could be like an eternity,
Em
Gonna get low down, gonna fly high,
Am
All the truth in the world adds up to one big lie.
Em B7 Em
I'm in love with a woman who don't even appeal to me.

Pre-chorus 4

C B7 Em
Mr. Jinx and Miss Lucy, they jumped in the lake,
C B7
I'm not that eager to make a mistake.

Chorus 4

Em
People are crazy and times are strange,
Am
I'm locked in tight, I'm out of range,
Em B7 Em
I used to care but things have changed.

Coda

| Em | Em | Am | Am |
| Em | Em B7 ||

Fade out

Vincent

Words & Music by
Don McLean

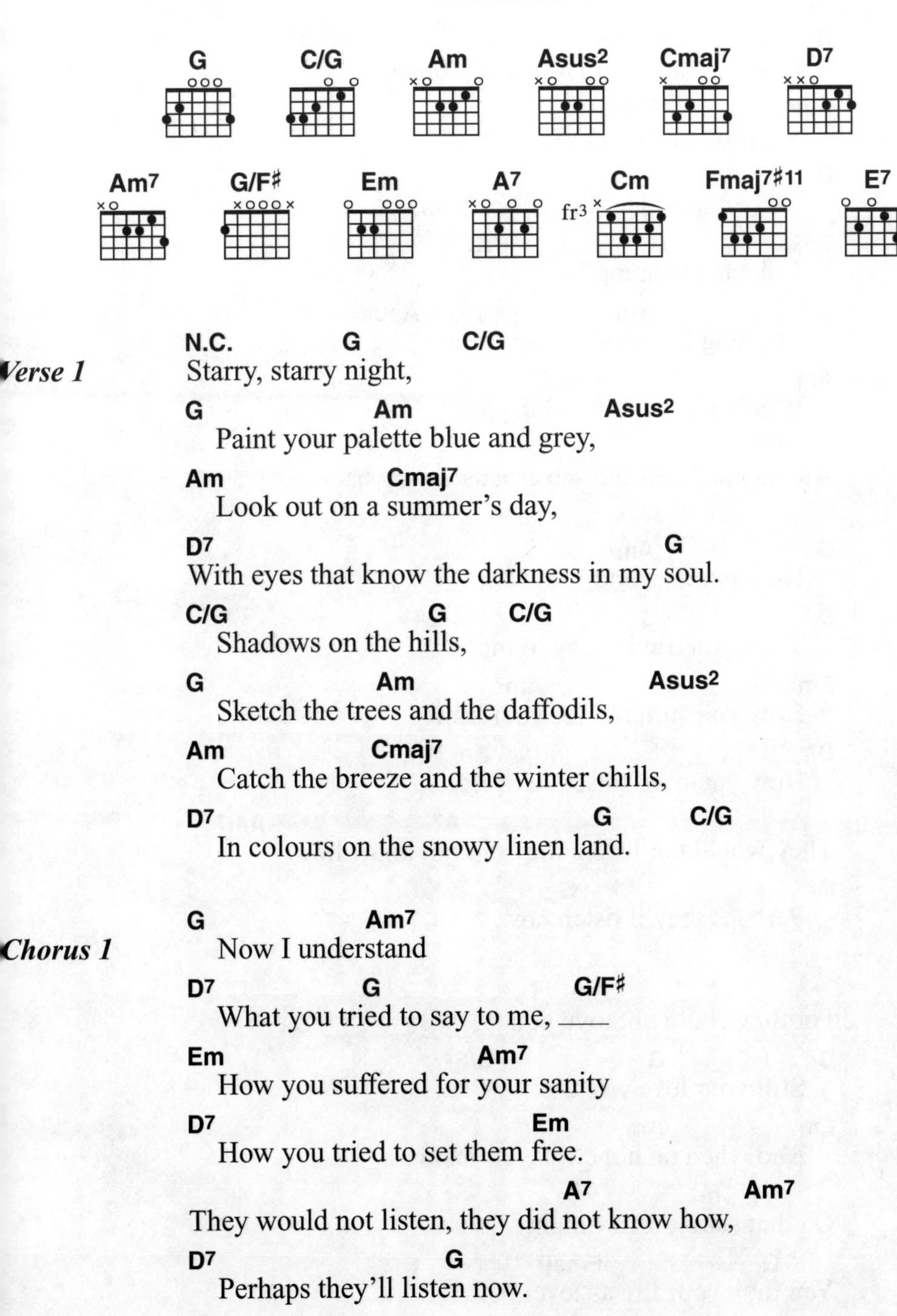

Verse 1

N.C. G C/G
Starry, starry night,

G Am Asus2
Paint your palette blue and grey,

Am Cmaj7
Look out on a summer's day,

D7 G
With eyes that know the darkness in my soul.

C/G G C/G
Shadows on the hills,

G Am Asus2
Sketch the trees and the daffodils,

Am Cmaj7
Catch the breeze and the winter chills,

D7 G C/G
In colours on the snowy linen land.

Chorus 1

G Am7
Now I understand

D7 G G/F♯
What you tried to say to me, ____

Em Am7
How you suffered for your sanity

D7 Em
How you tried to set them free.

A7 Am7
They would not listen, they did not know how,

D7 G
Perhaps they'll listen now.

Verse 2

N.C. G C/G
Starry, starry night,
G Am Asus2
Flaming flowers that brightly blaze,
Am Cmaj7
Swirling clouds in violet haze,
D7 G
Reflect in Vincent's eyes of china blue.
C/G G C/G
Colours changing hue,
G Am Asus2
Morning fields of amber grain,
Am Cmaj7
Weathered faces lined in pain,
D7 G
Are soothed beneath the artist's loving hand.

Chorus 2

G Am7
Now I understand
D7 G G/F♯
What you tried to say to me, ___
Em Am7
How you suffered for your sanity
D7 Em
How you tried to set them free.
A7 Am7
They would not listen, they did not know how,
D7 G
Perhaps they'll listen now.

Middle

Am7
For they could not love you,
D7 G G/F♯
Still your love was true;
Em Am
And when no hope was left inside
Cm
On that starry, starry night
G Fmaj7♯11 E7
You took your life as lovers often do;
Asus2
But I could have told you Vincent
Cmaj7 D7 G
This world was never meant for one as beautiful as you.

```
            N.C.               G         C/G
Verse 3     Starry, starry night,
            G                 Am                   Asus2
               Portraits hung in empty halls,
            Am                  Cmaj7
               Frameless heads on nameless walls,
            D7                                                G
               With eyes that watch the world and can't forget.
                                                C/G
            Like the strangers that you've met,
            G                        Am              Asus2
               The ragged men in ragged clothes,
            Am                 Cmaj7
               The silver thorn of bloody rose,
              D7                                     G
            Lie crushed and broken on the virgin snow.

                               Am7    D7
Chorus 3    Now I think I know ___
                            G          G/F#
            What you tried to say to me,
            Em                                Am7
               And how you suffered for your sanity,
            D7                          Em
               How you tried to set them free.
                                                    A7             Am7
            They would not listen, they're not listening still,
            D7                      G     C/G   G
            Perhaps they never will.
```

Waltzing Back

Words & Music by
Dolores O'Riordan

Em G C Am G/A C/G

fr10

Intro ‖: Em G | C Am | Em G | C Am :‖

Verse 1

```
      Em              G
Who gave them the right
C                Am        Em
Waltzing back into your life,
      G          C       Am
Your life, your life?
Em          G
Now I feel fear,
  C                   Am           Em
I wish that they'd never come here,
G     C       Am
Here, here.
```

Chorus 1

```
Em
What they're gonna do,
G
What they're gonna say,
C                     Am        Em
Taking you away  from my life,
    G          C       Am
My life, my life?
Em
What they're gonna do,
G
What they're gonna say,
C                     Am        Em
Taking you away  from my life,
    G          C      Am       Em  G  C     G/A
My life, my life?  La, ah.               La-ah.
Em  G  C  G/A  Em  G  C       G/A
                           La-ah.
Em  G  C  G/A
```

```
              Em              G
Verse 2       Who gave them the right
              C           Am          Em
              Turning it back into light,
              G      C        Am
              Light, light?
              Em          G
              Then I felt fear,
                C                       Am             Em
              I wish that they'd never come here,
              G      C        Am
              Here, here.

              Em
Chorus 2      What they're gonna do,
              G
              What they're gonna say,
              C                        Am          Em
              Taking you away  from my life,
                  G          C        Am
              My life, my life?
              Em
              I don't wanna know,
              G
              I don't wanna say,
              C                         Am                  Em
              I don't wanna say  'cause it's your life,
                    G            C      Am        Em  G  C   G/A
              Your life, your life.    La, ah.            La-ah.
              Em  G  C  Am  G/A  Em  G  C    G/A
                                           La-ah.
              Em  G  C  G/A

Instrumental  ||: Em  G  | C   Am  | Em  G   | C   Am  :||

                 Em            G
Outro         ||: Who gave them the right,
                 C          Am
              The right, the right?   :||  Play 3 times
                Em              G
              Who gave them the right,
                 C          Am     Em  C/G  C  Am  Em  C/G  C  Am
              The right, the right? ________________________
                                                     Play 3 times
              ||: Em  C/G | C   Am  | Em  C/G | C   Am  :||
                                                     Play 3 times
              ||: Em  G   | C   Am  | Em  G   | C   Am  :|| Em       ||
```

What A Beautiful Day

Words & Music by Mark Chadwick, Simon Friend,
Jonathan Sevink, Jeremy Cunningham & Charles Heather

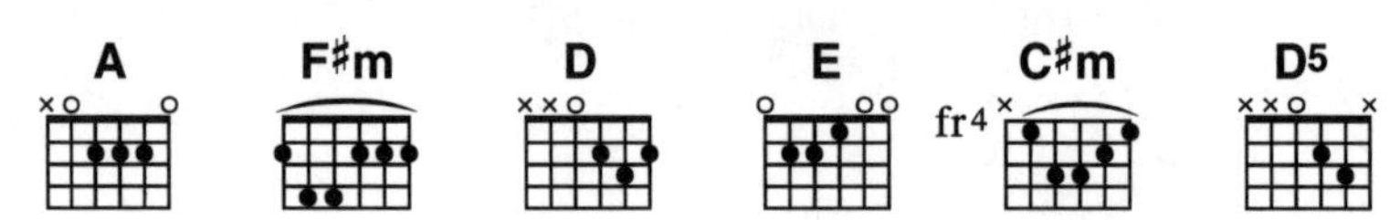

Chorus 1

A F♯m
What a beautiful day, I'm the king of all time,
D E F♯m
And nothing is impossible in my powerful mind.

Verse 1

F♯m C♯m
Was on the fifth of November when time it went back,
D
Well some would say that that's impossible,
E F♯m
But you and I we never looked back,
(F♯m) C♯m
And wasn't it incredible, oh so beautiful and above all,
D
Oh just to see the fuse get lit this time,
E F♯m
to light a real bonfire for all time.

Chorus 2

As Chorus 1

Instrumental 1

| F♯m | F♯m | C♯m | C♯m |

| D | E | F♯m | F♯m ||

Verse 2

F♯m C♯m
I was drinking in a night-club, it felt good to be back,
D
When Hepburn said "I love you,"
E F♯m
And Flynn said "Make mine a double Jack."
(F♯m) C♯m
Was then we planned a revolution to make things better for all time,
D E F♯m
When Guevara said "That's crazy," and ordered up a bottle of wine.

Chorus 3 As Chorus 1

Chorus 4 As Chorus 1

Verse 3

```
F♯m                          C♯m
In there on the big screen, every night I've seen
     D       E           F♯m
The way all things could be ___
            C♯m              D           E            F♯m      | D5    ||
Oh for me, ___  oh for me, ___  for me, ___  for me.
```

Inst. 2

```
| A        | A        | F♯m      | F♯m      |
| D        | E        | F♯m      | F♯m      ||
```

Verse 4

```
     F♯m
The news broke after midnight,
         C♯m
And we pulled the temples down without a sound,
         D
But the generals were hiding out,
     E                         F♯m
The ministers, well - they'd all gone to ground.
(F♯m)                        C♯m
Wealth redistribution became the new solution,
    D                       E                          F♯m
So I got a paper bag, and you got the one with all the holes.
```

Chorus 5 As Chorus 1

Chorus 6 As Chorus 1

Outro

```
(F♯m)          D                          E                F♯m
Oh yeah and nothing is impossible in my all powerful mind,
                  D                          E             F♯m
That's because nothing is impossible in my powerful mind.
```

When Will I Be Loved

Words & Music by
Phil Everly

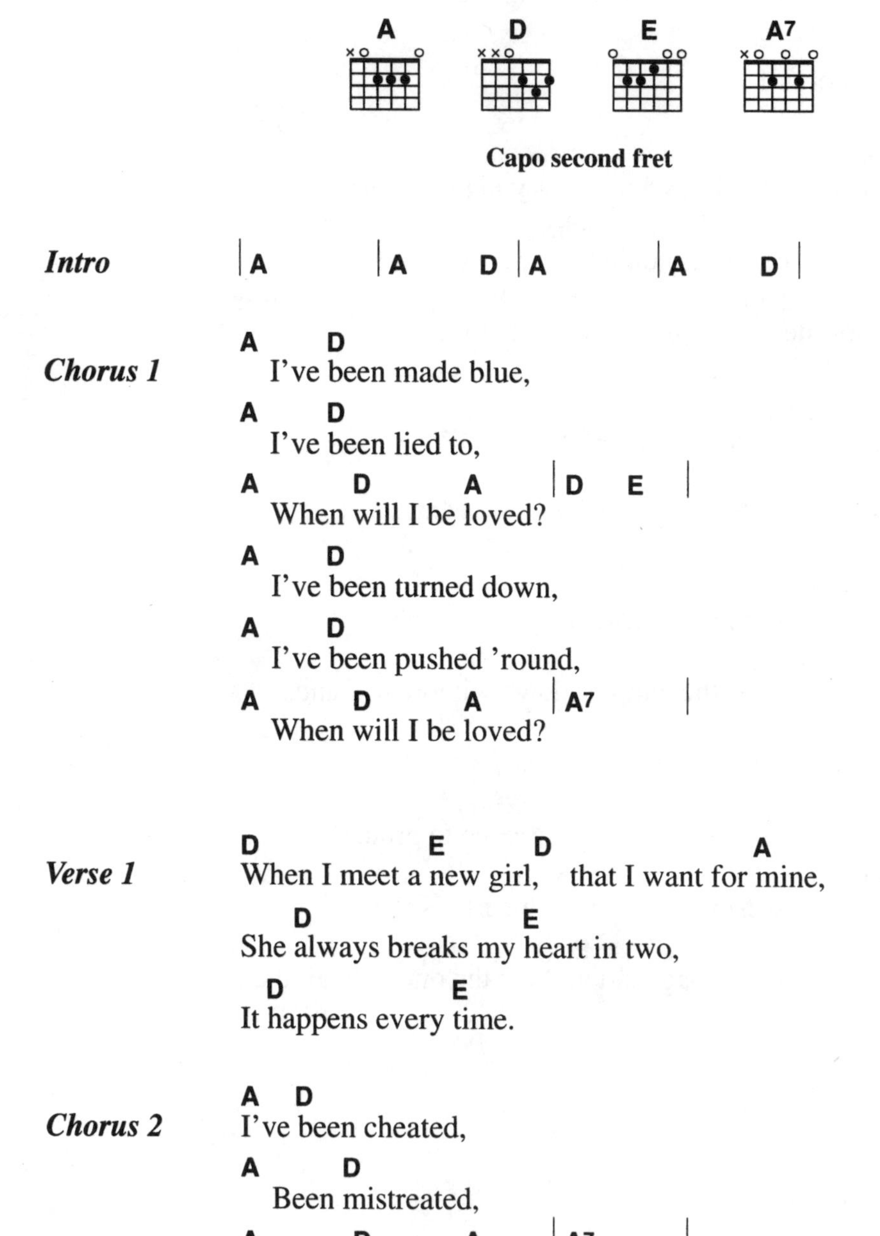

Capo second fret

```
Intro       | A        | A      D | A        | A      D |

            A    D
Chorus 1      I've been made blue,
            A    D
              I've been lied to,
            A        D        A     | D    E    |
              When will I be loved?
            A    D
              I've been turned down,
            A    D
              I've been pushed 'round,
            A        D        A     | A7        |
              When will I be loved?


            D              E        D                A
Verse 1     When I meet a new girl,   that I want for mine,
                D                  E
            She always breaks my heart in two,
              D             E
            It happens every time.

            A   D
Chorus 2    I've been cheated,
            A       D
              Been mistreated,
            A        D        A     | A7        |
              When will I be loved?
```

Verse 2

```
D              E        D               A
   When I meet a new girl,   that I want for mine,
   D               E
She always breaks my heart in two,
  D           E
It happens every time.
```

Chorus 3

```
A   D
I've been cheated,
A     D
   Been mistreated,
A        D       A    | A7        |
   When will I be loved?
```

Outro

```
A             D  A    | A7        |
   When will I be loved?
```

Repeat to fade

Where Did You Sleep Last Night

Words & Music by
Huddie Ledbetter

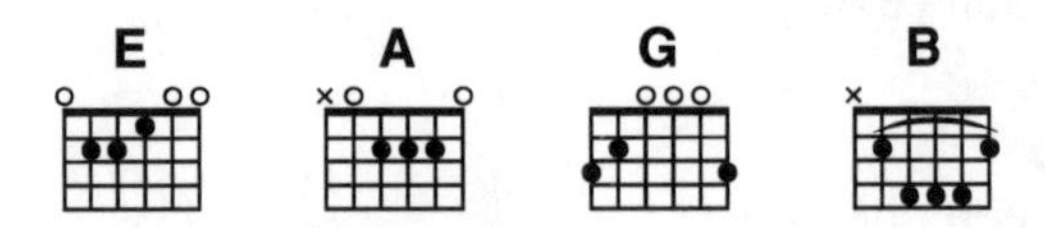

Tune guitar down one semitone

Intro ‖: E | A G | B | E :‖

Verse 1

```
    E                 A   G
My girl, my girl, don't lie to me,
          B                  E
Tell me where did you sleep last night ?

"In the pines, in the pines
          A              G
Where the sun don't ever shine,
         B                E
I would shiver the whole night through."
```

Verse 2

```
    E                  A     G
My girl, my girl, where will you go?
     B                        E
 "I'm going where the cold wind blows

In the pines, in the pines
          A              G
Where the sun don't ever shine,
         B                E
I would shiver the whole night through."
```

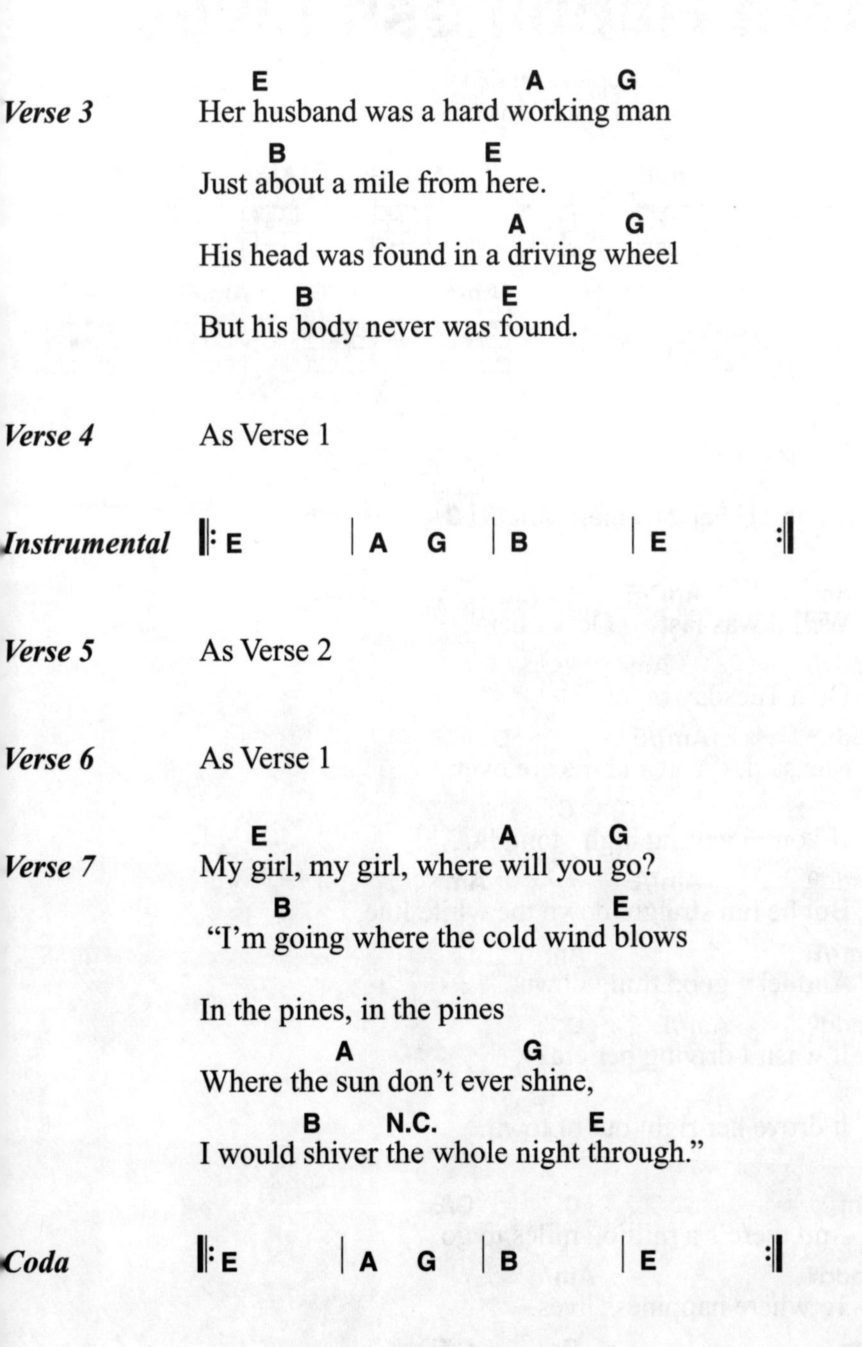

```
               E                  A       G
Verse 3        Her husband was a hard working man
                 B                E
               Just about a mile from here.
                                 A        G
               His head was found in a driving wheel
                  B                E
               But his body never was found.

Verse 4        As Verse 1

Instrumental   |: E        | A   G | B      | E      :|

Verse 5        As Verse 2

Verse 6        As Verse 1

               E                   A       G
Verse 7        My girl, my girl, where will you go?
                 B                        E
               "I'm going where the cold wind blows

               In the pines, in the pines
                           A            G
               Where the sun don't ever shine,
                     B       N.C.           E
               I would shiver the whole night through."

Coda           |: E        | A   G | B      | E      :|
```

Where Happiness Lives

Words & Music by
Even Johansen

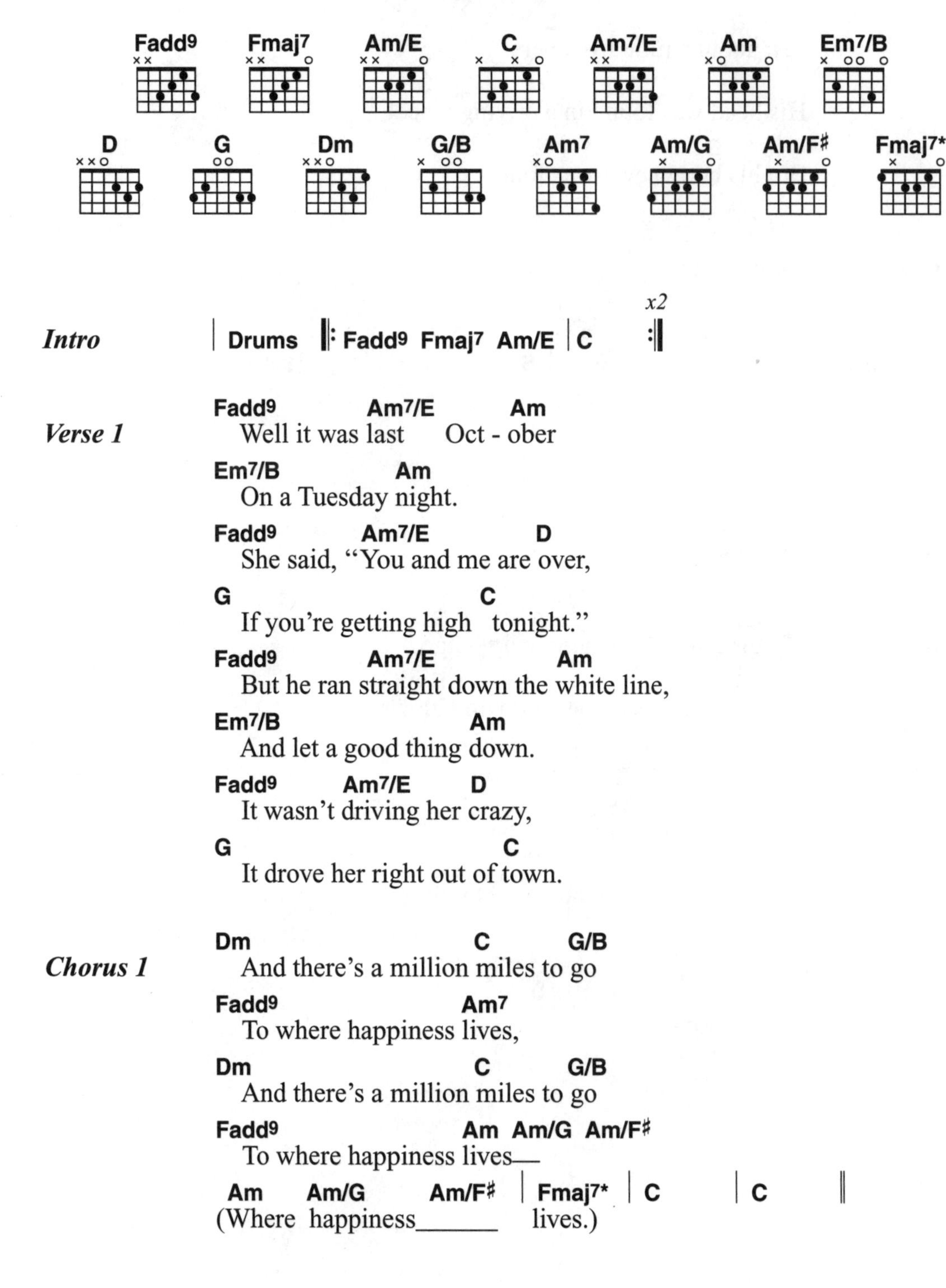

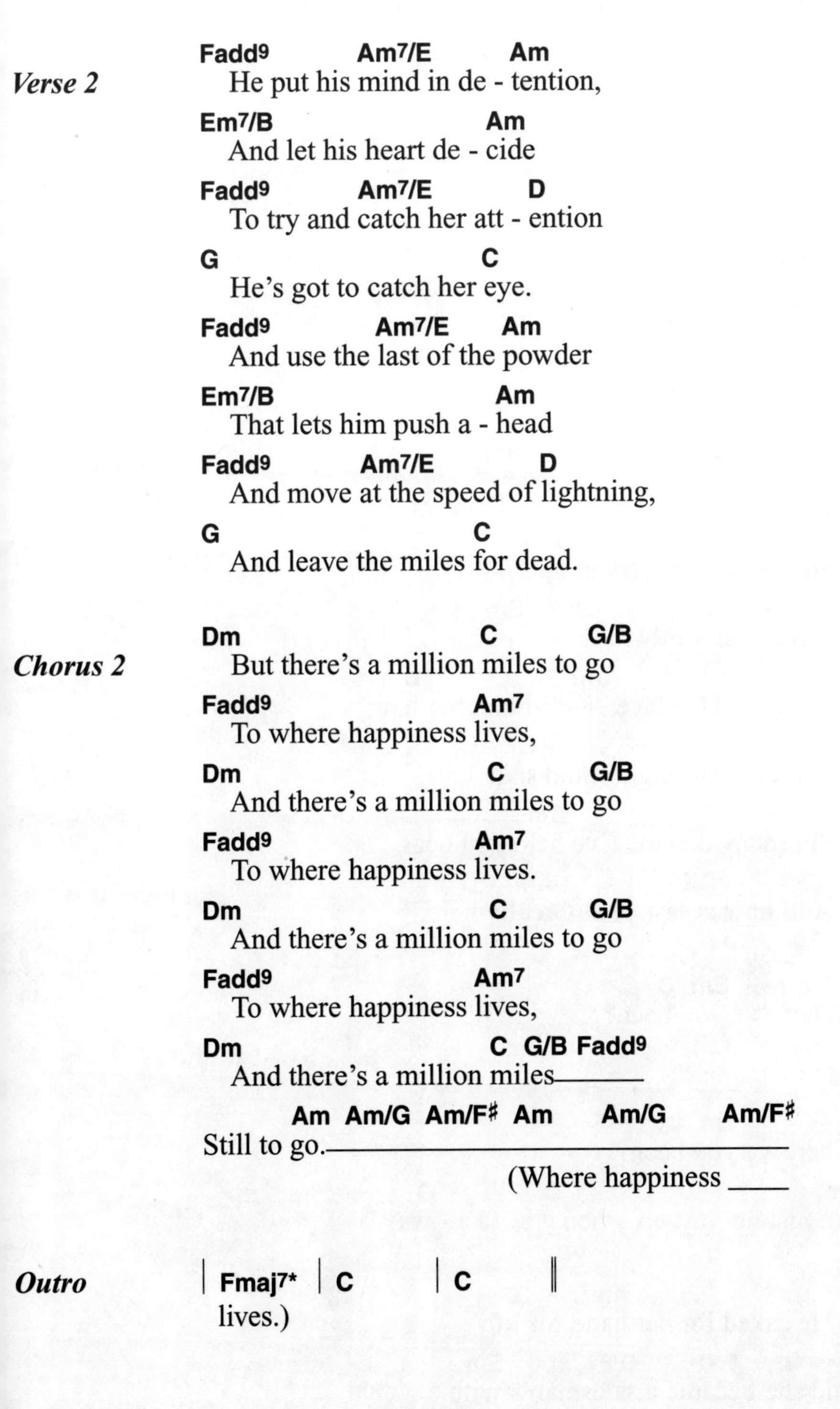

Verse 2

Fadd9 Am7/E Am
He put his mind in de - tention,
Em7/B Am
And let his heart de - cide
Fadd9 Am7/E D
To try and catch her att - ention
G C
He's got to catch her eye.
Fadd9 Am7/E Am
And use the last of the powder
Em7/B Am
That lets him push a - head
Fadd9 Am7/E D
And move at the speed of lightning,
G C
And leave the miles for dead.

Chorus 2

Dm C G/B
But there's a million miles to go
Fadd9 Am7
To where happiness lives,
Dm C G/B
And there's a million miles to go
Fadd9 Am7
To where happiness lives.
Dm C G/B
And there's a million miles to go
Fadd9 Am7
To where happiness lives,
Dm C G/B Fadd9
And there's a million miles______
Am Am/G Am/F♯ Am Am/G Am/F♯
Still to go.____________________
(Where happiness ____

Outro

| Fmaj7* | C | C ‖
lives.)

Where've You Been

Words & Music by
Jon Vezner & Don Henry

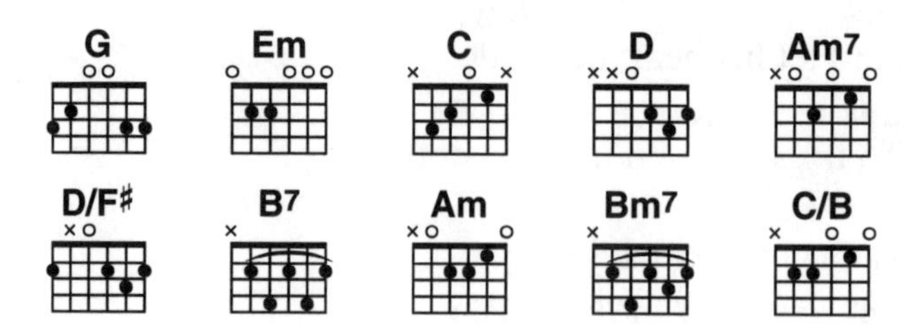

Intro | G Em | C | C | G ||

Verse 1

```
D                    Am7     D/F♯
Clare had all but   given up,
      G                 D/F♯  Em
When she and Edwin fell in love,
D                       Am7              D
She touched his face,  and shook her hair,
   G            D/F♯          B7
In disbelief she sighed and said
Am                              Bm7
   "In many dreams I've held you near,
C               C/B          Am     D
   And now at last you're really here."
```

Chorus 1

```
G             Em  C
"Where've you been?
                                     G
I've looked for you forever and a day.
G            Em  C
Where've you been?
Em                            C        G
I'm just not myself when you're a - way."
```

Verse 2

```
D                        Am7      D
   He asked for her hand for life
      G               D/F♯       Em
And she became a salesman's wife.
```

cont.

```
D                                Am7      D/F#
   He was home each night by eight,
          G                       D/F#    B7
But one stormy evening he was late.
Am                              Bm7
   Her frightened tears fell to the floor,
C           C/B          Am        D
   Until his key turned in the door.
```

Chorus 2

As Chorus 1

```
| C  D  | G     ||
```

Middle

```
C
   They'd never spent a night apart,
   Em
For sixty years she heard him snore.
C
   Now they're in a hospital,
   Am                              D    | D
In separate beds, on different floors.
```

Verse 3

```
D                           Am7    D/F#
Clare soon lost her memo - ry,
     G                      D/F#   Em
Forgot the names of fami - ly.
D                             Am7     D
   She never spoke a word a - gain,
G                     D/F#        B7
Then one day they wheeled him in,
Am                             Bm7
   He held her hand and stroked her hair,
C                C/B  Am        D
   With a fra - gile voice she said:
```

Chorus 3

```
G              Em  C
"Where've you been?
                                         G
I've looked for you forever and a day.
G             Em  C
Where've you been?
                                           Em
I'm just not myself when you're a - way.
   D                                          C
No I'm just not myself when you're a - way."
```

Will You?

Words & Music by
Hazel O'Connor & Wesley Magoogan

Dm F B♭ C A Dm/A G G/B

Intro

```
| Dm        | Dm        ||
```

Verse 1

```
Dm                  F             B♭      C
   You drink your coffee, and    I sip my tea
             Dm          F
And we're    sitting here playing so cool, thinking
B♭                     A
   'What will be will be'.
```

Chorus 1

```
F                            C
   But it's getting kind of late now,
Dm                        Dm/A  A      Dm/A  A      Dm/A  A      Dm/A  A
   Oh I wonder if you'll stay    now, stay    now, stay    now, stay    now
    Dm         F           G     G/B           Dm      A  | A          |
Or will you just pol - itely,       say goodnight?
```

Verse 2

```
Dm                    F                  B♭                    C
   I move a little closer to you,    not knowing quite what to do
             Dm              F                                   B♭              A
And I'm    feeling all fingers and thumbs, I spill my tea, oh silly me.
```

Chorus 2

```
F                            C
   But it's getting kind of late now,
Dm                     Dm/A  A      Dm/A  A      Dm/A  A      Dm/A  A
   I wonder if you'll stay    now, stay    now, stay    now, stay    now.
    Dm         F           G     G/B           Dm      A
Or will you just pol - itely,       say goodnight?
```

Bridge

```
                     F                   C
And then we touch much too much,
       Dm                                         A
This moment has been waiting for a long, long time.
                   F                   C
Makes me shiver, it makes me quiver,
```

cont.

Dm
This moment I am so unsure,

C
This moment I have waited for

B♭ A | A |
Was it something you've been waiting for, waiting for too?

Verse 3

Dm F B♭ C
Take up your eyes, bare your soul, gather me to you and make me whole

Dm F B♭ A
Tell me your secrets, sing me the song, sing it to me in the silent dawn.

Chorus 3

F C
But it's getting kind of late now,

Dm Dm/A A Dm/A A Dm/A A Dm/A A
I wonder if you'll stay now, stay now, stay now, stay now.

Dm F G G/B Dm A
Or will you just pol - itely, say goodnight?

Sax solo

| Dm F | G G/B | Dm | A (fermata) | Dm |

| Drum break ||

| Dm | F | B♭ | C | Dm | F | B♭ | A |

| F | C | Dm | A | A | Dm F | G G/B | Dm | A |

| F | C | Dm | A | F | C | Dm | Dm |

| C | C | B♭ | B♭ | A | A |

| Dm | F | B♭ | C | Dm | F | B♭ | A |

| F | C | Dm | A | A | Dm F | G G/B | Dm | A |

| Dm F | G G/B | Dm | A (fermata) | Dm ||

Wonderful Tonight

Words & Music by
Eric Clapton

G D/F♯ C D Em

Intro ‖: G | D/F♯ | C | D :‖

Verse 1

G D/F♯
It's late in the evening,
C D
She's wondering what clothes to wear.
G D/F♯
She puts on her make-up
C D
And brushes her long blonde hair.
C D
And then she asks me,
G D/F♯ Em
"Do I look alright?"
C D G
And I say, "Yes, you look wonderful tonight."

Link | G | D/F♯ | C | D ‖

Verse 2

G D/F♯
We go to a party
C D
And everyone turns to see
G D/F♯
This beautiful lady
C D
That's walking around with me.
C D
And then she asks me,
G D/F♯ Em
"Do you feel alright?"
C D G
And I say, "Yes, I feel wonderful tonight."

Bridge

```
       C              D
I feel wonderful because I see
     G              D/F#    Em
The love-light in your eyes,
          C             D
And the wonder of it all
             C              D                   G
Is that you just don't realise how much I love you.
```

Link

|: G | D/F# | C | D :|

Verse 3

```
G                D/F#
It's time to go home now
C                     D
And I've got an aching head,
G                  D/F#
So I give her the car keys,
C                 D
She helps me to bed.
C             D
And then I tell her
G    D/F#        Em
As I turn out the light,
            C                  D              G       D/F#  Em  D
I say, "My darling, you were wonderful tonight.
         C                D             G
Oh my darling, you were wonderful tonight."
```

Coda

|: G | D/F# | C | D :| G ||

Wouldn't It Be Nice

Words & Music by
Brian Wilson, Tony Asher & Mike Love

```
             Dmaj7              Gmaj7
Bridge          Maybe if we think and wish and hope and pray
                  F♯m7                  Bm7
             It might come true.
             Dmaj7                 Gmaj7                            F♯m7          Bm7
                Maybe then there wouldn't be a single thing we couldn't do.
                           F♯m7                     Bm7
             We could be married (we could be married)
                                 F♯m7                       C
             And then we'd be happy, (and then we'd  be happy)
                              F
             Ah, wouldn't it be nice.


Link         | F     | F     | F     | F     ||


             Dm/A                                         E♭/F
Verse 3         You know it seems the more we talk about it
             Dm/A                               Am      Gm
                It only makes it worse to live without it,
                       Am   Gm      C
             But let's talk about it
                           F
             Wouldn't it be nice.

                F
Coda         ||:   Good night, baby, sleep tight, baby.  :||   Repeat to fade
```

Writing To Reach You

Words & Music by
Fran Healy

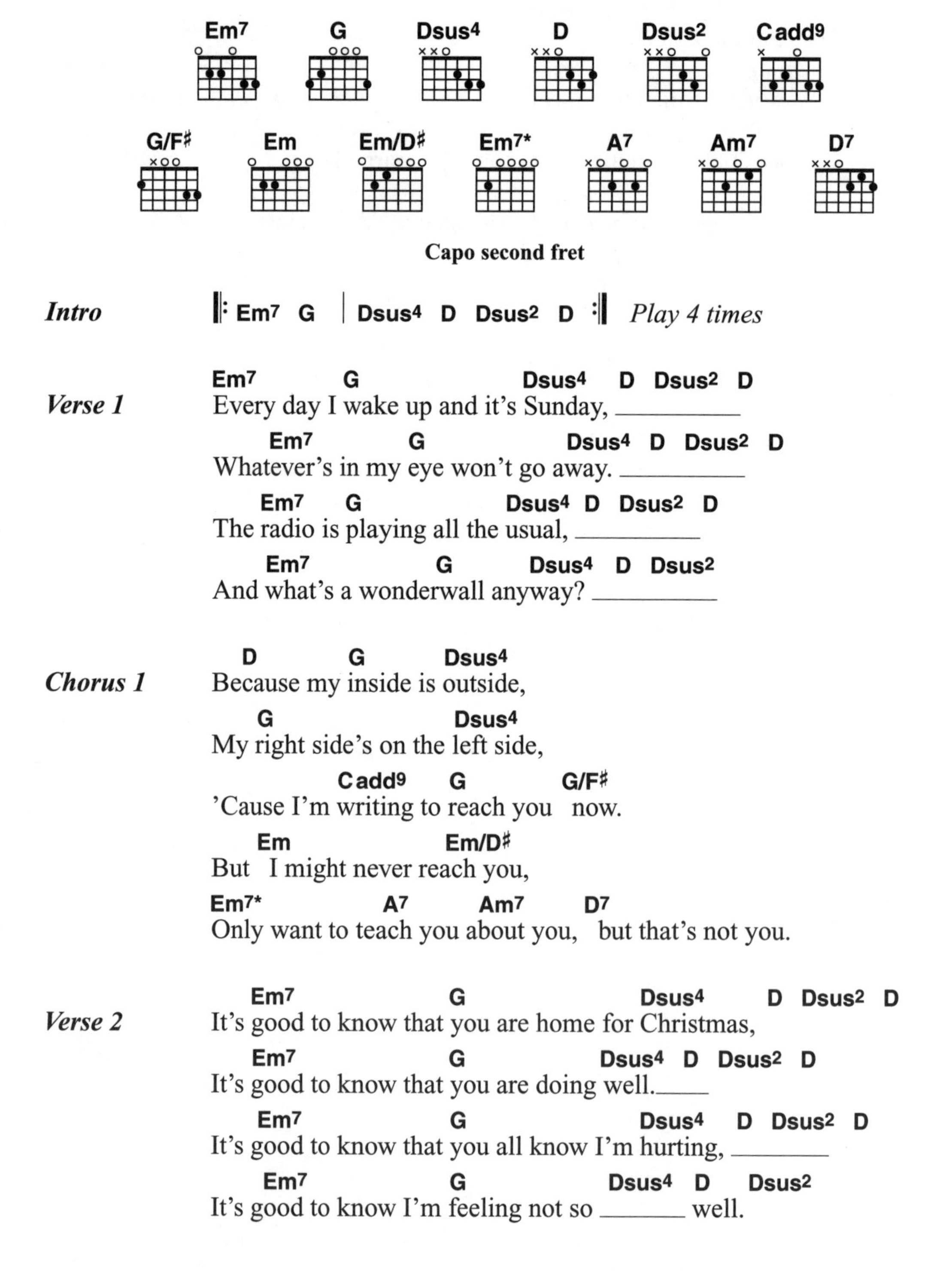

Capo second fret

Intro ||: Em7 G | Dsus4 D Dsus2 D :|| *Play 4 times*

Verse 1

Em7 G Dsus4 D Dsus2 D
Every day I wake up and it's Sunday, ______

Em7 G Dsus4 D Dsus2 D
Whatever's in my eye won't go away. ______

Em7 G Dsus4 D Dsus2 D
The radio is playing all the usual, ______

Em7 G Dsus4 D Dsus2
And what's a wonderwall anyway? ______

Chorus 1

D G Dsus4
Because my inside is outside,

G Dsus4
My right side's on the left side,

Cadd9 G G/F♯
'Cause I'm writing to reach you now.

Em Em/D♯
But I might never reach you,

Em7* A7 Am7 D7
Only want to teach you about you, but that's not you.

Verse 2

Em7 G Dsus4 D Dsus2 D
It's good to know that you are home for Christmas,

Em7 G Dsus4 D Dsus2 D
It's good to know that you are doing well.____

Em7 G Dsus4 D Dsus2 D
It's good to know that you all know I'm hurting, ______

Em7 G Dsus4 D Dsus2
It's good to know I'm feeling not so ______ well.

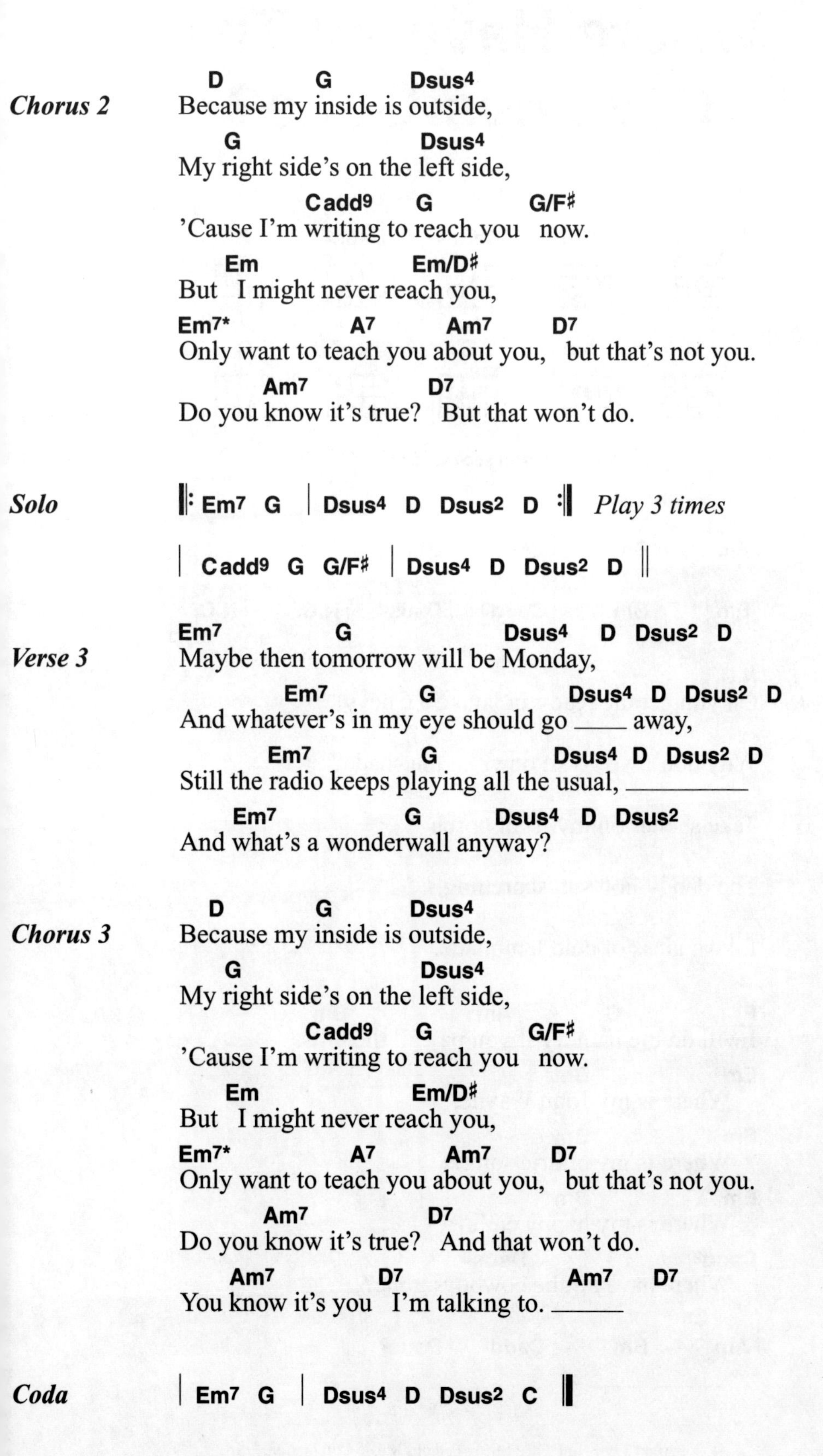

Chorus 2

D G Dsus4
Because my inside is outside,
G Dsus4
My right side's on the left side,
Cadd9 G G/F♯
'Cause I'm writing to reach you now.
Em Em/D♯
But I might never reach you,
Em7* A7 Am7 D7
Only want to teach you about you, but that's not you.
Am7 D7
Do you know it's true? But that won't do.

Solo

|: Em7 G | Dsus4 D Dsus2 D :| *Play 3 times*

| Cadd9 G G/F♯ | Dsus4 D Dsus2 D ||

Verse 3

Em7 G Dsus4 D Dsus2 D
Maybe then tomorrow will be Monday,
Em7 G Dsus4 D Dsus2 D
And whatever's in my eye should go ___ away,
Em7 G Dsus4 D Dsus2 D
Still the radio keeps playing all the usual, ________
Em7 G Dsus4 D Dsus2
And what's a wonderwall anyway?

Chorus 3

D G Dsus4
Because my inside is outside,
G Dsus4
My right side's on the left side,
Cadd9 G G/F♯
'Cause I'm writing to reach you now.
Em Em/D♯
But I might never reach you,
Em7* A7 Am7 D7
Only want to teach you about you, but that's not you.
Am7 D7
Do you know it's true? And that won't do.
Am7 D7 Am7 D7
You know it's you I'm talking to. _____

Coda

| Em7 G | Dsus4 D Dsus2 C ||

Where Have All The Cowboys Gone?

Words & Music by
Paula Cole

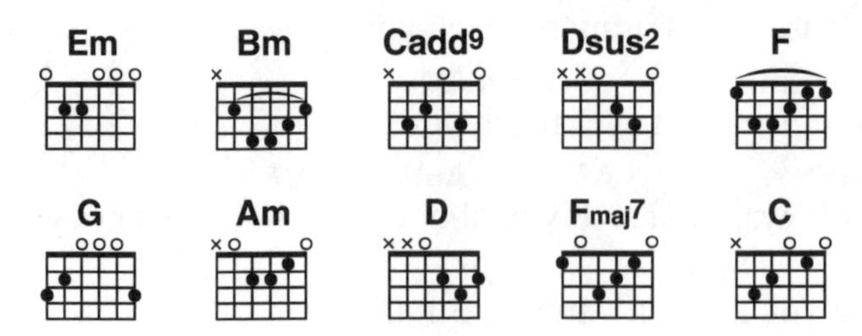

Capo second fret

Intro | Em | Bm | Em | Bm |

| Em | Bm | Cadd9 | Dsus2 | N.C. | N.C. |

```
                    N.C.
Verse 1 (spoken)    Oh you get me ready in your 56 Chevy

                    Why don't we go sit down in the shade?

                    Take shelter on my front porch

                    The dandy lion sun scorching,

                    Like a glass of cold lemonade.

                    F          G         Am            Bm
Chorus 1            I will do the laundry if you pay all the bills,
                    Em             Bm
                       Where is my John Wayne,
                    Em             Bm
                       Where is my prairie song?
                    Em             Bm
                       Where is my happy ending,
                    Cadd9                   Dsus2
                       Where have all the cowboys gone? ____
```

Link 1 | Am | Bm | Cadd9 | Dsus2 |

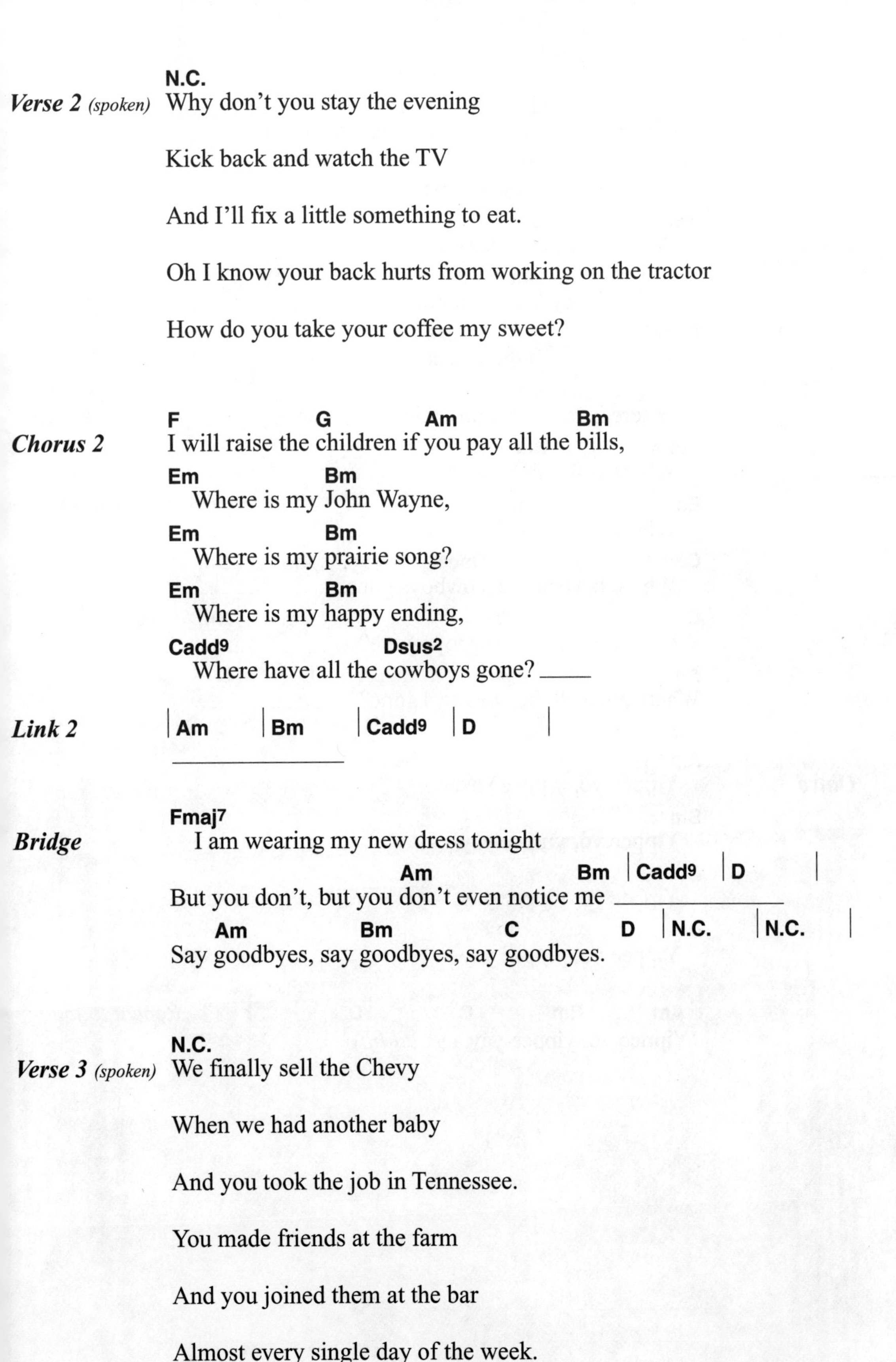

Verse 2 *(spoken)*

N.C.
Why don't you stay the evening

Kick back and watch the TV

And I'll fix a little something to eat.

Oh I know your back hurts from working on the tractor

How do you take your coffee my sweet?

Chorus 2

F **G** **Am** **Bm**
I will raise the children if you pay all the bills,

Em **Bm**
Where is my John Wayne,

Em **Bm**
Where is my prairie song?

Em **Bm**
Where is my happy ending,

Cadd9 **Dsus2**
Where have all the cowboys gone? ____

Link 2

| **Am** | **Bm** | **Cadd9** | **D** |

Bridge

Fmaj7
I am wearing my new dress tonight

Am **Bm** | **Cadd9** | **D** |
But you don't, but you don't even notice me ________

Am **Bm** **C** **D** | **N.C.** | **N.C.** |
Say goodbyes, say goodbyes, say goodbyes.

Verse 3 *(spoken)*

N.C.
We finally sell the Chevy

When we had another baby

And you took the job in Tennessee.

You made friends at the farm

And you joined them at the bar

Almost every single day of the week.

Chorus 3

F G Am Bm
I will wash the dishes while you go have a beer

Em Bm
Where is my John Wayne,

Em Bm
Where is my prairie song?

Em Bm
Where is my happy ending,

Cadd9 Dsus2
Where have all the cowboys gone?

Em Bm
Where is my Marlboro man,

Em Bm
Where is his shiny gun?

Em Bm
Where is my lonely ranger,

Cadd9 Dsus2 | Am | Bm |
Where have all the cowboys gone? ______

C D | Am | Bm | C | D |
Where have all the cowboys gone? ______

Am Bm | C | D |
Where have all the cowboys gone? ______

Outro

Am
Yippee yo, yippee yay,

Bm
Yippee yo, yippee yay,

C
Yippee yo, yippee yay,

D
Yippee yo, yippee yay.

|: Am | Bm | C | D :| *Repeat to fade*
(Yippee yo, yippee yay, *etc. ad lib*)

You Can Call Me Al

Words & Music by
Paul Simon

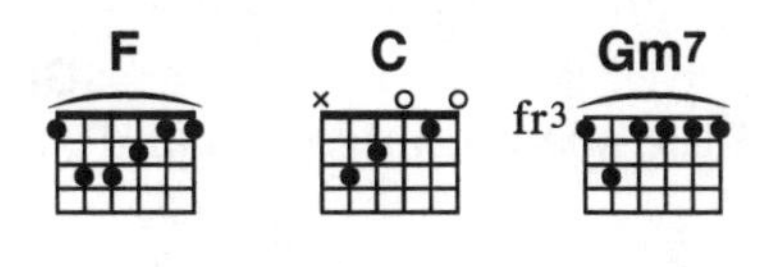

Intro ‖: F C | Gm7 C | F C | Gm7 C :‖

Verse 1

F
A man walks down the street,
Gm7 C
He says, "Why am I soft in the middle now,
F
Why am I soft in the middle?
Gm7 C F
The rest of my life is so hard.
Gm7 C
I need a photo-opportunity, I want a shot at redemption;
F Gm7 C
Don't want to end up a cartoon, in a cartoon graveyard:
F
Bonedigger, bonedigger.
Gm7 C F Gm7 C
Dogs in the moonlight, far away my well-lit door.
F Gm7 C
Mister Beerbelly, Beerbelly get these mutts away from me,
F Gm7 C
I don't find this stuff amusing anymore."

Chorus 1

F C
If you'll be my bodyguard
Gm7 C F C Gm7 C
I can be your long lost pal.
F C
I can call you Betty
Gm7 C
And Betty when you call me
F C Gm7 C
You can call me Al.

Verse 2

F
A man walks down the street,
Gm7 C
He says, "Why am I short of attention?
F Gm7 C F
Got a short little span of attention and oh my nights are so long.

Where's my wife and family?
Gm7 C F
What if I die here? Who'll be my role-model
Gm7 C F
Now that my role-model is gone, gone."
Gm7 C
He ducked back down the alley
F Gm7 C
With some roly-poly little bat-faced girl.
F Gm7 C
All along, along there were incidents and accidents,
F Gm7 C
There were hints and allegations.

Chorus 2

F C
If you'll be my bodyguard
Gm7 C F C Gm7 C
I can be your long lost pal.
F C
I can call you Betty
Gm7 C
And Betty when you call me
F C Gm7 C F
You can call me Al, call me Al.

Instrumental

|: F | Gm7 C | F | Gm7 C :| *Play 4 times*

|: F C | Gm7 C | F C | Gm7 C :|

Verse 3

F Gm7 C
A man walks down the street: It's a street in a strange world.
F Gm7 C F
Maybe it's the Third World, maybe it's his first time around,
Gm7 C
Doesn't speak the language, he holds no currency,
F
He is a foreign man.

```
        Gm7           C                F
cont.      He is surrounded by the sound, the sound
           Gm7          C
        Of   cattle in the marketplace,
        F                                 Gm7
           Scatterlings and orphanages.
        C                 F
           He looks around, around,
                Gm7           C
        He sees angels in the architecture
        F
        Spinning in infinity,
                  Gm7          C
        He says, "Amen! and Halleluiah!"

        F                  C
Chorus 3 If you'll be my bodyguard
        Gm7             C         F     C  Gm7  C
        I can be your long lost  pal.
        F                C
        I can call you Betty
             Gm7              C
        And Betty when you call me
                F    C    Gm7  C
        You can call me Al.

           F                 Gm7  C
Coda    ||:  Na na na na,     na na na na,
        F                Gm7      C
           Na na na na,   na na,  na na na na.  :||
        F         Gm7  C  F          Gm7  C
        Hm, hm,               hm, hm,
        F         Gm7  C  F
        Hm, hm,               hm, hm.
           N.C.
        | Bass break |

        ||: F   C  | Gm7  C  | F    C  | Gm7   C  :||
           F                  C
        ||: If you'll be my bodyguard

        | Gm7  C | F   C | Gm7  C |
        F                C
        I can call you Betty.

        | Gm7  C | F   C | Gm7  C  :||  Repeat to fade
```

You Do

Words & Music by
Aimee Mann

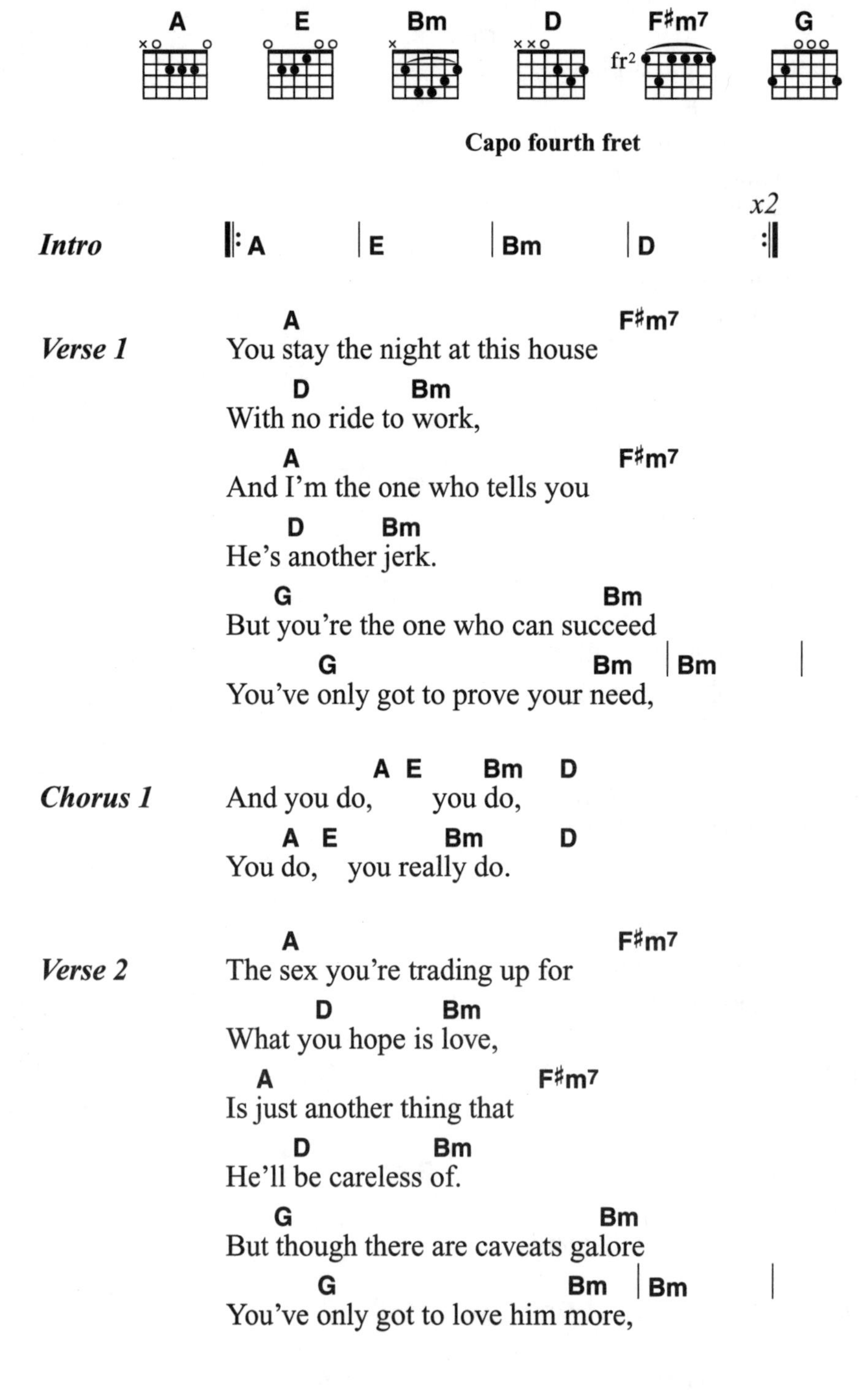

Capo fourth fret

Intro ‖: A | E | Bm | D :‖ x2

Verse 1
A F♯m7
You stay the night at this house
D Bm
With no ride to work,
A F♯m7
And I'm the one who tells you
D Bm
He's another jerk.
G Bm
But you're the one who can succeed
G Bm | Bm |
You've only got to prove your need,

Chorus 1
A E Bm D
And you do, you do,
A E Bm D
You do, you really do.

Verse 2
A F♯m7
The sex you're trading up for
D Bm
What you hope is love,
A F♯m7
Is just another thing that
D Bm
He'll be careless of.
G Bm
But though there are caveats galore
G Bm | Bm |
You've only got to love him more,

Chorus 2

```
                    A  E      Bm    D
And you do,         you do
      A   E           Bm        D
You do,    you really do
                         C  Bm   A
Even when it's all too    clear.
```

Link 1

```
| F#m7  | D      | Bm     | Bm     |
```

Verse 3

```
      A                         F#m7
You write a little note that
      D               Bm
You leave on the bed.
      A                                     F#m7
And spend some time dissecting
      D           Bm
Every word he said.
      G                    Bm
And if he seemed a little strange
       G                   Bm   | Bm      |
Well, baby anyone can change.
```

Chorus 3

```
                    A  E      Bm    D
And you do,         you do,
      A   E           Bm        D
You do,    you really do.
      A   E      Bm    D
You do,    you do,
      A   E           Bm        D
You do,    you really do,
            Bm   D               A
You really do,    you really do.
```

You Do Something To Me

Words & Music by
Paul Weller

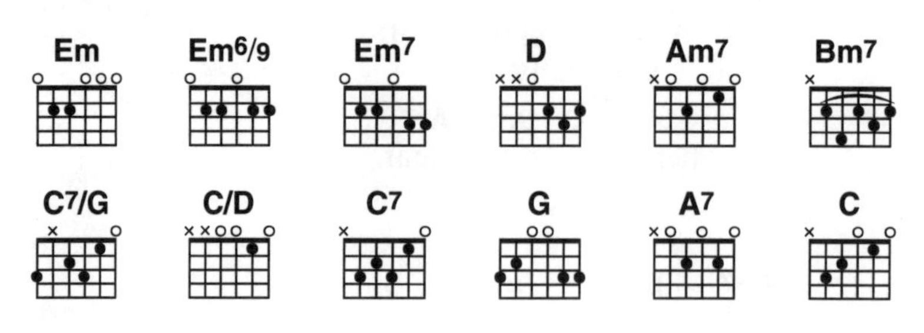

Intro | Em Em6/9 Em7 | Em Em6/9 Em7 | Em Em6/9 Em7 | Em ||

Verse 1

(Em) D Am7
You do something to me,
Bm7 Em
Something deep inside.
D Am7
I'm hanging on the wire
Bm7 Em
For the love I'll never find.

Verse 2

D Am7
You do something wonderful
Bm7 Em
Then chase it all away.
D Am7
Mixing my emotions,
Bm7 Em
That throws me back again.

Chorus 1

C7/G Am7
Hanging on the wire, yeah,
C/D Em
I'm waiting for the change.
C7 G
I'm dancing through the fire
A7 C C/D Em
Just to catch a flame and feel real again.

Guitar solo ‖: D | Am7 Bm7 | Em | Em :‖

Chorus 2 As Chorus 1

Verse 3

```
(Em)                      D      Am7
You do something to me,
Bm7                     Em
Somewhere deep inside.
                          D        Am7
I'm hoping to get close to
   Bm7                Em
A peace I cannot find.
```

Chorus 3

```
                              C7/G       Am7
Dancing through the fire, yeah,
C/D                   Em
Just to catch a flame.
C7              G
  Just to get close to,
     A7                 C7           C/D   Em
Just close enough to tell you that:
                          D       Am7
You do something to me,
Bm7                       Em   Em6/9  Em7
  Something deep inside.
```

| Em Em6/9 Em7 | Em Em6/9 Em7 | Em Em6/9 Em7 | Em ‖

Ziggy Stardust

Words & Music by
David Bowie

Intro |: G5 D | Cadd9 G/B Dsus4/A :| *Play 4 times*

Verse 1

G5 Bm C
Ziggy played guitar, jamming good with Weird and Gilly
D
And the spiders from Mars.
G Em
He played it left hand but made it too far, ___
A C
Became the special man, then we were Ziggy's band.

Verse 2

G Bm C
Ziggy really sang, screwed up eyes and screwed down hairdo
D
Like some cat from Japan,
G Em
He could lick 'em by smiling, he could leave 'em to hang,
Am C
They came on so loaded man, well hung and snow white tan.

Chorus 1

A5 G5* F5 G5*
So where were the Spiders
A5 G5* F5 G5*
While the fly tried to break our balls?
A5 G5* F5
Just the beer light to guide us,
D E
So we bitched about his fans and should we crush his sweet hands?

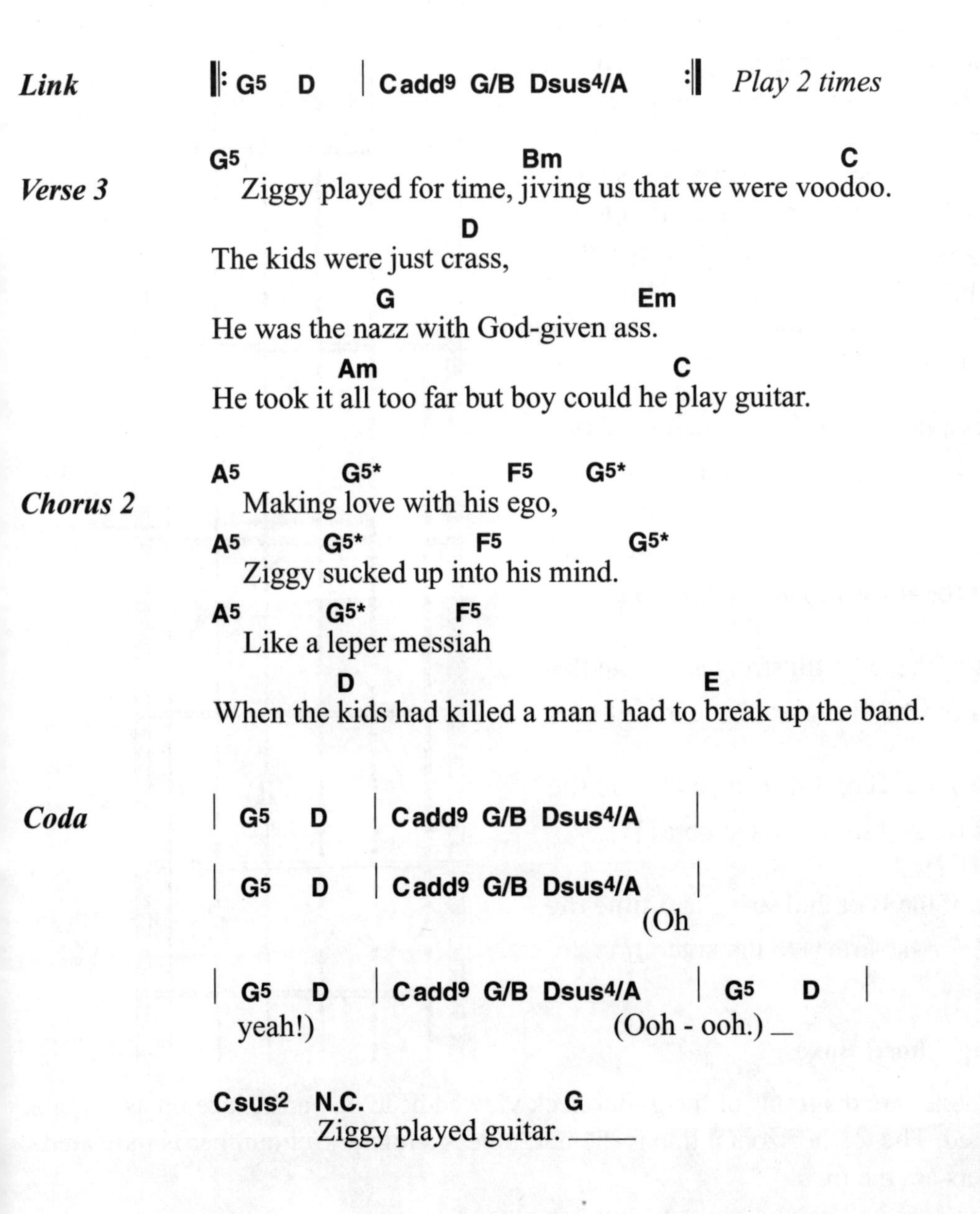

Link 𝄆 G5 D | Cadd9 G/B Dsus4/A 𝄇 *Play 2 times*

Verse 3

G5 Bm C
Ziggy played for time, jiving us that we were voodoo.
D
The kids were just crass,
G Em
He was the nazz with God-given ass.
Am C
He took it all too far but boy could he play guitar.

Chorus 2

A5 G5* F5 G5*
Making love with his ego,
A5 G5* F5 G5*
Ziggy sucked up into his mind.
A5 G5* F5
Like a leper messiah
D E
When the kids had killed a man I had to break up the band.

Coda

| G5 D | Cadd9 G/B Dsus4/A |

| G5 D | Cadd9 G/B Dsus4/A |
(Oh

| G5 D | Cadd9 G/B Dsus4/A | G5 D |
yeah!) (Ooh - ooh.) _

Csus2 N.C. G
Ziggy played guitar. ___

Relative Tuning

The guitar can be tuned with the aid of pitch pipes or dedicated electronic guitar tuners which are available through your local music dealer. If you do not have a tuning device, you can use relative tuning. Estimate the pitch of the 6th string as near as possible to E or at least a comfortable pitch (not too high, as you might break other strings in tuning up). Then, while checking the various positions on the diagram, place a finger from your left hand on the:

5th fret of the E or 6th string and **tune the open A** (or 5th string) to the note (A)

5th fret of the A or 5th string and **tune the open D** (or 4th string) to the note (D)

5th fret of the D or 4th string and **tune the open G** (or 3rd string) to the note (G)

4th fret of the G or 3rd string and **tune the open B** (or 2nd string) to the note (B)

5th fret of the B or 2nd string and **tune the open E** (or 1st string) to the note (E)

E or 6th
A or 5th
D or 4th
G or 3rd
B or 2nd
E or 1st
Head
Nut
1st Fret
2nd Fret
3rd Fret
4th Fret
(B)
5th Fret
(A) (D) (G) (E)

Reading Chord Boxes

Chord boxes are diagrams of the guitar neck viewed head upwards, face on as illustrated. The top horizontal line is the nut, unless a higher fret number is indicated, the others are the frets.

The vertical lines are the strings, starting from E (or 6th) on the left to E (or 1st) on the right.

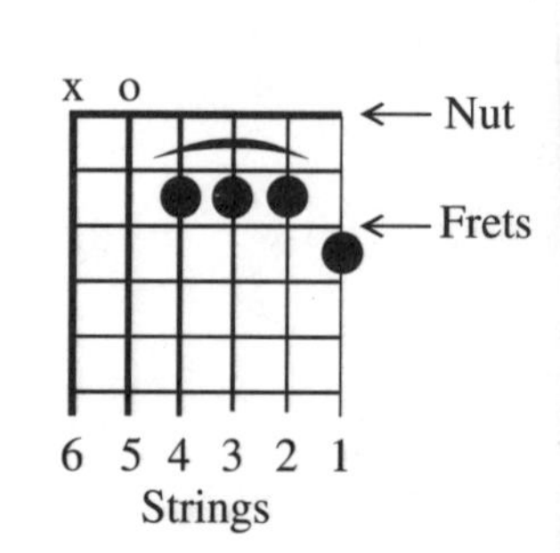

The black dots indicate where to place your fingers.

Strings marked with an O are played open, not fretted. Strings marked with an X should not be played.

The curved bracket indicates a 'barre' - hold down the strings under the bracket with your first finger, using your other fingers to fret the remaining notes.

1/05 (53768)